AQA Science

Exclusively endorsed and approved by AQA

Gerry Blake • David Brown • James Hayward

Jo Locke • Kevin Ward

Series Editor: Lawrie Ryan

GCSE Applied Science

Nelson Thornes
a Wolters Kluwer business

Published in 2006 by:
Nelson Thornes Ltd
Delta Place
27 Bath Road
CHELTENHAM
GL53 7TH
United Kingdom

06 07 08 09 10 / 10 9 8 7 6 5 4 3 2 1

A catalogue record for this book is available from the British Library

ISBN 0 7487 9657 6

Cover bubble illustration by Andy Parker
Cover photographs: oil rig/sun, Photodisc 22 (NT); radio telescopes/sun, Photodisc 54 (NT); wheat/grass field, Corel 227 (NT)

Illustrations by Oxford Designers and Illustrators, Kevin Jones Associates, Roger Penwill, David Russell and Angela Lumley

Page make-up by Design Practitioners Ltd

Printed and bound in Slovenia by DELO tiskarna by arrangement with Korotan-Ljubljana

With thanks to Christine Hodges and Stewart Chenery, for their contribution to this book

Contents

Welcome to AQA Applied Science!

LEARNING OBJECTIVES

By the end of the lesson you should be able to answer the questions posed in the learning objectives; if you can't, review the content until it's clear.

Nelson Thornes AQA GCSE Applied Science (Double Award) is the new work-related qualification that puts science to work in an everyday context.

Designed specially for the AQA 4861 specification, *Nelson Thornes AQA GCSE Applied Science* is the only course material endorsed by the AQA examination board.

Your student book covers all four units of the specification and emphasises science in the world of work. It includes both scientific principles and laboratory procedures. Advice is given to help you produce quality coursework. In-text questions allow you to check your understanding and progress.

For clarity your student book is broken down into units and chapters. Each idea is set out in a double page spread and starts with the learning objectives. Chapters begin with introductions and end with useful additional work, on related issues or case studies. You will quickly get used to the way your student book is set out.

Your teachers will decide on the most appropriate practical work and coursework tasks for you to carry out. They will also assess your coursework portfolio for units 1, 3 and 4. This work accounts for 65% of your GCSE marks. Your portfolio must be kept safe. At the end of the course it will go to a moderator for inspection.

Our aim is to help you to prepare for tomorrow and help you to see how science works in society. We hope you understand the science and acquire new scientific skills. We certainly hope you develop an interest and enthusiasm for science.

GET IT RIGHT!

Avoid common mistakes and gain marks by sticking to this advice.

a) What are the yellow boxes?

To check you understand the science you are learning, questions are integrated into the main text. The answers are always on the same page, so you don't waste your time flicking through the entire book.

 You'll also find questions about hot topics in science to talk about as a class or in small groups.

STANDARD PROCEDURE

What do we mean by 'standard procedures'? A standard procedure describes exactly how we carry out a practical or scientific task. It ensures that whoever carries out the experiment does it in exactly the same way. A simple diagram and questions make this feature a short introduction, reminder or basis for practical work.

DID YOU KNOW?

Curious examples of scientific points that are out of the ordinary, but true…

The four units of this double award course (worth two GCSEs) are as follows:

Unit 1 'Science in the Workplace' carries 10% of the total marks. In this unit you write two reports, investigating:

A How Science is Used

B Working Safely in Science.

Unit 2 'Science for the Needs of Society' carries 35% of the marks and is assessed by a $1\frac{1}{2}$ hour written examination paper. Your student book contains helpful exam-style questions.

Unit 3 'Developing Scientific Skills' carries 27.5% of the marks. In this unit you write at least three practical reports. The final mark comes from the best mark you get for each skill. In these practical investigations you follow 'standard procedures', to show how:

1 Microbiologists investigate living organisms

2 Analytical chemists find out about substances

3 Material scientists investigate the properties of materials.

Unit 4 'Using Scientific Skills for the Benefit of Society' carries 27.5% of the marks. In this unit you write reports based on four activities:

1 Monitoring Living Organisms (17 marks)

2 Making a Useful Product (17 marks)

3 Assembling Electronic/Electrical Devices (9 marks)

4 Using Machines (7 marks).

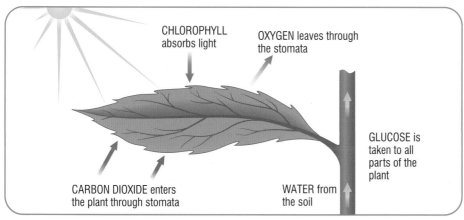

CHLOROPHYLL absorbs light

OXYGEN leaves through the stomata

GLUCOSE is taken to all parts of the plant

CARBON DIOXIDE enters the plant through stomata

WATER from the soil

Diagrams can help explain concepts too—refer to these throughout the book to check you understand.

TEST YOURSELF!

Did you understand everything? Get these questions right, and you can be sure you did. Get them wrong, and you might want to take another look.

KEY FACTS

Keys facts appear throughout the book and can be used in your revision to help summarise your knowledge.

1.1 Using science

People often think of scientists wearing white lab coats. However, we use scientific skills in so many jobs: vets, nurses, engineers, pharmacists, photographers, chefs, beauticians and gardeners, to name but a few.

A range of scientific jobs

Not all scientists wear lab coats

Science is big business in the UK.

a) Name a big manufacturing firm near where you live.
b) Name a large employer in your area that uses science and provides a service to the public.

As Applied Science students you will write a portfolio report *(Unit 1 – Task A)* on 'How Science is Used in the Workplace'. You will do research using books and computers. You might find information on visits and on your work experience. You will also interview people and write letters to companies.

  Discuss the best methods to get different types of information for a project.

c) Draw a table showing different methods of collecting information and when you have used them.

Method of collecting information	Where I have used it before
Surveys	Geography project on where people live

Making an excellent portfolio

The most important thing to remember is that other people are going to read your report. They will make decisions based on the information you give them. Imagine inventing the best ever engine but trying to sell it in a really ugly and unstylish car. It wouldn't sell. To be successful, make sure your ideas are both good and well presented.

The 'assessment evidence grid' or mark scheme for this report follows:

Back to the drawing board?

1A *You should be able to*:	2A *You should be able to*:	3A *You should be able to*:
• Produce a simple study on a range of organisations that use science • State the products made or services provided • Identify the jobs of those employed	• Identify organisations as local, national or international • Describe their location • Describe the products made or services provided • Describe the jobs and qualifications of the employees and how they use science • Describe the types of skills scientists need in addition to their qualifications, and a range of careers that are available in science	• Produce an in-depth study of **one** particular organisation • Explain its location • Describe the products made or services provided and explain their importance to society • Give a detailed account of the skills and qualifications needed by scientists who work there • Describe the effect on the local environment of the organisation
1–3 marks	4–8 marks	9–11 marks

'How Science is Used' coursework checklist

1 Identify one local, one national and one international organisation that use science.

2 What does each organisation do? Describe the products they make and/or the services they provide.

3 Where are the organisations located and why are they located there?

4 Explain their importance to society and their effect on the local community.

5 How many people does each organisation employ?

6 Put the employees of each organisation into one of three classes: major, significant and small users of science.

7 Identify the job titles and qualifications of the people who perform scientific tasks.

8 Describe the types of scientific activity they carry out on a daily basis.

9 What skills do the scientists need in addition to their qualifications?

10 As an appendix to your report, write about the careers that are available in science-related areas and their importance.

Students must show that they have studied one organisation in detail to obtain a stage 3A mark.

GET IT RIGHT!

- Divide up your work into easy to understand sections.

- Include copies of letters, questionnaires, and replies from organisations, etc., as appendices to your report. Write down all your sources of information at the end.

- Write the contents page and put the page numbers on last, after you have finished your project.

GET IT RIGHT!

Use a mind map to help plan your work.

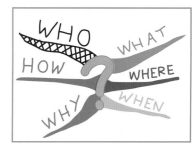

Mind map

TEST YOURSELF!

1 Which friends or family members work in an organisation that uses science? (You could interview them.)

2 Which three organisations could you use in the project?

3 Using the checklist above as a guide, write a questionnaire to help you get the information you need from the three organisations.

1.2   Reporting to impress

Gathering information

1 How can I get information for my portfolio?

Interviewing – Asking a scientist questions about their work is a very good way of getting information for your portfolio. Prepare your questions and include them, as well as the replies you got, in your portfolio.

E-mails and letters – If you e-mail or send letters to a company to ask questions about their work, make sure you include your e-mail or letter in your portfolio.

Ask a librarian – Ask a librarian to help you search for the right information.

Work experience – There is always some science that is going on in every business. At the start of your work experience, make sure you find out all about the health and safety issues. You should include this information in your portfolio.

Surveys – Surveys are very effective to get lots of information from lots of people quickly. You should show your teacher the questions that you are going to ask before you start. By asking multiple choice questions, you can analyse the answers you get if your sample is large enough.

Websites – Websites often show lots of information about companies. It is important that you don't just download and print off loads of pages. The projects you do should show your ideas, not someone else's.

1.3 Location, location, location

The location of a business has a huge impact on how that business performs.

A town centre location would allow businesses easy access to potential customers. Likewise, an out of town shopping complex would be easy for people to visit and park their cars. This is not useful for some businesses, as they may need excellent road and rail links for staff and to transport their products.

Research or business parks are useful for companies who need lots of parking for their staff, but customers may find it difficult to get there. Internet-based companies and research companies tend to be in these parks.

a) Find out about a local business park. What businesses are there, and what do they do?

An out of town shopping complex

Out of town shopping malls are very popular shopping and leisure destinations.

b) What sorts of businesses would be successful at an out of town shopping centre? What sorts of businesses would be unsuccessful?

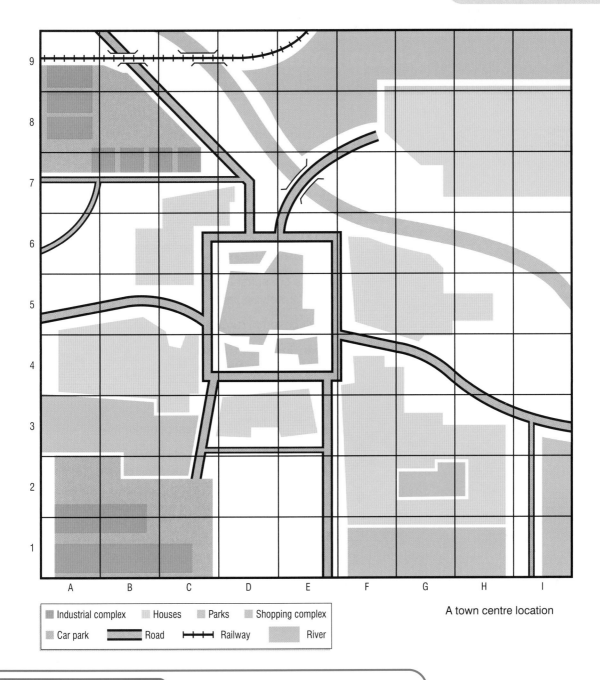

Legend:
- Industrial complex
- Houses
- Parks
- Shopping complex
- Car park
- Road
- Railway
- River

A town centre location

TEST YOURSELF!

1 Match these businesses to a suitable location from the list:

Business

Opticians, chemists, chemical factory, gymnasium, doctor's surgery, new university, car manufacturers, greengrocer, boat builder, car mechanic

Location

Out of town shopping centre, business park, town centre, local shops

2 Where would you put them on the map? Use the map references to help.

3 Look at the information you need for your project on page 7: you must explain the location of the scientific workplaces you research.

1.4   Group Lotus Plc

GET IT RIGHT!

For your portfolio choose workplaces:

- near to where you live
- where you know the name of a contact
- where you can visit.

Lotus logo

Look at this interview with Laura of Lotus Engineering. Plan your own interviews with people from your three chosen workplaces.

STUDENT: What does Group Lotus Plc do?

LAURA: **Lotus Cars** manufacture and sell sports cars, the *Elise* and *Exige*. We built the *Vauxhall Speedster* and make crash structures for the *Aston Martin V12 Vanquish*.

Lotus Engineering are consultants to many manufacturers, helping design, develop and produce prototype cars.

STUDENT: Why is Lotus based in rural Norfolk?

LAURA: Colin Chapman, looking for a suitable location, drew a circle on a map 100 miles from central London. Within that area fell Hethel, near Norwich. It is on the former US Air Force base, where today's purpose-built factory and 2.5-mile test track are located.

STUDENT: How important is Lotus to the local community?

LAURA: **Group Lotus** employs 1100 people at Hethel, making it the biggest employer in South Norfolk. The company also has staff in Germany, the USA, China and Malaysia. Lotus tries to be a good neighbour. For example, we stagger the start times for different areas of the company, to ease the flow of traffic. Lotus also works with the Police on safer driving initiatives. This includes providing a police-branded *Lotus Elise* for summer 'car cruise' events.

STUDENT: Do all employees use science?

LAURA: All employees of Lotus are involved with science at some level. Everybody understands the scientific concepts behind the cars.

Colin Chapman moved Lotus to Hethel, near Norwich in Norfolk, in 1966

Major users of science	Significant users of science	Small users of science
Engineers	Factory workers	Directors
Technicians	Designers	Sales & Marketing Dept.
		PR team
		Administrative roles

STUDENT: What are the qualifications of the people who do scientific tasks?

LAURA: Not everybody working at Lotus has a degree in Engineering, but many receive on-the-job training and study for qualifications throughout their time here. Engineers carry out various scientific tasks, depending on their specialism. We have designers making 3D digital images, clay modellers, and business graduates working with our technical specialists.

Design in clay! In the Lotus Design styling studio

STUDENT: Can you describe some of the other scientific activities that Lotus carries out on a daily basis?

LAURA: Lotus engineers carry out many automotive activities, from crash-testing new components to improving engine management systems. From the chassis and suspension to the engine and traction control – every aspect of the car's make up – our engineers at Lotus can design from scratch. We use the latest computer systems when designing 3D models. This is not just for aesthetic perfection, but also to improve the aerodynamics and performance.

Scientific developments also mean our technicians now bond the aluminium chassis together using adhesive. This produces a stronger join than by welding. Similarly, we discovered that water-based paints create the best finish. They also do less damage to the environment.

STUDENT: Apart from their scientific qualifications, what skills do your employees need?

LAURA: Lotus 'scientists' need vision and adaptability to 'change the rules' and look at new solutions to engineering projects. We are an innovative company, always aiming for top-quality products.

STUDENT: Laura, thank you so much for your help today.

Engine power – an engineer performing combustion tests to monitor improvements

Precise measurements – engine design

A *Lotus Elise* being tested in an 'anechoic chamber', where no sound can echo off the walls of the room

TEST YOURSELF!

1 What three organisations are you using in your project?

   (*Remember: one local, one national, one international.*)

2 Who are your contacts in these organisations?

3 Plan your interview questions and arrange your meeting.

   (*Remember: you must study one organisation in more detail to obtain a stage 3A mark – see the table on page 7.*)

1.5   Forensic science at work

Sherlock Holmes was a detective in novels written in Victorian times. He was brilliant at solving crimes from clues left by criminals.

Nowadays, finding the evidence and figuring out what it means is the work of a forensic scientist.

a) Hair, fibres, insects, fingerprints, handwriting, and teeth! Explosives, bite marks, bullets, and blood! What's the link between all these things?

Who committed the crime? When? Was she drinking? Was he using drugs? Is this really her signature? How long has he been dead? What was the cause? How fast were they going? Is this the gun? These kinds of questions come up in crimes like murders, drug cases, and burglaries.

Crime officers (SoCOs) entering a crime scene

Finding out when somebody died and how, a factory or an office was broken in to, and what caused an accident are just a few of the everyday mysteries that need to be investigated.

There are many kinds of forensic science jobs. Scene of crime officers (SoCOs) go out to find evidence on the spot. Others, like toxicologists (experts in harmful substances), concentrate on lab work. A ballistics expert deals with firearms and bullets. An entomologist knows all about insects and how to use them in solving mysteries, such as finding out when somebody died.

Detective Sherlock Holmes on the case!

Using fingerprints to identify people was a big step forward in Sherlock Holmes' day. Nowadays, we also use 'DNA profiling' to identify people.

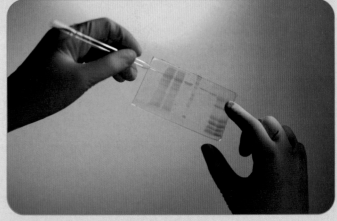

DNA profiling is based on each person's own unique genetic code

FINDING OUT MORE

Today, science plays a key part in policing. Why not contact your local police force and arrange to meet someone from 'scientific services' or 'specialist units'? See what information is available on-line at www.**mycounty**.police.uk (substitute suffolk, warwickshire etc. for '**mycounty**'). You could use the police Special Services Department for one of your three organisations to research.

Would forensic science be right for you?

To test your interest, read a few mysteries and play some crime-solving computer games. Forensics can be fascinating, but it also involves careful thinking and precise testing. The skills you need come from studying science.

CRIME SCENE DO NOT ENTER CRIME SCENE DO NOT ENTER

Outside the kitchen

Murder most foul
– reconstruction of the crime scene

Outside the kitchen:

Underneath the broken window, the scene of crime officer (SoCO) sees a shoe print in the flower bed. She makes a cast of this and puts glass fragments into bags, for future comparison. There is a smear of blood and some clothing fibres on the broken pane. After collecting these, the officer dusts the window sill and pane for fingerprints.

Inside the kitchen:
Some more fingerprints are on the inside of the frame. On the work top there is a faint shoe print. The SoCO takes an impression of these using a gelatin lift. There is a cigarette stubbed out on the worktop. The officer keeps it to get a DNA profile from the saliva on the butt.

Inside the kitchen

Inside the bedroom:
On the floor by the door is a crumpled note, written to a man and signed by the victim. This is sent off for document analysis. On the walls are spots of blood. The SoCO photographs the stains and records their size and splatter pattern. She takes a sample for DNA analysis. She also dusts for fingerprints on the door and around the room. The bedding, the victim's clothing and the body are 'taped' to recover any hairs or fibres. Finally, at the post mortem, body fluid samples are taken from the victim for toxicological testing.

b) How many pieces of evidence has the SoCO collected?

Inside the bedroom

2.1   Working safely – the hidden costs if you don't

Workplace hazards

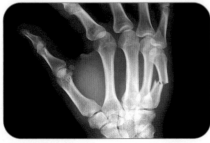

A broken bone

Power cables

Imagine if you lived under these power cables:

a) Why could this be hazardous (dangerous)?
b) Is the risk (chance of being harmed) high?

There are hidden dangers in the workplace. More than 2500 16 to 24-year-olds will be seriously injured at work this year, involving broken bones and serious burns.

We cannot remove the hazards completely, but we can reduce the risks.

Think about the main reasons people get injured:

- Slips and trips – 33% of all major injuries. The cost to employers is £512 million and the cost to the heath service is £133 million, per year. The human cost cannot be calculated.
- Unsafe lifting and carrying, causing back pain.
- Falling from a height – causing 70 deaths and 4000 serious injuries each year.
- Being struck by a moving object. Each year, 3500 people are killed on our roads and 40 000 are seriously injured.

 Discuss ways to reduce these risks.

c) Why do you think young people face the highest risk of injury?

More than 1 million people have days off work each year because of problems with muscles and joints.

Half a million people are ill because of work-related stress. Although pressure keeps us motivated, excess pressure causes illness.

 Discuss practical ways in which we can reduce these illnesses.

In scientific workplaces, we have hazardous substances and dangerous equipment to deal with. There are also electrical, noise and manual handling problems. Scientific work can be dangerous.

d) Why do you think accidents among scientists are rare?

The 'assessment evidence grid' or mark scheme for this report follows:

You should be able to:	You should be able to:	You should be able to:
1B ● Carry out research into working safely in the school or college laboratory, including hazards and risks and their assessment, first aid and fire prevention 1–4 marks	**2B** ● Carry out research into the issues of working safely in a workplace that uses science or scientific skills, including hazards and risks and their assessment, first aid and fire prevention 5–8 marks	**3B** ● Carry out research into the issues of working safely in a scientific workplace and compare these with the school or college laboratory, including hazards and risks and their assessment, first aid and fire prevention 9–11 marks
1C ● Use a limited range of sources and information, to present findings in your portfolio 1 mark	**2C** ● Use a range of sources and information to present findings clearly in your portfolio 2 marks	**3C** ● Use a wide range of sources and information to present findings clearly and logically throughout your portfolio 3 marks

➡ **WORKING MORE INDEPENDENTLY** ➡

In the school or college laboratory, you could start by identifying:

● Hazard warning signs.
● Biological, chemical and physical hazards, including radioactive substances, and their risks.
● Health and safety procedures.
● How we use risk assessments.

You can find out more about your chosen scientific workplace by identifying:

● Health and safety checks.
● Risk assessments for tasks carried out.
● What they do to prevent accidents from the hazards that exist.
● Emergency procedures followed if an accident does happen.

Ideas for your questionnaire about health and safety at your chosen scientific workplace

● What hazards have you identified at *[name of company]*?
● What have you done to control the risk of these hazards?
● What new safe working practices have you introduced, if any?
● Have these reduced accidents, absence rates and saved your company money?

 Discuss with a partner what other questions you could ask.

Produce your own questionnaire.

Case study

Sarah was using an unguarded drilling machine. The sleeve of her jumper caught on the rotating drill, entangling her arm. Both bones in her lower arm were broken and she suffered extensive tissue and muscle injury. She spent 10 days in hospital and was off work for 3 months. She was unable to operate machinery for 8 months. Her manager was prosecuted.

The cost to the business was £45 000. Two other employees were made redundant to prevent the company going out of business.

As Applied Science students you will write a report *(Unit 1 – Task B)* on:

● 'Working Safely in a Scientific Workplace', comparing this with
● the health and safety precautions in your own school or college.

TEST YOURSELF!

1 How do we all take risks in life?

2 How could you avoid having a certain accident and so reduce the risk to yourself and to others? (Think about protective clothing, checking equipment and training.)

3 a) How could working all week long at a computer screen be hazardous?
   b) How could the risks be minimised?

2.2 Laboratory safety – who is it for?

Marie Curie

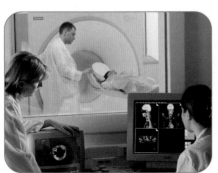

A PET scan machine

A Geiger counter

In 1911, Marie Curie won her second Nobel Prize for her work on radioactivity. She started the use of mobile X-ray units to help wounded soldiers in the First World War. Almost 100 years later, X-rays are common. Marie Curie did not know the dangers of radiation when she first started working with radioactive materials. Sadly, Marie died of leukaemia (cancer of the blood) due to radiation exposure.

Today, doctors get the clearest medical images with positron emission tomography (PET) scans. Doctors inject very small amounts of radioactive materials into the patient. Gamma-ray cameras placed round the patient can then show exactly where diseases such as cancer are. Notice that the technicians work behind a protective screen. Then they will be joined by the nurse.

a) Why do you think they need a safety screen?

Imagine in 5 years time – you could be working in a laboratory preparing materials to use in hospitals.

You have probably seen an experiment with a Geiger counter.

b) What safety precautions did your teacher take?
c) Look at the two photographs below. How do the suits protect the workers from radiation?

 Have a discussion about the hazards of radioactivity.

Space suit   Hostile environment suit

Hazard symbols

- Yellow and black triangles **warn of danger**, e.g. radioactivity.
- A red crossbar is something you **must not do,** e.g. no smoking.
- A blue circle is something you **must do**, e.g. wear eye protection.
- A green background gives **safety information**, e.g. first aid.
- **Hazard labels** are orange and black, e.g. biohazard.

Hazard warning signs

Hazard signs in the lab: corrosive, highly flammable, oxidising, toxic, harmful/irritant, explosive. Which of these hazard signs have you seen before?

 Discuss how your laboratories are protected.

Consider mains electricity, gas, fumes and explosions.

 Think about the safety rules in your school or college laboratory.

Discuss which 5 rules you think are the most important and why.

You already know some risks of using poor techniques in experiments.

The school laboratory technicians have to be careful too, when they prepare chemicals. For example, sodium hydroxide is corrosive, causing severe burns. It is particularly dangerous to eyes. It gets hot when added to water.

Sodium hydroxide is an alkali. You sometimes use sodium hydroxide solution in science experiments.

Technicians prepare your solutions by dissolving solid sodium hydroxide in water.

d) When preparing solutions of sodium hydroxide, what safety precautions should the technician use to reduce the risk?

DID YOU KNOW?

High levels of ionising radiations can damage body cells, cause loss of hair and radiation sickness. They also cause cancer.

Some people work with radioactive substances. Not surprisingly, their levels of exposure to radiation are checked.

They wear 'film badges' that are sensitive to radioactivity. (See pages 87 and 89.)

TEST YOURSELF!

1. What do these words mean? a) flammable; b) biohazard; c) toxic; d) harmful; e) corrosive; f) irritant; g) explosive; h) oxidising.

2. Some sodium hydroxide solution spills on the table. What should you do if you accidentally wipe some of the solution in your eye?

3. If radiation can cause cancer, why do we expose cancer patients to radiation during radiotherapy or chemotherapy?

4. Research task. Find out about how unwanted or waste materials, including radioactive substances, are disposed of safely.

GET IT RIGHT!

Organise a tour of the laboratories and the preparation rooms with your science technicians.

2.3 Risk assessments – thinking first

LEARNING OBJECTIVES

What are the following:

1 Hazards and risks?
2 Accident prevention?
3 Health and safety?
4 Risk assessments?

An unexpected hazard

Fork-lift truck driver

DID YOU KNOW?

There are 1.6 million injuries at work each year.

70% of these could be prevented if employers put control measures in place.

The rate of injuries in firms with fewer than 50 employees is over twice the rate of that in firms employing more than 1000 people.

Find out lots more at www.youngworker.co.uk

Some people like taking risks, e.g. skiing or bungee jumping.

Sometimes the hazards come with the job, like being a policeman.

Sometimes we are not aware there is a risk.

A **hazard** is anything that can cause harm. Examples include chemicals, electricity and gas, noise, careless behaviour, microorganisms, etc. The **risk** is the chance that someone will be harmed by the hazard.

a) Think of a fork-lift truck. When might it pose a risk?
b) Who might be harmed?
c) How could accidents with fork-lift trucks be limited?

250 people each year lose their lives at work in Britain. More than 150 000 are injured or badly hurt.

Safety slogans

In your school or college laboratory, minor burns to hands caused by touching hot tripods and test tubes are fairly common. The hazard (or danger) is minor, as the burns are small and heal quickly. The risk is high, but the consequences are not very serious.

d) What **control measures** (or safety precautions) would you use to reduce the number of minor burns in schools and colleges?
e) What is the **emergency action** (first aid) for a minor burn accident?

Electric shock from a faulty appliance could result in death. It is a major hazard. However, with properly designed and maintained equipment, the risk is insignificant.

Concentrated sulfuric acid is corrosive. It causes severe burns and can permanently damage eyes. It is a major hazard. If it is left out in a laboratory, the risk is significant.

f) What control measures can we use to reduce the risk when using sulfuric acid?
(See the CLEAPSS CD-ROM Student Safety Sheet 22.)

We make risk assessments to ensure that we control or get rid of risks. If you think it's just a form-filling exercise you've missed the point! In a risk assessment we:

1 Identify **hazards**, i.e. things that could cause harm – materials, procedures and equipment.

2 Work out the **risk** – how likely is it that harm could occur and how serious could the consequences be?

3 Put **control measures** (safety precautions) in place to avoid or reduce the risk as far as possible.

4 Decide on the **emergency action** (first aid) to take if the controls fail and there is an accident.

The Table below shows how to set out a risk assessment:

Risk Assessment Form   Name of student: _____   Date: _____

Task: _____

Hazards	Risks	Control measures	Emergency action
Think about the material, procedure or equipment. What makes it dangerous and what could go wrong?	(high / moderate / low) **Probability of harm and Seriousness of consequence**	Safety precautions	First aid

TEST YOURSELF!

1 There is a 95% probability of infection after a gnat bite.

  Chose the correct word to describe the risk of a gnat bite:

  • Probability of harm is [high / moderate / low].
  • Seriousness of consequence is [high / moderate / low].

2 Copy and add to this hazard prompt list:

  Slips and trips; lifting; electricity; radiation; stress; transport; chemicals; computer screens; biohazards..

  (Your list will help you when writing your safety report.)

3 You have probably been sunburnt.

  a) How does **time of exposure** increase your **risk** of sunburn?
  b) What **control measures** can be used to avoid being burnt?
  c) What **emergency action** can you take if you get sunburnt?

GET IT RIGHT!

You will find the terms **hazard**, **risk** and **risk assessment** in **health and safety** legislation, like the Control Of Substances Hazardous to Health (COSHH) regulations.

The job of the Health and Safety Executive (HSE) is to see that risks to people's health and safety from work activities are properly controlled.

See www.hse.gov.uk

2.4 Preventing fires

Fighting a major fire at a warehouse

Think about how this company should avoid such a disaster in the future.

Fire doors form a barrier to stop fire spreading. They must be kept shut but not locked!

Sprinkler facts

- A sprinkler costs less than a carpet.
- Sprinklers are completely automatic. They work by themselves and can stop heat and smoke from trapping people.
- Only the sprinklers over a fire open. All the others stay shut.
- In a fire you are 20 times more likely to die in a building without a sprinkler.
- Smoke is the main cause of death and damage to property in fires.
- In buildings protected by sprinklers, 99% of fires are controlled.
- Fire fighters often use 10 000 times more water from hoses to do the same job as a sprinkler.

The liquid-filled glass bulb shatters at 65 °C. The sprinkler head opens and sprays water onto the fire.

a) How do sprinklers reduce the amount of water needed to put out a fire?
b) How can sprinklers also reduce the amount of smoke?
c) Why does less damage occur in buildings that have sprinkler systems?

Sprinklers are not the answer for every place of work. In schools, for example, we have fire alarms, fire extinguishers and fire blankets.

A fire blanket

d) Why are these preferred, rather than sprinklers? (Think about old buildings and vandalism.)

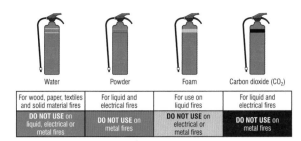

For wood, paper, textiles and solid material fires	For liquid and electrical fires	For use on liquid fires	For liquid and electrical fires
DO NOT USE on liquid, electrical or metal fires	**DO NOT USE** on metal fires	**DO NOT USE** on electrical or metal fires	**DO NOT USE** on metal fires

Types of fire extinguisher

DID YOU KNOW?

Cigarettes burn at 700°C.

Every 3 days, someone dies from a fire caused by a cigarette.

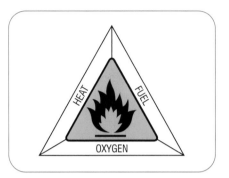

The fire triangle

Classes of fire

- Class A: **solids** such as paper, wood, plastic etc.
- Class B: **flammable liquids** such as paraffin, petrol, oil etc.
- Class C: **flammable gases** such as propane, butane, methane etc.
- Class D: **metals** such as aluminium, magnesium, titanium etc.
- Class E: fires involving **electrical apparatus**.

Types of extinguisher

Water: Works by cooling material to below its ignition point. Used for Class A fires. Not suitable for Class B (liquids) or Class E (electricity) fires.

Dry powder: Works by smothering (by excluding oxygen) and knocking down flames. For Class A, B and E fires, but best for fires involving flammable liquids. *It can be dangerous to extinguish a gas fire without first turning off the gas supply.*

Foam: Works by forming a foam blanket to smother the fire and stop combustion. For Class A and B fires. (Not recommended for home use or electrical fires, but safer than water.)

Carbon dioxide (CO_2): Carbon dioxide smothers the fire by displacing oxygen. Is ideal for fires in electrical apparatus, and will extinguish Class B (flammable liquid) fires. *Carbon dioxide can be dangerous in confined areas.*

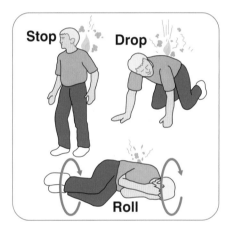

What should you do if your clothes catch fire?

TEST YOURSELF!

1. What are the missing words?

   When you find a fire: sound the **a**...., shut **d**.... and **w**...., switch off **g**.... and **e**...., walk to **a**.... **a**....

2. a) Why should you '*stop, drop and roll*' even if there is a fire blanket?
   b) '*Push the button, not your luck. Excuses kill.*' What does this mean?
   c) Fire doors create a '*fire wall*'. Explain.

3. a) Why is water dangerous on oil fires?
   b) Powder on upholstery can put out a fire, only for it to re-light. Why?
   c) Why are foam extinguishers not suitable in homes?
   d) Why is CO_2 dangerous in confined areas?

4. Design a fire safety poster for a local company. Include these ideas:

   - People before property, but prevention is better than cure.
   - The greatest danger is at night. Keep low. Know your way out.
   - Each year about 700 people die from fires in their own homes and 14 000 are injured. 60% of home fires occur during cooking.
   - Only 6% of deaths and 10% of injuries occur in workplace fires.
   - Good management and safe storage reduce fire risks.
   - Care is needed with processes involving heat and electricity.

A smoke alarm

2.5 First aid – 'I'm glad my friend knew what to do.'

The recovery position

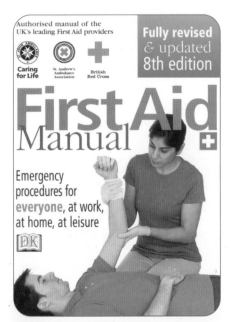

Most people who train in first aid use this manual
(see www.dk.com/firstaidmanual).
You can train with St John Ambulance (www.sja.org.uk) and British Red Cross (www.redcross.org.uk).

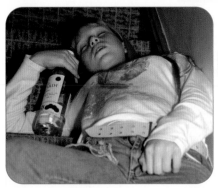

Sam after the party!

You've been to a party with friends. Sam has had too much to drink and collapses.

a) What should you do?

If Sam is clearly having difficulty breathing, she could choke on her vomit. Call 999 for advice.

If Sam comes round, give her water or fruit juice to drink. (Coffee won't sober her up. It just increases the rate alcohol goes round her body.)

Sam was glad her friend knew what to do.

An accident happens. Someone is injured. It's important to treat them as soon as possible.

Imagine an accident in a science laboratory. It is important to know what to do while waiting for a qualified first-aider. The following advice covers common laboratory accidents:

Chemical splashes in the eye. Wash the eye under tap water for at least 10 minutes. The flow should be slow and the eyelid should be held back. Afterwards, take the casualty to hospital.

Chemical splashes on the skin. Wash the skin until all traces of the chemical have disappeared. Remove clothing as necessary.

Chemicals in the mouth, perhaps swallowed. Do not wash out the mouth, as the chemical may be swallowed. After the *first-aider* washes the mouth out, take the casualty to hospital.

Burns. Cool under gently running water until first aid arrives.

Toxic gas. Sit the casualty down in the fresh air.

Clothing on fire. Smother by pushing the casualty to the ground. Spread the laboratory fire blanket on top of the flames.

Asthma attacks. Make sure that their personal medication is available, so they can use it immediately.

Find out the answers to questions b) to d) below.
b) What should you do if a friend gets:
   i)   an electric shock?
   ii) a bad cut?
c) Can we use rubber gloves to move an electric shock casualty?
d) Why don't we take large objects out of a bad cut?

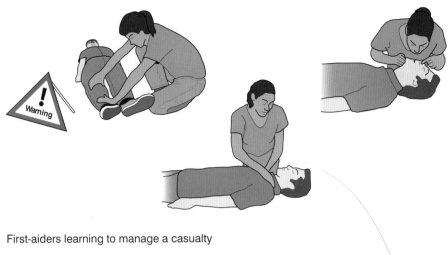

First-aiders learning to manage a casualty

First aiders begin by assessing the **Danger**:

- Are you or the casualty in any danger?

They continue with **Response**:

- Does the casualty respond to you?

Then we have the **ABC**:

- **Airway, Breathing, Circulation**.

e) The Table shows some common laboratory injuries. Refer to a First Aid Manual and design a first aid poster for your school or college. The poster must give information for each injury.

Injury	Your aims	First aid steps	Risks to your safety Cautions / Warnings
Minor burns / scalds			
Chemical burn			
Inhalation of fumes			
Swallowing chemicals			
Electric shock			
Cuts and grazes			
Foreign object in the eye			
Chemical in the eye			

Check your poster design with a qualified first-aider.

TEST YOURSELF!

1 Why is it useful to have a first aid qualification?

2 Students sometimes wipe their eyes and transfer chemicals from their hands into their eyes. What ways do you recommend to reduce these accidents?

2.6   Risky business at the brewery

LEARNING OBJECTIVES

1 Where are there potential hazards in scientific workplaces?
2 When are health and safety regulations important in scientific workplaces?
3 How can risks arise?

The cleaner in the photo needs a permit to enter a fermentation vessel. For cleaning he wears a full body suit, with a harness attached. He has a carbon dioxide (CO_2) monitor on his waist. He also wears a motion sensor. If he stops moving, an alarm goes off.

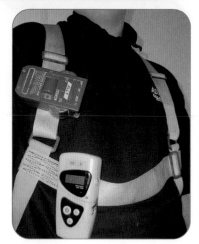

Why might it be risky to clean out one of these containers?

 Discuss the cartoon (below) with a partner.

WHAT'S THE POINT OF MONITORING CARBON DIOXIDE? ISN'T IT IN THE AIR ANYWAY?

YES, AND THEY PUT LOTS OF CO₂ INTO FIZZY DRINKS AND THAT'S NOT A PROBLEM

Why monitor carbon dioxide?

BACKGROUND SCIENCE

To make beer we use yeast to break down sugar to make alcohol. Scientists call this **fermentation**:

| Glucose (sugar) | → | ethanol (alcohol) | + | carbon dioxide |

$$C_6H_{12}O_6 \rightarrow 2C_2H_5OH + 2CO_2$$

The froth on top of the beer is filled with carbon dioxide gas. Carbon dioxide is more dense than air. It falls to the bottom of the fermentation vessel when we pump the beer out of the container.

An automatic sodium hydroxide spraying head in a fermentation vessel

The cleaner sprays sodium hydroxide (NaOH) on the walls of the vessel. This kills any bacteria that might start to grow there. Bacteria will ruin the flavour of the beer. Sodium hydroxide is an **alkali**. It is caustic and kills bacteria by attacking their protein.

a) How does the full body suit protect the cleaner?
b) Why might the cleaner have too little oxygen when breathing?
c) What **emergency action** could we take in the event of an accident?

The brewery are replacing their old fermentation vessels. The new ones are sealed containers. These vessels contain automatic sodium hydroxide spraying heads.

d) How are the newer vessels safer?

What happens when carbon dioxide levels increase?

| **0.04%** The approximate amount of CO_2 naturally in the atmosphere

| **0.5%** The normal International Safety Limit

| **0.7%** Workers have 20 minutes to evacuate the area

| **1.2%** Workers leave the area immediately

| **1.5%** The normal Short Time Exposure Limit

| **3%**

You will be breathing at twice your normal rate. Your heart rate and blood pressure increase. You feel dizzy, your head aches and your hearing is impaired.

| **5%**

You breathe much faster and feel a choking sensation. You quickly become tired and become confused.

People move heavy objects in the brewery. This is also a hazard. Using fork-lift trucks reduces the risk to workers. However, **manual handling** is still needed. The management provides training in safe lifting. Its rules are:

- Face the way you need to move.
- Bend your knees and lift with a straight back.
- Hold the load close to your body.

These rules are strictly enforced.

A worker not following the safe lifting rules gets a warning. *"You've heard it before: Lift with your legs, not with your back. So how come you bent your waist lifting that case of beer?"*

 Discuss what should happen next if a worker is seen not lifting safely. (Is it unreasonable for the worker to get the sack?)

Back injury

TEST YOURSELF!

1 Copy and complete the following sentences, using these words:

alkali   carbon dioxide   oxygen   sodium hydroxide

The cleaner of a fermentation vessel in a brewery is at risk because there is a hazard posed by the solution of _____ _____ and the gas _____ _____. Sodium hydroxide is an _____. An increase in CO_2 limits the amount of _____ that can be absorbed into the blood.

2 Describe potential hazards in scientific workplaces due to:
a) careless behaviour
b) not using equipment properly
c) not using protective and safety equipment
d) not following correct procedures.

3 Explain why there is a CO_2 risk in:
a) mushroom farms and greenhouses
b) soft drink production
c) residential homes for the elderly.

GET IT RIGHT!

In your portfolio write about:

1 Health and safety checks.

2 Risk assessments for hazardous materials and procedures.

3 What to do to prevent accidents.

2.7   Health warning

a) What is the difference between a hazard and a risk?

Hazards and risks of a new game

Imagine that a new game takes off as the next school craze. Your head teacher has had a complaint from a school governor. So your Applied Science class has been given the task of completing a risk assessment for the game.

Your head teacher warns you that different people must not blow into the same balloon. "I don't want anyone passing on their germs," are the head teacher's stern words. "We've just had an outbreak of 'flu and you've all heard of MRSA, haven't you?"

 Discuss your ideas of what should be included in the risk assessment.

Complete a risk assessment form for the game:

Hazards	Risks	Control measures	Emergency action

Fighting the superbug

You have probably seen newspaper headlines such as 'Superbug killed my husband' or 'Dirty hospital disgrace.'

But what is MRSA?

MRSA is a bacterium, which causes infections. It is a 'superbug', because MRSA is resistant to antibiotics (see page 80). MRSA is short for Multiple Antibiotic-Resistant *Staphylococcus aureus*.

Staphylococcus aureus is a common bacterium. It lives on the skin of many healthy people without them even knowing it. People in hospital tend to be old, sick, weak and at risk of infections. While their defences are low, MRSA is a potential killer.

Sadly, infections of MRSA in hospitals lead to approximately 5000 deaths every year.

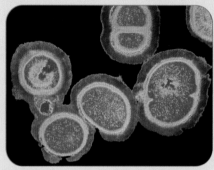

Staphylococcus aureus

b) What is an antibiotic? (See page 80.)
c) How could an infection of MRSA on the skin get into the blood stream? (Clue: think about a wound.)
d) Why is an infection in the blood more dangerous than one on the skin?

What do doctors say about MRSA?

Hygiene has always protected patients from dangerous diseases.

- Moving from patient to patient, doctors and nurses must always wash their hands.
- Visitors must also use the 'alcohol-based hand-rubs'. These are designed to reduce the number of micro-organisms on their hands.
- To be safe hospitals must also be clean.

'Cleanyourhands' campaign logo

Hospitals are currently spending £1 billion each year fighting infections such as MRSA. However, in school, healthy young people are not in danger of MRSA infections.

 "Whether a dirty ward rather than a dirty hand is a breeding ground for *Staphylococcus* is a matter of debate". What do you think? Discuss the issues around MRSA.

1 | Health and Medicine

In this section you will learn about:

The healthy body

- What is inside cells?
- What are specialist cells?
- What is homeostasis?
- What are genes and what do they do?

The unhealthy body

- What causes diseases?
- How do diet and excercise affect your body?
- What are the effects of drugs and alcohol on your body?
- What are genetic disorders?

Preventing, diagnosing and treating illnesses

- What effect do pharmaceuticals have?
- How can immunisations prevent diseases being spread?
- What are the medical uses of x-rays and gamma rays?

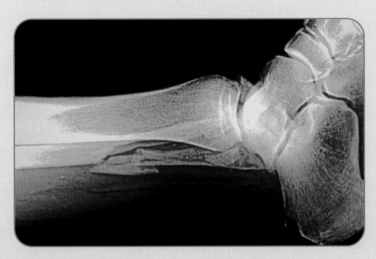

This section is tested by examination

Paramedic

"In order to save lives, I need to know how systems in the body function."

Nurse

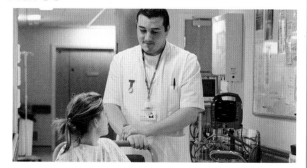

"Science is very important in my job. I need to understand how the body works."

Radiographer

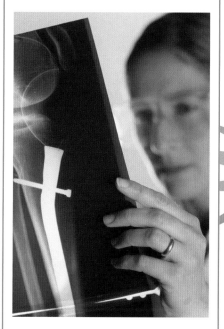

"I use X-rays to detect broken bones and diagnose medical conditions."

Career opportunities

Pathologist

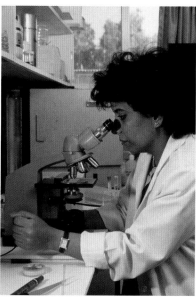

"I need to recognise all the features in body cells. If I spot anything unusual it might mean a person has developed a disease."

Pharmacist

"People come to me for advice on a range of conditions. I need to know how drugs affect the body."

Dietician

"Knowing how different foods affect the body allows me to help patients manage their medical conditions."

1.1   What are we made of?

This is how the chloroplasts in moss cells appear when you look down a light microscope.

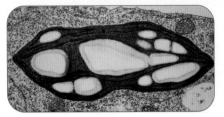

This is what a chloroplast in a moss cell looks like under an electron microscope. Scientists use electron microscopes to see structures inside cells more clearly.

Your body is made up of millions of **cells**. In fact, cells make up all living organisms. However, they are so small that you can only see them clearly using a microscope. Around 100 animal cells would fit across the width of a full stop!

Scientists use microscopes to look at cells. From this work we now know what happens inside cells. People working in the medical profession can use this information to help fight diseases. For example, doctors view the results of smear tests to look for signs of **cancer**.

a) Approximately how many cells are there in the human body?
b) Look at the two photos on the left. Which microscope would you use if you wanted to see the smallest features of a cell clearly?

Animal cells

All animal cells have four main features:

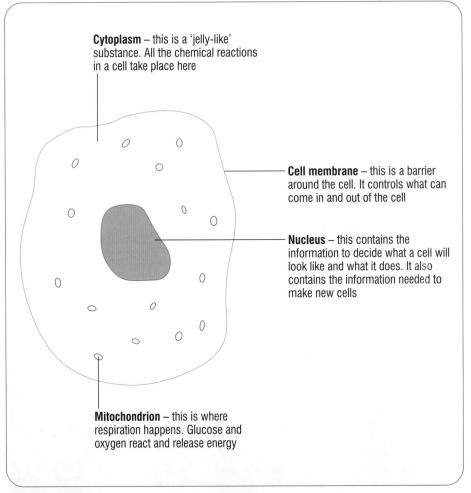

Cytoplasm – this is a 'jelly-like' substance. All the chemical reactions in a cell take place here

Cell membrane – this is a barrier around the cell. It controls what can come in and out of the cell

Nucleus – this contains the information to decide what a cell will look like and what it does. It also contains the information needed to make new cells

Mitochondrion – this is where respiration happens. Glucose and oxygen react and release energy

An animal cell

c) Which part of the cell controls the cell's activities?

Comparing animal and plant cells

Plant cells also contain a nucleus, cell membrane, mitochondria (plural of mitochondrion) and cytoplasm. Plus they have three extra important features:

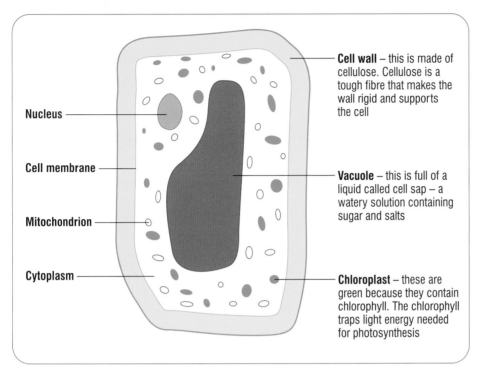

Nucleus

Cell membrane

Mitochondrion

Cytoplasm

Cell wall – this is made of cellulose. Cellulose is a tough fibre that makes the wall rigid and supports the cell

Vacuole – this is full of a liquid called cell sap – a watery solution containing sugar and salts

Chloroplast – these are green because they contain chlorophyll. The chlorophyll traps light energy needed for photosynthesis

A plant cell

You can read more about the important role that chloroplasts play in photosynthesis on pages 98–99.

d) What are the 3 features that we only find in plant cells, and not in animal cells?

e) What is the function of the cell wall?

DID YOU KNOW?

Dust in your house is mainly made from dead skin cells.

TEST YOURSELF!

1 Which of the following features are found in an animal cell? Which of the following features are found in a plant cell?
   a) Nucleus
   b) Vacuole
   c) Cell membrane
   d) Cytoplasm
   e) Mitochondria
   f) Chloroplasts
   g) Cell wall

2 What do you find in the vacuole of a plant cell?

3 Why do the cells found in a plant's root not contain chloroplasts?

4 Why do animal cells not require a cell wall?

1.2 What goes into and out of your cells?

All the cells in your body need food and oxygen. These substances get carried around your body in the blood. Food and oxygen move out of the blood and into the cells.

Some chemical reactions that take place inside the cells make waste products. These can be toxic. So carbon dioxide and other waste chemicals move out of the cells and into the blood.

a) What are the 2 main things that a cell needs to survive?

How do substances move in and out of cells?

Substances move in and out of cells by **diffusion**; but what is diffusion? As bacon cooks in the kitchen, you can soon smell it in the other rooms of your house. The particles that make up the smell move from a place of high concentration (the kitchen) to one of low concentration (the rest of the house). This is an example of diffusion. It takes place in all liquids and gases.

b) Name another everyday example of diffusion.

Diffusion: the smell of bacon frying

WELL, WHAT DO YOU THINK OF MY NEW AFTERSHAVE?

Diffusion: not always welcome!

c) Explain why the smell from a strong aftershave will fill a room after a few minutes.

How does water move in and out of cells?

Water moves into and out of cells by **osmosis**. This is a special type of diffusion. The cell membrane is partially permeable (some things can pass through it). It contains tiny holes that water molecules can pass through. Larger molecules such as glucose can't get through. You can see this in the diagram at the top of the next page:

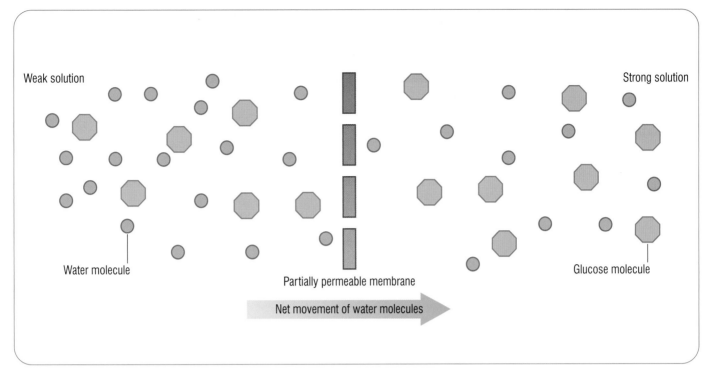

Weak solution

Strong solution

Water molecule

Glucose molecule

Partially permeable membrane

Net movement of water molecules

Water moves in and out of cells by **osmosis**

The diagram shows osmosis taking place. Water molecules move from an area where they are in a high concentration to an area where they are in a low concentration.

d) Explain how water molecules travel into a cell.

Why do plants wilt?

It is very important for farmers to water their crops regularly. If they don't, their plants will wilt, and eventually die.

Water moves into the plant cells by osmosis, filling the vacuole. This puts pressure on the cell wall and makes the cell **turgid** (rigid).

If the plant lacks water, the vacuole shrinks. The cell then becomes **flaccid** (floppy). The plant wilts, and starts to fall over.

e) Why do plants wilt if you forget to water them?

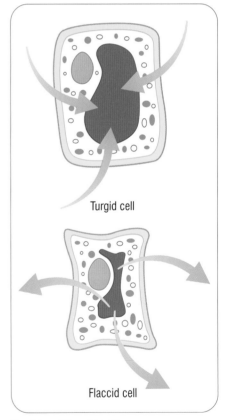

Turgid cell

Flaccid cell

Turgid and flaccid cells

TEST YOURSELF!

1 Copy and complete the following sentences with these words:

diffusion   osmosis   partially permeable

Food and oxygen move into cells by_____. Cells have a _____ membrane. Some substances can pass through it. Water moves into and out of cells by _____.

2 Why must you remember to water your plants on hot, dry days?

3 If you placed an animal cell in a beaker of water, why would it burst?

4 Why would a plant wilt if you watered it with sea water?

1.3

How do your cells change food into energy?

LEARNING OBJECTIVES

1 What is aerobic respiration?
2 How does respiration release energy?

How do your cells release energy?

Your body needs energy to do everything. For example, you need it to move, to grow and to stay warm. We get energy from our food, but to release energy, food has to be 'burned' in oxygen. This reaction is called **aerobic respiration**:

glucose   +   oxygen   →   carbon dioxide   +   water   +   **energy**
(a type of sugar)   (waste products)

$$C_6H_{12}O_6 \quad + \quad 6O_2 \quad \rightarrow \quad 6CO_2 \quad + \quad 6H_2O \quad + \quad energy$$

a) Why do all the cells in your body need to respire constantly?

Where does respiration take place?

Respiration happens inside tiny structures inside your cells called **mitochondria**. Muscle cells need lots of energy, so they are packed with large numbers of mitochondria.

How can you measure how fast someone is respiring?

People who are physically active like rugby players and athletes need lots of energy. They need to eat lots of 'high-energy' food. (See page 66.) That's so their bodies can release the energy from the glucose they get from food. Their bodies have to respire at a fast rate.

b) Apart from playing sports, when might your rate of respiration increase?

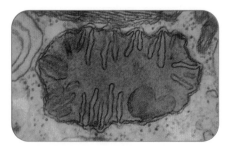

A mitochondrion

You can measure your rate of respiration with a respirometer. This tells us how quickly a person uses up oxygen. Athletes use this in training to monitor their fitness levels.

Respiring without oxygen

Your body can only 'burn' glucose in oxygen at a certain rate. There are times when you need to produce energy more quickly. The body can make this extra energy for short periods of time without oxygen. We call this **anaerobic respiration**. It often happens during strenuous exercise.

$$\text{glucose} \rightarrow \text{lactic acid} + \text{energy}$$

Lactic acid is toxic, and can give you cramp in your muscles. When you have finished exercising you keep on breathing heavily. This extra oxygen breaks down the lactic acid. The oxygen needed for this process is called the **oxygen debt**.

This athlete has run a hard race!

c) Explain why the body sometimes needs to respire anaerobically.
d) Why can anaerobic respiration cause pain?

DID YOU KNOW?

Sprinters often hold their breath during a 100 m race. This results in an oxygen debt of 7 litres.

TEST YOURSELF!

1 Copy and complete the following sentences with these words:

all   mitochondria   respiration   time

Energy is released in the _____ inside your cells by the process of _____. Respiration occurs in _____ of your cells all of the _____.

2 Why do muscle cells contain lots of mitochondria?

3 Explain why your rate of respiration increases during exercise.

4 Gyms often have steamed-up windows. Explain why, using ideas about respiration.

1.4 Do all cells look the same?

LEARNING OBJECTIVES

1 Which cells are specialised cells in animals?
2 What are the specialised cells in plants?

Most cells in your body contain these four important features:

- nucleus
- cell membrane
- cytoplasm
- mitochondria.

However, they do not look the same. Your cells have different jobs to do and this affects their design. These cells are called **specialised cells**.

a) Why are cells specialised?

Specialised animal cells

This is a smear of human blood cells. Pathologists study this information to spot diseases or anything abnormal in the body:

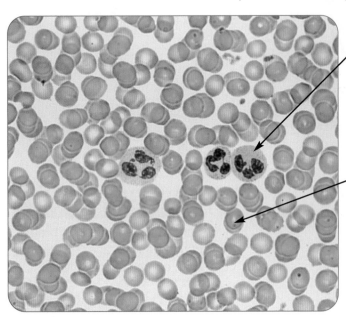

White blood cells fight disease. They:

- are large
- have a nucleus
- can change shape so the cells can engulf microorganisms. (See pages 64–65.)

Red blood cells carry oxygen around the body. They:

- are small
- have no nucleus and a disc-like shape. This increases their surface area for carrying oxygen
- contain haemoglobin (red pigment). (See page 71.)

Human blood cells

b) Look at the photo above. What type of blood cell is most common in your blood?

Nerve cells

Nerve cells, called **neurones**, transmit electrical impulses around your body. They:

- are long and thin – in your leg they are over 1 m long!
- are covered in fat – to insulate you from the impulse and to stop the message being confused with other messages
- have receptors – to detect stimuli like light, sound, and heat. (See pages 44–45.)

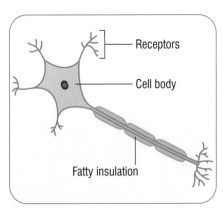

Receptors
Cell body
Fatty insulation

A nerve cell

c) What types of information do nerve cells transmit?

Specialised plant cells

Plants also contain cells that carry out specific jobs:

Leaf palisade cells are found near the top of a leaf. They are the main site of photosynthesis. The cells:

- are long and thin – so have a large surface area for absorbing light
- contain lots of chloroplasts for photosynthesis.

Root hair cells absorb water and nutrients from the soil. They have:
- a root hair – which has a large surface area for absorbing water
- no chloroplasts – as there is no light underground!

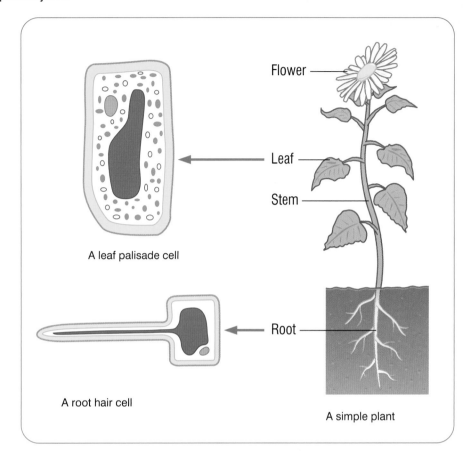

A leaf palisade cell

A root hair cell

Flower

Leaf

Stem

Root

A simple plant

d) Why do palisade cells contain lots of chloroplasts?
e) Why do root hairs have a large surface area?

TEST YOURSELF!

1 Copy and complete the following sentences with these words:

**chloroplasts   disease   photosynthesis
oxygen   red   specialised**

Cells that perform different jobs in an organism are called _____ cells.

Your _____ blood cells carry _____ around the body.

White blood cells fight _____.

Leaf cells are packed full of _____ to carry out _____.

2 What would happen if nerve cells were not covered in a layer of insulation?

3 Do some research to answer this question:

Cells that line your nose (the nasal epithelium) perform two special jobs – what features do these specialised cells need?

1.5   How are substances transported around the body?

LEARNING OBJECTIVES

1 How does your circulatory system work?
2 What does your heart do?
3 What is your blood made of?

Your **heart** is a muscle about the size of your fist. It is constantly pumping blood around your body. It delivers oxygen and nutrients to your cells and removes waste.

a) What is the function of the heart?

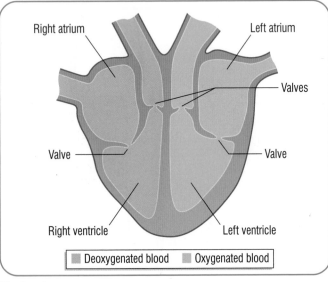

The heart

The right side of your heart contains **deoxygenated blood**. This means it has low levels of oxygen. This blood has to be pumped to the lungs by the right ventricle. Once at the lungs, it collects more oxygen.

The left side of your heart contains **oxygenated blood**. This is rich in oxygen, which all body cells need. The muscle in the left ventricle has to be very thick, to pump blood at a high pressure. This makes the blood travel all the way around your body.

The valves in your heart stop the blood from flowing backwards.

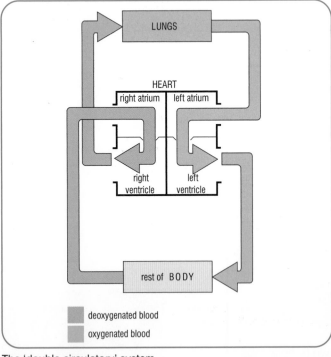

The 'double circulatory' system

This diagram shows how the heart circulates blood through the body. Blood flows through the heart twice during each circuit of the body. It is called a 'double circulatory' system.

b) Why does the wall of the left ventricle need to be thicker than the right ventricle?
c) What is the difference between oxygenated and deoxygenated blood?

What is your blood made of?

You have about 5 litres of blood in your body. Blood is made up of:

- **Red blood cells** – carry oxygen.
- **White blood cells** – fight disease by **engulfing** microbes and making antibodies.
- **Plasma** – a straw coloured liquid mainly composed of water. It carries digested food, waste (e.g. carbon dioxide), hormones, blood cells and antibodies.
- **Platelets** – fragments of cells which help the blood to clot.

Blood travels around your body in blood vessels. There are three types:

An artery	**A vein**	**A capillary**

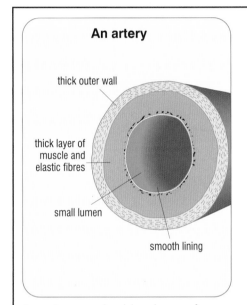

thick outer wall

thick layer of muscle and elastic fibres

small lumen

smooth lining

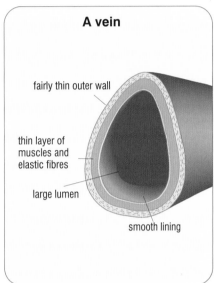

fairly thin outer wall

thin layer of muscles and elastic fibres

large lumen

smooth lining

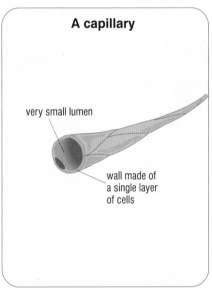

very small lumen

wall made of a single layer of cells

An **artery** carries blood away from the heart under high pressure.

Veins return blood to the heart. They have valves to stop blood flowing backwards.

Capillaries are tiny vessels. The wall is only 1 cell thick, so substances can easily move through them.

d) What 4 things is blood made up of?

TEST YOURSELF!

1 Copy and complete the following sentences using these words:

deoxygenated   left   right

lungs   muscle   four

The heart is a _____ containing ____ chambers. The _____ side is very thick because it has to pump blood around the body. The _____ side contains _____ blood. This has to be pumped to the _____ to collect more oxygen.

2 How is carbon dioxide carried around the body?

3 How is the structure of each of the blood vessels related to its function?

4 a) What is the function of the valves in your heart?
   b) Why is this important for your body?

1.6

What happens when we breathe?

LEARNING OBJECTIVES

1 What is the structure of your thorax?
2 How do you breathe?
3 What is gas exchange in your lungs?

You breathe in oxygen and breathe out carbon dioxide. This process is called **gas exchange**. It takes place inside your lungs.

Your lungs are found inside the **thorax**. They are protected by your rib cage. You can see this on the chest X-ray.

Below the lungs there is a large sheet of muscle called the **diaphragm**. This separates your thorax from the abdomen below. It plays an important part in our breathing.

a) What happens during gas exchange?
b) How are your lungs protected?

Have a look inside your thorax

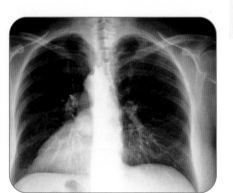

Chest X-ray

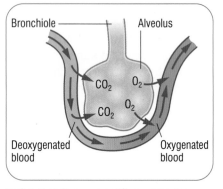

In the alveoli, oxygen diffuses into the blood. CO_2 diffuses from the blood into the alveoli to be exhaled.

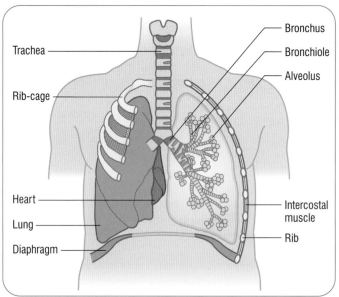

Inside the thorax

Air enters your body via your mouth and nose

↓

Down the trachea

↓

Down a bronchus

↓

Through a bronchiole

↓

Into an alveolus (air sac)

↓

Here oxygen diffuses into the blood

DID YOU KNOW?

When patients cannot breathe through the mouth and nose, a hole can be cut into the windpipe through the throat. This operation is known as a tracheotomy.

c) Describe, step by step, how carbon dioxide leaves the body.

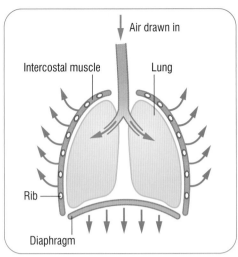

Air drawn in

Intercostal muscle

Lung

Rib

Diaphragm

The inhaling process

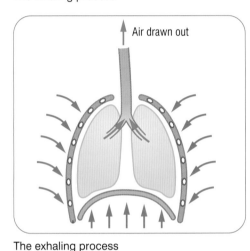

Air drawn out

The exhaling process

How do you breathe?

Inhaling (breathing in):

- Intercostal muscles contract – pulling your ribcage up and out
- Diaphragm contracts – moving down.

This increases the volume in the thorax. The pressure decreases and you draw air into your lungs.

Exhaling (breathing out):

- Intercostal muscles relax – lowering your ribcage down and in
- Diaphragm relaxes – moving up.

This decreases the volume in the thorax. The pressure increases and forces air out of your lungs.

d) What are the muscles called that alter the position of your ribs?

TEST YOURSELF!

1 Copy and complete the table using the following words:

up   down   up and out   down and in   decreases   increases

	Inhaling	Exhaling
Ribs move		
Diaphragm moves		
Thorax volume		

2 Look at the pie charts on the right:

a) Explain why the percentage of nitrogen is the same in inhaled and exhaled air.
b) Explain why you exhale more carbon dioxide than you inhale.
c) Name some other differences between inhaled and exhaled air not shown on the pie charts.

3 Research how paramedics treat people who have stopped breathing.

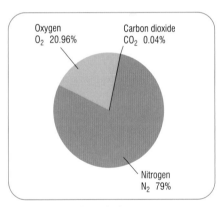

Oxygen O_2 20.96%

Carbon dioxide CO_2 0.04%

Nitrogen N_2 79%

Composition of inhaled gases

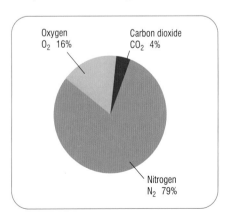

Oxygen O_2 16%

Carbon dioxide CO_2 4%

Nitrogen N_2 79%

Composition of exhaled gases

1.7

How do we react to changes in our environment?

LEARNING OBJECTIVES

1 How does your body control reactions?
2 What is a reflex action?

Your body responds to stimuli (changes in the environment) via your nervous system.

The nervous system works by sending electrical impulses around your body. Most information detected by your body is sent to the brain. The brain then decides what to do. It sends another impulse to some part of your body telling it how to respond.

There are three stages to a nervous response:

1 **stimulus** – a change in the environment

2 **receptors** – groups of cells that detect the stimulus

3 **effectors** – cause a response (they are muscles or **glands**)

a) How are messages sent along nerves?

Receptor cells

Receptor cells are found in your sense organs and are sensitive to a range of stimuli. They change the stimulus into electrical impulses that travel along **sensory neurones** to the central nervous system (CNS). The CNS is made up of the brain and spinal cord.

Sense organ	Receptor cells	Stimulus
Eye	Light	Light
Ear	Sound	Sound
Tongue	Taste	Chemical
Skin	Pressure Temperature	Touch Heat
Nose	Smell Taste	Chemical (smell)

b) Name 4 stimuli that the body responds to.

There are three types of neurone, as shown below:

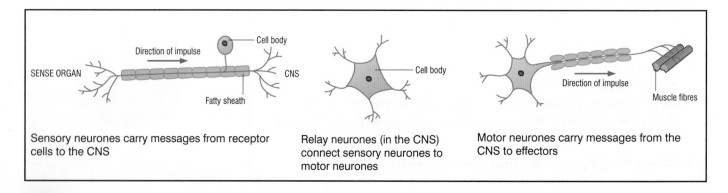

Sensory neurones carry messages from receptor cells to the CNS

Relay neurones (in the CNS) connect sensory neurones to motor neurones

Motor neurones carry messages from the CNS to effectors

Controlled reactions

The diagram below shows the steps involved in a nervous response.
This process only takes around 0.7 seconds!

Stimulus → Receptor cells → **Sensory neurone** → Spinal cord → Brain → Spinal cord → **Motor neutrone** → Effector → Response

CNS

The steps that occur in a controlled reaction

c) Which type of neurone is only found in the CNS?

Reflex actions

Reflex actions do not involve the brain. By missing out the brain, the body reacts even quicker than normal. So we use these reactions when we are in danger.

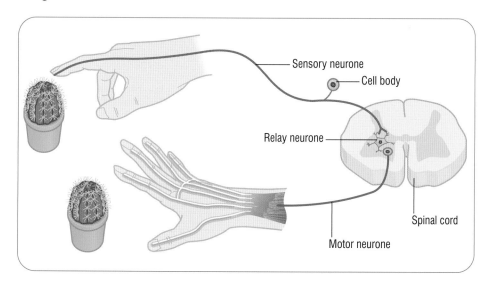

A reflex!

d) Which is the fastest type of nervous response?
e) Describe 2 situations where your body would respond by a reflex action.

TEST YOURSELF!

1 Match the parts of the nervous system to their function:

Receptor cells	Cause a response
Effectors	Carry electrical impulses
Neurones	Decide on a response
Brain	Detects changes in your environment

2 Are the following reactions controlled or reflex actions?
   a) Pupils in your eyes shrinking in bright light.
   b) Tying your shoe lace.
   c) Signing your name.
   d) Taking your hand off a hot coal.

3 Draw a flow diagram showing the steps involved in a reflex action.

1.8   Why do we have hormones?

Hormones are chemical messengers that travel around your body. They are made in **glands** and secreted into the blood, which carries the hormones all around your body.

Hormones cause a response only in **target cells**. Hormones control body processes that need constant adjustment – such as body temperature.

Keeping the conditions in your body constant is called **homeostasis**.

Hormones and nerves carry out similar roles, but act in very different ways:

	Nerves	Hormones
Speed of response	Very fast	Slower
Length of response	Short acting	Longer acting
Area targeted	Very precise area	Larger area
Time of reaction	Immediate	Longer term

a) Where are hormones produced in the body?
b) What role do hormones play in the body?

The diagram below shows some important glands and the hormones they produce:

Adrenal glands
Produce adrenaline – involved in the 'fight or flight' reaction that occurs in response to danger.

Pancreas
Produces insulin – controls blood sugar level.

Ovaries (females)
Produce oestrogen – causes eggs to mature, pubic hair to grow, breasts to enlarge, etc.

Testes (males)
Produce testosterone – causes sperm production, hair growth, shoulders to widen, etc.

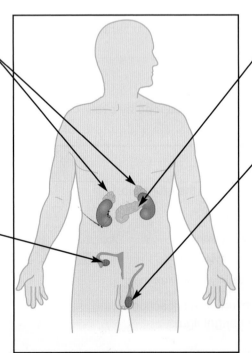

Some important glands

c) Name the 2 hormones that are responsible for changes that take place during puberty.

How does insulin control your blood sugar level?

After eating (especially carbohydrate-rich foods), your blood sugar level rises. The carbohydrates get broken down into **glucose**. If your blood sugar level stays high, it can lead to a diabetic coma, and if this is untreated you can die.

Special cells in the pancreas detect high blood sugar levels and release the hormone insulin. Insulin tells cells in the liver to store some of the glucose by converting it into **glycogen**. As glucose is removed from the blood, the blood sugar level falls.

If the blood glucose level is too low, insulin is not released. The pancreas releases another hormone. This one tells the liver to turn stored glycogen back into glucose. Then the glucose is released into the blood stream and the blood sugar level rises.

How do doctors control diabetes?

In a person who has diabetes, the pancreas cells do not produce enough insulin. This means that their blood sugar levels can rise to a level which can be fatal. Doctors may advise patients to visit a dietician.

Dieticians advise diabetic people to avoid eating large quantities of carbohydrate-rich foods. They are also advised to exercise after they have eaten, to help use up excess glucose.

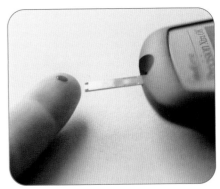

A blood testing kit, which is used to monitor blood glucose levels

For some people, just controlling their diet is not enough to manage their condition. In this case, doctors prescribe insulin. These diabetic people have to inject themselves with insulin several times a day.

d) Why do people with diabetes have to test their blood sugar level before injecting themselves with insulin?

TEST YOURSELF!

1 Copy and complete the following sentences using these words:

blood   glands   pancreas   sugar   target

Hormones are produced in _____. They travel in the _____ and cause a response in _____ cells. Insulin is produced by the _____. It controls blood _____ level.

2 Name some foods which diabetics must avoid eating in large quantities.

3 Explain how the body uses glycogen to control the amount of glucose in the blood.

4 Find out about how diabetes is linked to diet and obesity.

1.9

How do we avoid getting too hot or too cold?

Your body works best at 37°C. Whatever conditions you are in, your body will try to maintain this temperature. Your brain monitors the temperature of your blood and receptors in your skin receive information about the external temperature.

Your brain processes this information, and sends messages to tell the body how to respond.

a) What is the normal body temperature?

Exercise, sunbathing and physical labour can cause the body to overheat. Exposure to cold weather can cool the body down. It only takes a couple of degrees difference in your body's temperature to stop the body from working efficiently.

Your body is designed to protect itself from these variations in several ways, mainly using the skin.

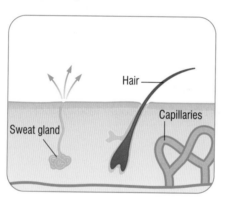

Hairs on hot skin

What happens when you get too hot?

- Hairs on your skin lie flat.
- Sweat glands produce sweat.
- Capillaries near the surface of your skin widen (**vasodilation**).

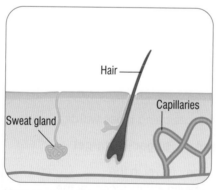

Hairs on cold skin

What happens when you get too cold?

- Hairs on your skin stand on end. This traps a layer of air close to the skin, preventing heat loss.
- Sweat glands do not produce sweat.
- Capillaries near the surface of your skin narrow (**vasoconstriction**).
- Shivering (rapid muscle contractions). This requires extra energy, so your cells respire more, producing extra heat.

b) Why do the hairs on your arm stand up when you are cold?
c) Why does shivering help you warm up?

Why do you go red when you are hot?

When you are hot the capillaries in your skin widen (dilate). This allows more blood to flow close to the surface of the skin and makes you look red. So more heat is lost from the blood by radiation, cooling you down.

Why do we sweat?

Sweat is mainly water, but it also contains salt and urea (a waste material). The water in sweat uses heat energy from your body to evaporate. As heat energy is lost from your body, you feel cooler.

The more you sweat, the more you cool down; but you also lose more water and salt. These substances need to be replaced by drinking and eating, otherwise you will dehydrate.

d) What is sweat made of?

Someone is hot!

What happens if you get too cold?

As your body cools it starts to function at a slower rate. If your temperature drops by 2°C your brain will be affected. Body movements will slow and your speech will begin to slur.

If your body temperature continues to drop, you will go into a coma. Eventually you will die. This condition is called **hypothermia**. It is a major problem for explorers in extreme weather conditions, but can also affect the elderly if they have poor heating.

e) How would you know if someone is suffering from hypothermia?

Explorers need to make sure they don't get too cold by wearing protective clothing

---

TEST YOURSELF!

1 Copy and complete the table with the following words:

lie flat   make sweat   narrow   stand up
stop making sweat   widen

	Too hot	Too cold
Hairs		
Blood vessels		
Sweat glands		

2 Explain what the words vasodilation and vasoconstriction mean.

3 If you tasted your skin after you exercised, why would it taste salty?

4 How is a polar bear adapted so that it doesn't get hypothermia?

1.10   Why does everyone look different?

LEARNING OBJECTIVES

1 How do people vary?
2 What is variation?

It is easy to tell the difference between a lion and a fish. This is because they have lots of different **characteristics** (features). However, it is more difficult to tell the difference between two frogs. This is because, within a species, lots of characteristics are shared.

Every person in the world is different – even identical twins differ in some ways. These differences within a species are called **variation**. People vary in many ways including height, build, hair colour and intelligence.

There are two factors which cause variation:

- The characteristics you inherit from your parents (genetics).
- The environment in which you live.

a) What is variation?

How do people vary?

Very intelligent

Speaks English

Good swimmer

Average height

Rides a bike

Blood group AB

Tall

Speaks Spanish

How people can vary

These two children vary in a number of ways. Some of this variation is due to characteristics they have inherited from their parents. However, most is due to factors in their environment. These include where they live and what they learn from their parents, teachers and friends.

b) State 3 characteristics that are caused by genetic variation.
c) Give 3 characteristics that are influenced by environmental variation.

Hair colour

This characteristic could be classified as an **inherited** feature – people generally have the same colour hair as one of their parents. However, look at the girl in the picture on the right:

Do you think her parents also have blue spiky hair? Probably not!

This is an example of environmental variation. The person has chosen to dye and style their hair in this way.

Is this person's hair colour inherited?

Height

Height is another characteristic that is mostly determined by inheritance. If your parents are tall, you are also likely to be tall. However, if you live in a deprived area with very little to eat, your growth is likely to be stunted as a result of poor diet.

Many characteristics are affected by both environmental and genetic variation.

d) Name 2 other characteristics that are influenced by both environmental and genetic variation.

Characteristics that are not influenced by the environment

In humans there are only four such features:

- Eye colour.
- Natural hair colour.
- Blood group.
- Genetic diseases – like cystic fibrosis and haemophilia.

Variation in height

TEST YOURSELF!

1 Copy and complete the table using the words provided below:

weight **intelligence**
blood group **skin colour**
eye colour **hair length**

Type of variation	Characteristic
Genetic variation	
Environmental variation	
Both types of variation	

2 a) Are plants more or less likely than animals to be influenced by environmental variation?

 b) Name some factors in the environment which could affect plant growth.

3 Why are identical twins the best people to study if you want to find out how the environment influences characteristics?

1.11   Why do we look like our parents?

1 How is information passed on from your parents?
2 What are chromosomes and genes?

The picture below shows a child and his parents. The child shares some features with his mother and some with his father. These are called **inherited** features. They have been passed on from the parents to the child.

Parents

Offspring

The different features of a child and his parents

a) Make a list of the features the child has inherited from his mother and those he has inherited from his father.

Where is this information stored?

You inherit characteristics from your parents through genetic material. Inside the nucleus of your cells are **chromosomes**. These are strands of the chemical **DNA**, which contain all the information needed to make a human being.

Each chromosome is divided into sections of DNA. Each contains the information needed to produce a single characteristic like eye colour or hair colour. These coding sections are called **genes**. One chromosome contains thousands of genes.

b) What is a chromosome?
c) What is a gene?

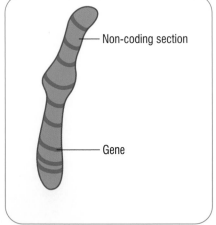

Non-coding section

Gene

Chromosome

How do we inherit features from our parents?

Inside the nucleus of your normal body cells, there are 23 pairs of chromosomes (so 46 altogether). One chromosome of each pair comes from your mother. The other comes from your father.

Egg and sperm cells are the only cells in the body to contain 23 chromosomes. They only have one copy of each pair.

During fertilisation, these cells join together to form an embryo. This means that inside each cell of the embryo there are 46 chromosomes.

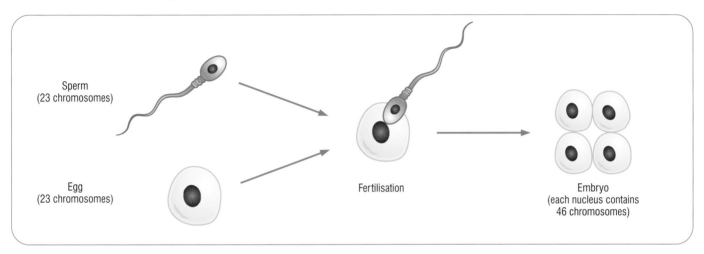

Sperm
(23 chromosomes)

Egg
(23 chromosomes)

Fertilisation

Embryo
(each nucleus contains
46 chromosomes)

Fertilisation

d) How many chromosomes are there inside a human nucleus?

Out of your 46 chromosomes, 22 pairs are identical, but the 23rd pair do not always match. These are the sex chromosomes. They determine whether you are a boy or a girl.

Girls have two identical X chromosomes, whereas boys have one X chromosome and a shorter Y chromosome. Only males carry this chromosome, so it is the father who determines the sex of their children!

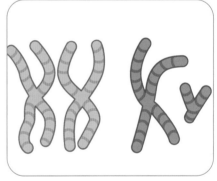

Females have two X chromosomes, males have one X and one Y chromosome

TEST YOURSELF!

1   Copy and complete the following sentences using these words:

   chromosomes   DNA   genes   nucleus

   Inside each of your normal body cells there is a _____. This

   contains 46 _____ made up of the chemical _____.

   Sections of DNA which code for a characteristic are called _____.

2   Fruit flies have only 4 pairs of chromosomes in each nucleus.
   a) How many chromosomes do they have in a normal body cell?
   b) How many chromosomes do they have in a sex cell?

3   Explain why identical twins look the same, but brothers and sisters only look similar.

1.12

Why don't we look identical to our parents?

LEARNING OBJECTIVES

1 What are alleles?
2 What are dominant and recessive genes?

You have two genes for each characteristic – one from your mother and one from your father. These two genes may be the same. For example, they may both code for blonde hair. In this case you will have blonde hair.

However, they may be different. Different forms of the same gene are called **alleles**. For example, there is also a gene that codes for brown hair and one that codes for black hair.

a) What is an allele?

How do we know which gene will be expressed?

Some genes will always be **expressed** (shown) – these are called **dominant genes**. If a gene that codes for black hair is present in the nucleus, that person will have black hair. If the gene for blonde hair is also present, it will not be shown. This is because the black hair gene is stronger.

Weaker genes like the blonde hair gene are called **recessive genes**. Recessive genes will only be expressed if you have two of them.

b) Which type of gene will always be expressed if it is present?

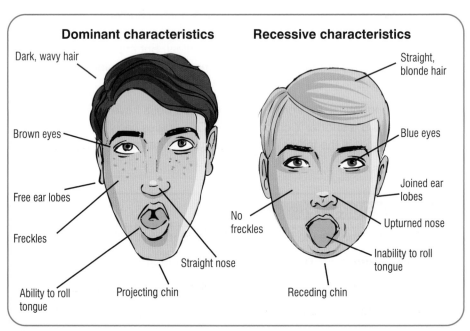

Dominant and recessive characteristics

c) Make a list of some recessive characteristics shown in the picture above.
d) Make a list of some dominant characteristics shown in the picture above.

How do you inherit eye colour?

We can represent the genes on your chromosomes using letters. The dominant gene is always represented with a capital letter. For eye colour, brown eyes are dominant and blue eyes are recessive. In the example below – **B** = brown eyes allele, **b** = blue eyes allele. During fertilisation, one gene from the mother's egg joins with one gene from the father's sperm. This is shown in the diagram below:

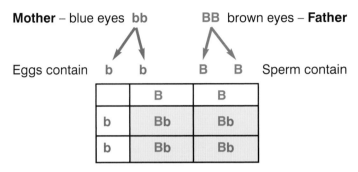

These are the possible combinations of alleles from these parents. Studying the inheritance of one gene is called monohybrid inheritance.

All children will have the genes **Bb**. This means that they will all have brown eyes, as **B** is the dominant allele. Remember – you have two genes for each characteristic.

What would happen if both your parents had brown eyes, but they also carried the recessive gene for blue eyes? This is no trickier – just follow the diagram step by step.

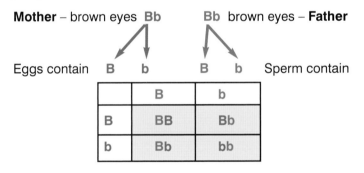

During fertilisation, any of the combinations shown in the yellow area of the table could be produced.

Children would be born in the ratio of 1 **BB** : 2 **Bb** : 1 **bb**. For every three children with brown eyes there will be one child with blue eyes.

TEST YOURSELF!

1 Copy and complete the following sentences using these words:

   alleles   dominant   recessive

   Many forms of a gene exist; these are called ____. The _____ alleles will always be shown, whereas _____ alleles will only show up if a person has two copies of this form of the gene.

2 If you had dominant alleles for hair colour and style, what would your hair look like?

3 **F** is the gene for freckles and **f** is the gene for no freckles. If a mother has freckles (**Ff**) but the father doesn't (**ff**), what type of skin will their children inherit? Draw a diagram like the one above to explain your answer.

1.13   Saving lives

DO SOMETHING AMAZING!

Doctors and nurses use blood from donors to save thousands of lives each year. Each donation can benefit more than one person, as the blood is normally divided into different parts. Each part has different medical uses:

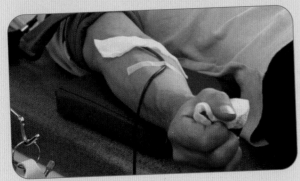

A blood donor

RED BLOOD CELLS

These are given to people suffering from severe anaemia, rheumatoid arthritis or cancer. They are also used to 'top-up' blood after major surgery or accidents.

PLATELETS

These are given to patients who have suffered bone marrow failure, been treated for cancers with chemotherapy, and after receiving an organ transplant.

PLASMA

This is used for patients who have lost blood during childbirth, after heart surgery and for patients who have suffered liver failure.

Only around 6% of the population who could give blood actually do so. Blood can be stored for only a short period of time, so it is essential to maintain a regular supply.

Activity

The National Blood Service have asked you to design a poster to promote 'giving blood'. You need to include as much information as possible to convince people that their help is needed.

TSUNAMI STRIKE

** Newsflash** 26th December 2004 **

A tsunami

Information has reached the UK of a huge Tsunami. It has struck the Maldives, a small group of islands in the Indian Ocean. This tidal wave has covered the low-lying islands completely, and caused widespread death and devastation.

Activity

Imagine you are an agricultural scientist.

You have been sent to the Maldives at the end of January 2005. You need to write a report on the long-term impact of the tsunami on the islands' agriculture. You observe scenes of farmland like the ones below. Many trees and crops have died, despite surviving the impact of the tidal wave.

Agricultural after-effects of a tsunami

Some areas, which suffered heavy rains soon after the tsunami, have partially recovered, with 30–50% of crops surviving.

Your report needs to explain how salt water has killed most of the crops, and why some crops in areas which had heavy rains have survived.

Are you exercising hard enough?

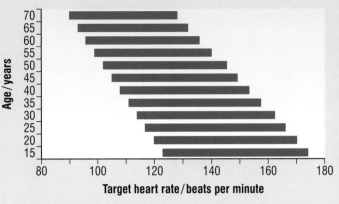

A graph showing target heart rate during exercise

To improve your aerobic fitness, you need to exercise to increase your heart rate. The required rate depends upon your age. You can measure your heart rate during exercise by taking your pulse.

Activities

a) Why does your pulse rate increase during exercise?

b) If you wanted to increase your fitness level, within what range would your heart need to beat during exercise?

c) What happens to the target heart rate as a person's age increases?

d) Professional athletes often train at levels that exceed these target heart rates. This significantly increases their rate of aerobic respiration. How does this help the athlete?

Would you know what to do?

Every year many lives are saved by people knowing basic first aid. If a person stops breathing you would give them 'the kiss of life' (artificial respiration). In 2005, the St John's Ambulance guide to artificial respiration was:

- Ensure the airway is open.
- Pinch nose firmly closed.
- Take a deep breath and seal your lips around the casualty's mouth.
- Blow into the mouth until the chest rises.
- Remove your mouth and allow the chest to fall.
- Repeat once more then check for circulation.
- Check for circulation after every 10 breaths.

If breathing starts, place in Recovery Position.

Activities

a) Before giving the kiss of life, you should place your ear over the person's mouth, and look for movement in their chest. Explain why this is important.

b) Why would giving the kiss of life to a person who is not breathing help to save their life?

c) Explain why the term 'artificial respiration' is misleading.

d) Why should you 'check for circulation after every 10 breaths'?

e) You need to use a different technique, called CPR, if a person's heart stops beating. Find out how this is carried out, and write a method (similar to the one above) for this technique.

SUMMARY QUESTIONS

1

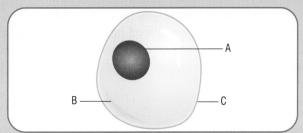

A student is looking at an animal cell through a microscope.

a) Name parts A, B and C.

b) Where in the cell do chemical reactions take place?

c) What are the 3 extra structures that you would find in a plant cell?

2 Copy and complete the table below using the pictures to help you.

Cell	Name	Function
A		Carries oxygen
B	Neurone	
C		Carries out photosynthesis
D	Root hair	

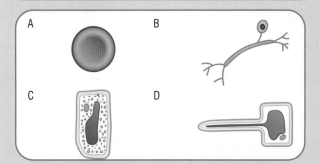

3 Match the parts of the blood with their function.

Part	Function
Red blood cells	Carries substances around the body
White blood cells	Carry oxygen
Platelets	Fight disease
Plasma	Help to clot the blood

4 A chef accidentally puts his hand on the hot plate.

a) Which receptor cell detects this?

b) What effector is involved in the reaction?

c) How do impulses travel along a nerve?

d) Is this a controlled or a reflex response?

5 How many chromosomes are found in:

a) Hair cells?   b) Sperm cells?   c) A fertilised egg?

6 Look at the diagram of the thorax:

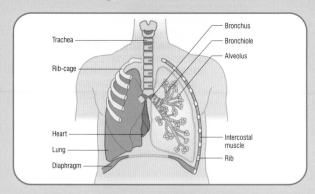

a) Which structure protects the lungs?

b) What is the diaphragm made of?

c) What do the intercostal muscles do?

d) Where does gas exchange take place?

e) Explain how air is drawn in and out of the lungs.

7 During respiration, glucose is 'burnt' in oxygen to release energy.

a) What 2 waste products are made during this process?

b) Where in the cell does this reaction happen?

c) Explain why the rate of respiration changes when you exercise.

8

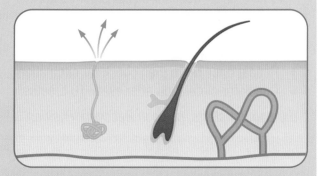

The picture above shows the skin of a gardener when she is working hard. What 3 things in the picture show you that she is hot?

9 The night before a marathon an athlete eats a large bowl of pasta. Their blood sugar level rises.

a) Why does this happen?

b) What hormone regulates this level?

c) Where is this hormone made?

d) Explain how this hormone acts to reduce your blood sugar level.

EXAM-STYLE QUESTIONS

1 A chef put some potatoes in water and noticed that they increased in size. He wanted to know why. He was told the cells in potatoes absorb water by osmosis.

The diagram below was used to explain osmosis but the labels are missing.

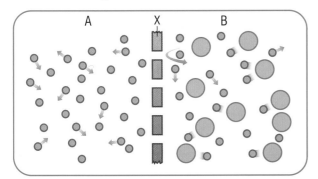

a) i)   Which half of the diagram (A or B) shows water and which a sucrose solution? (1)
   ii) What is X on the diagram? (1)
   iii) In which direction on the diagram will most of the water move? (1)
   iv) Explain to the chef why his potatoes increased in size. (3)

2 The diagrams show the position of the ribs and diaphragm during inhalation and exhalation.

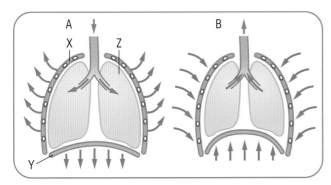

a) i)   Which diagram (A or B) shows inhalation and which shows exhalation? (1)
   ii) Name structures X, Y and Z. (3)
   iii) Write down three differences between inhalation and exhalation. (3)

b) When you breath you obtain oxygen. This allows a process called respiration to take place.

   i)   Copy and complete the following word equation to show this process.

   ……………. + oxygen ➤ …………. + water + energy

(2)

   ii) If 1 g of carbohydrate releases 17 kJ of energy, how much energy would be released from 6 g of carbohydrate?
   (Use a calculator if you need to.) (1)

3 A childminder responsible for the care of young children needs good reflex actions. The diagram shows the nervous pathway of a reflex action.

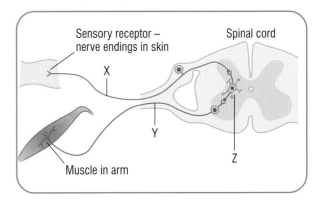

a) i)   What is meant by a reflex action? (2)
   ii) What is the name of the sensory receptor found in the skin? (1)
   iii) Give the names of neurones X, Y and Z. (3)

b) Explain the advantages of reflex actions to the childminder. (2)

4 The graph below shows the body temperature of a yachtsman and air temperature over 24 hours.

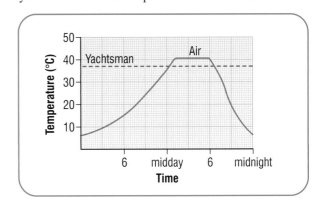

a) What is the yachtsman's body temperature? (2)

b) Explain how the yachtsman might be controlling his body temperature at 3pm. (4)

2.1   What are harmful microorganisms?

LEARNING OBJECTIVES

1 What are microorganisms?
2 Which microorganisms cause diseases?

Microorganisms are very tiny living things – at least 100 times smaller than one of your cells. Most cause no harm to animals or plants. However, some can cause disease when they enter the body. These are called **pathogens**. They are studied by microbiologists.

a) What are pathogens?
b) What are the scientists who study pathogens called?

There are three groups of microorganism: bacteria, viruses and fungi. We are going to look at the first two.

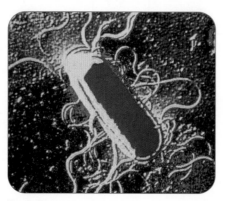

Bacteria

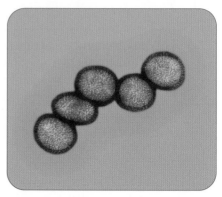

Virus

Features of bacteria:

- Have a cell wall
- No nucleus
- Genetic material floats around in the cytoplasm

Examples of disease they cause:

- Tuberculosis
- Salmonella
- Pneumonia

Features of a virus:

- Have a protein coat
- No nucleus
- A few genes which float inside the virus
- Smaller than bacteria

Examples of disease they cause:

- Measles
- Rubella
- Mumps
- 'Flu

c) Give 2 differences between bacteria and viruses.

How do pathogens make you feel ill?

Bacteria do this in two ways:

1 They damage your cells. For example, lung tissue is destroyed by tuberculosis bacteria.

2 They produce **toxins** – these are poisonous chemicals. *Salmonella* bacteria produce a toxin that causes one type of food poisoning.

Viruses make you feel unwell by damaging your cells.

How do bacteria and viruses reproduce?

There is a time delay between harmful microorganisms entering our body and when we start to feel unwell. This is called the **incubation period**. During this time, the microorganisms are rapidly reproducing.

d) What happens during the incubation period of a disease?

Bacteria can reproduce very quickly. In good conditions, they divide into two every 20 minutes. So within hours a few bacteria will have reproduced into several thousand. They will now start to have a big effect on your body.

Viruses cannot replicate by themselves. They can only reproduce using your cells (or those of another living organism).

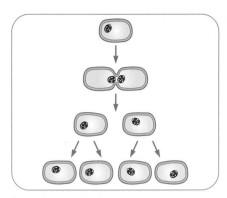

Bacteria reproducing

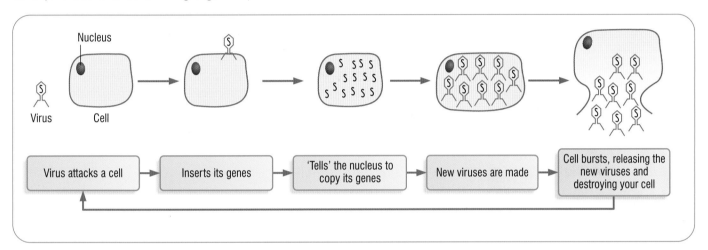

Virus attacks a cell → Inserts its genes → 'Tells' the nucleus to copy its genes → New viruses are made → Cell bursts, releasing the new viruses and destroying your cell

Viruses must invade your cells in order to reproduce

e) How do viruses cause disease?

TEST YOURSELF!

1 Copy and complete the following sentences using these words:

bacteria   mumps   pathogens   tuberculosis   viruses

We call harmful microorganisms _____.

The two main types of microorganism are _____ and _____ .

A disease caused by a virus is _____.

A disease caused by bacteria is _____.

2 The table below shows the number of bacteria in a person.

Time / minutes	Number of bacteria
0	20
20	40
40	80
60	
80	320
100	

a) Copy and complete the table.

b) Plot a graph of the data.

c) Using the graph, explain why the person feels ill after a short period of time.

2.2

How are diseases spread?

LEARNING OBJECTIVES

1 How do pathogens enter the body?
2 How do diseases spread?
3 How can you protect yourself from disease?

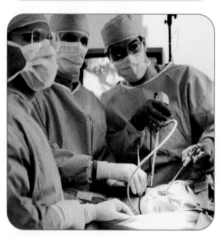

What steps do we take to prevent the spread of disease in an operating theatre?

When someone sneezes, you can catch a disease through droplet infection

In order to cause harm, pathogens have to enter our bodies. This can happen in five main ways:

- Through cuts in the skin.
- Through the digestive system – when you eat and drink.
- Through the respiratory system – when you breathe through your mouth and nose.
- Through the reproductive system – during sexual intercourse.
- Through insect / animal bites – mosquitoes, rats, etc.

You are more likely to become unwell if large numbers of microorganisms enter your body. The most common ways for this to happen is contact with a person infected with the pathogen, or by being exposed to unhygienic conditions.

a) Name the 5 ways pathogens can enter your body.

How can you prevent yourself catching a disease from an infected person?

By covering your mouth and nose. When somebody sneezes or coughs, tiny drops of liquid are released into the air – **droplet infection**. Colds and 'flu are spread by this method. This can be prevented by using a handkerchief. The only defence people had against the Asian bird 'flu epidemic in 2004 was wearing a protective mask.

By not sharing needles. People who inject medicines or illegal drugs should never share needles. Diseases can be passed on in blood. Needles must be disposed of carefully and new sterilised needles used every time. HIV and hepatitis can be spread in this way.

By not touching. Some diseases are **contagious**. They are spread by touching infected people. Some can even be spread by touching objects an infected person has touched. Mumps and chicken pox are spread like this.

By using protection. Body fluids are exchanged during sexual intercourse. Syphilis and gonorrhoea can be spread in this way. Using condoms can prevent diseases being transferred in this way.

b) How are colds and 'flu spread?

How being hygienic can help us to prevent disease spreading

Cook food properly. Some animals contain bacteria which could cause food poisoning, like *E. coli* and *Salmonella*. However, if the foods are cooked properly, the bacteria will be killed.

Restaurants are monitored by environmental health officers to ensure premises are clean, and that food is stored and cooked properly.

Drink clean water. Untreated water can contain microorganisms that cause diseases like cholera and typhoid. This may happen after flooding if sewage contaminates the fresh water supply. If water may be infected, you must boil it or use sterilisation tablets.

Protect yourself from animal bites. Mosquitoes spread malaria. By biting an infected person, and then someone else, the mosquito can pass the disease on. You can protect yourself from malaria by taking anti-malarial drugs, and using insect-repellent sprays.

Cover food. Flies are often found on animal dung. They then may land on your food, trampling germs all over it! Restaurants and delicatessens need to make sure all food is covered to prevent this happening.

Wash your hands. To reduce your risk of infection from microorganisms, wash your hands regularly. This is essential for employees in businesses involving the handling of foods.

Cover cuts and grazes. To prevent infection, you should thoroughly clean a cut. Then cover it with a plaster so microorganisms cannot enter your body.

c) State 5 ways you can help prevent the spread of infections.
d) Name 3 jobs where hygiene is important.

Lifeguards are trained to check water purity in swimming pools and to use chemicals to ensure that water is clean

---

TEST YOURSELF!

1 Copy and complete the table:

Method of transmission	Diseases spread in this way
Shared needles	
Touch	
Droplets	
Sexual intercourse	

2 Why must meat be thoroughly cooked before you eat it?

3 Why do diseases spread more easily in:
  a) Highly populated areas?
  b) Countries with poor hygiene?

2.3   How are microorganisms stopped from harming us?

LEARNING OBJECTIVES

1 How does your body mend cuts?
2 How do your white blood cells fight disease?

Although you come into contact with harmful microorganisms every day, you are not always ill. The main barrier to infection is your skin. However, if your skin is damaged, e.g. cut or grazed, pathogens can enter your body.

To prevent pathogens entering your body, the skin needs to seal a cut as quickly as possible. This also stops you losing too much blood.

a) What is your body's main defence against microorganism entry?

How does the blood clot?

Platelets are small pieces of cell that are made in the bone marrow. They are carried around the body in plasma. These pieces of cell are essential for helping the blood to clot.

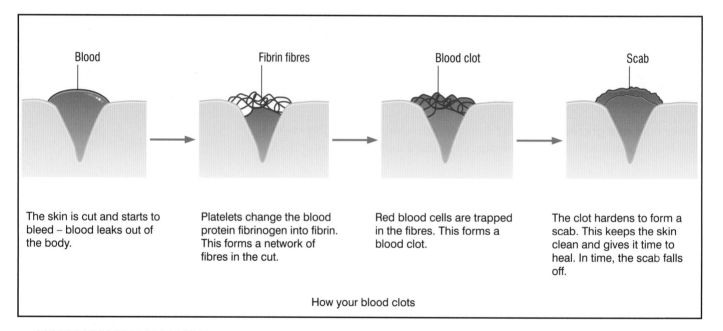

Blood	Fibrin fibres	Blood clot	Scab
The skin is cut and starts to bleed – blood leaks out of the body.	Platelets change the blood protein fibrinogen into fibrin. This forms a network of fibres in the cut.	Red blood cells are trapped in the fibres. This forms a blood clot.	The clot hardens to form a scab. This keeps the skin clean and gives it time to heal. In time, the scab falls off.

How your blood clots

DID YOU KNOW?

Leeches produce chemicals that stop the blood from clotting. These are used in hospital to help heal sores and in limb reattachment surgery. By stopping the blood clotting, oxygenated blood continuously enters the wound area (promoting healing) until the blood vessels regrow. Leeches also produce an anaesthetic, so you can't feel them sucking!

b) How do platelets help the blood to clot?

What happens if microorganisms enter our bodies?

Sometimes, harmful microorganisms do manage to enter our bodies. It is the job of white blood cells to prevent them causing disease. There are two types of white blood cells:

● **Lymphocytes** – make antibodies and anti-toxins.

● **Phagocytes** – engulf (swallow) microorganisms.

How do lymphocytes fight disease?

Lymphocytes detect that something 'foreign' has entered your body. They then make an **antibody** – a chemical to attack the microorganism.

The antibody reacts with the microorganism and de-activates it. Each antibody is specific for one type of microorganism. Every time a new microorganism enters the body, a new antibody needs to be made.

After they have fought the disease, some antibodies remain in your blood. These antibodies prevent you getting the disease again. This provides you with **immunity**.

Lymphocytes also make **anti-toxins**. These chemicals destroy poisonous toxins that some microorganisms make.

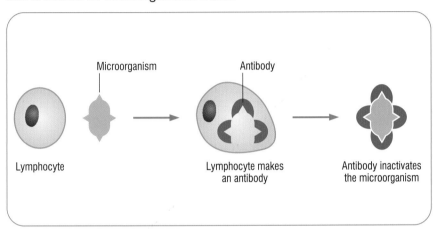

Microorganism Antibody

Lymphocyte Lymphocyte makes an antibody Antibody inactivates the microorganism

Lymphocyte fighting disease

c) What are antibodies?
d) What are anti-toxins?

How do phagocytes fight disease?

Phagocytes **engulf** (swallow) microorganisms. They then make enzymes which digest the microorganism. (See diagram on the right.)

e) How do phagocytes kill microorganisms?

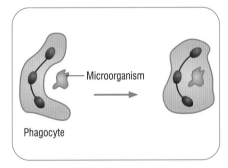

Microorganism

Phagocyte

Phagocyte fighting disease

TEST YOURSELF!

1 Match the parts of the blood with their function:

Part of the blood:	Function:
Lymphocyte	Engulfs microorganisms
Platelet	Makes antibodies and anti-toxins
Phagocyte	Helps blood to clot

2 Why is it important not to knock a scab off a cut?

3 What is the difference between an antibody and an anti-toxin?

4 If you have had chicken pox as a child, you should never suffer from the disease again. Explain why.

2.4   What makes a healthy diet?

LEARNING OBJECTIVES

1 What are the main food groups?
2 Which foods are healthy?
3 Which foods are unhealthy?

Dieticians and nutrition experts can advise us on eating healthily.

Your body needs food:

- For energy – to move and stay warm.
- For growth and repair – to make new cells, and to repair and replace old or damaged cells.
- To stay healthy.

There are seven food groups:

Carbohydrates – your main source of energy.

Proteins – you need proteins for building and repairing cells.

Fats – these provide you with a store of energy. They also help to keep you warm. Fat covers your vital organs, protecting them from damage.

Vitamins – you need vitamins in tiny amounts to keep you healthy. For example, vitamin C for resistance to disease. Vitamin A gives you good night vision.

Minerals – also needed in small quantities to keep you healthy. For example: iron for healthy red blood cells; calcium for strong teeth and bones.

Water – makes up two thirds of your body. All the reactions in a cell take place in water and substances have to dissolve in it to be carried around the blood. You can survive only a few days without water.

Fibre – we don't digest fibre, but it is important in your diet because it adds bulk to your food. This means that waste can be pushed out of the digestive system more easily. Fibre also absorbs poisonous waste made when we digest food.

Carbohydrates for energy

Fats provide you with a store of energy and help to keep you warm

Fruit and vegetables are a good source of vitamins and minerals

Proteins are needed to build and repair cells

a) Which type of food helps remove waste from the body?

b) What type of food would you need to eat if you were going to run a marathon?

Staying healthy

In order to stay healthy, you need to eat a **balanced diet**. This means that you need to eat a variety of foods in the right amounts. A healthy diet contains lots of fruit, vegetables and starchy foods (like cereal, pasta and potatoes). Such a diet is low in fat, salt and added sugar.

If you eat too much food (especially fats and sugars), the body will store it as fat. If you do this over a period of time, you may become overweight and eventually obese. Being obese carries an increased risk of heart disease, diabetes, some cancers and gout.

However, if you eat too little food then you will become weak and have little energy to do anything.

c) What is a balanced diet?

Why can fat be bad for you?

Saturated fat comes from animals. Unsaturated fat comes from plants.

If you eat too much saturated fat, it sticks to the lining of your blood vessels. This makes them narrower. Your heart then has to work harder to pump the blood through these vessels, which increases your risk of a heart attack.

d) What type of fat is found in bacon rind?

Which is the healthier option?

> ### DID YOU KNOW?
> Eating too much salt can raise your blood pressure. This triples your chance of having a heart attack, whatever your age!

TEST YOURSELF!

1 Copy and complete the following table:

Food group	Examples of food
Carbohydrates	
Proteins	
Fats	
Vitamins and minerals	
Fibre	

2 Why is it better for you to use olive oil for cooking than lard?

3 Why might pregnant women need to eat more food than other women?

4 Kate is 15 and normally has a burger, chips, coke and ice-cream for her dinner. Design a balanced meal that she could eat instead.

2.5   How can drugs harm your body?

LEARNING OBJECTIVES

1 How do drugs affect the body?
2 Which drugs can harm your body?
3 What is drug addiction?

Drugs are chemical substances that affect the way your body works. Some have a beneficial effect when you are ill, but many can seriously harm your health and even cause death.

Drugs work by altering the chemical reactions that take place inside your body. If your body gets used to these changes, it may become dependent on a drug. If this happens you are **'addicted'** – you crave the drug and think you can't survive without it. If an addict attempts to stop taking a drug, they suffer **withdrawal symptoms**. These can be very unpleasant and make it even harder to give up.

a) What effect do drugs have on the body?
b) What happens if a person becomes addicted to a drug?

Legal drugs

Some drugs which can harm our body are legal. These include alcohol, tobacco, and anti-depressants.

Many people think alcohol is perfectly safe, but it can cause serious damage to your body. It affects your nervous system and damages your liver.

Most people realise smoking is dangerous, but around 25% of the population smoke. Cigarettes contain nicotine, which is very addictive. This makes it very difficult to stop smoking once you have started. Smoking seriously increases your risk of cancer, and respiratory and heart diseases.

Anti-depressants are prescribed by doctors to help relieve depression. They provide patients with short-term benefits, but if they use them for a long time, it can lead to addiction.

c) What harmful effects does alcohol have on your body?

Some legal drugs

Illegal drugs

Some drugs that can damage your body, even in very small amounts, have been made illegal by the Government.

However, many young people will be offered these drugs. Some may want to experiment with these deadly chemicals. Others may feel pressurised by their friends to join in.

Look at the picture below and discuss the comments being made.

Some people think it is a good idea to take drugs

Drug	How it affects the body	Harmful effect on the body
Barbiturates	Depressants – slow down the nervous system	Addictive; hallucinations; heart attack
Heroin		Addictive; risk of coma
Amphetamines	Stimulants – speed up the nervous system	Addictive; memory loss
Cocaine		Addictive; aggression; brain damage

All these drugs can kill, even in small quantities.

d) Name four illegal drugs.

TEST YOURSELF!

1 Copy and complete the following sentences using these words:

addicted   drugs   withdrawal symptoms   unpleasant

Chemicals that affect the way your body works are called _____. If you take them too often you may become _____. When addicts stop taking drugs, they suffer _____. These can be very _____ and make it harder to give up.

2 State four reasons why people may be tempted to take drugs.

3 Why are some drugs illegal?

4 As well as being a highly dangerous drug, heroin carries additional risks if you inject it. What are they?

2.6

How does smoking tobacco harm your body?

LEARNING OBJECTIVES

1 Which diseases are caused by smoking tobacco?
2 How does smoking affect your blood?

Tobacco smoke contains over a thousand chemicals, many of which are harmful. Three examples are:

- **Tar** – this collects in the lungs when the smoke cools. It is a sticky black material which irritates and narrows your airways. Some of the chemicals it contains cause cancer.
- **Nicotine** – this is the addictive drug in tobacco. It affects the nervous system. It also makes the heart beat faster and narrows blood vessels.
- **Carbon monoxide** – this is a poisonous gas. It stops the blood from carrying as much oxygen as it should.

a) Why is smoking addictive?
b) Which part of cigarette smoke causes cancer?

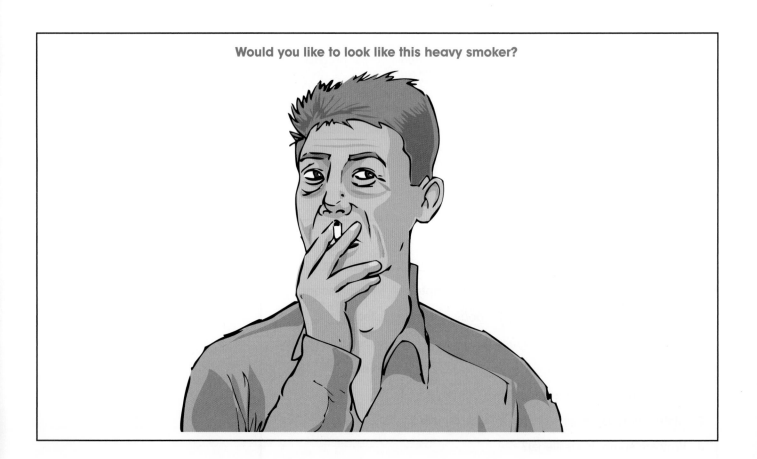

Would you like to look like this heavy smoker?

Heart disease

Three times as many smokers suffer from heart disease than non-smokers. Their arteries become blocked, which can cause a heart attack or stroke.

Diseases of the lungs

Chemicals in tobacco smoke cause the walls of the alveoli to weaken and lose their flexibility. They do not inflate properly when you inhale, and can burst during coughing. Not enough oxygen passes into the blood, leaving the person breathless. This disease is called **emphysema**.

Lung cancer is caused by chemicals in the tar found in lungs of smokers. In every 10 cases of lung cancer, 9 are smokers.

c) Name some of the diseases that smokers have an increased risk of developing.

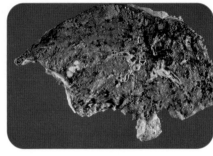

A diseased lung caused by smoking tobacco

The cells lining your windpipe have tiny hairs called cilia. They also produce mucus, which traps dirt and microorganisms. The cilia sweep the mucus up the trachea and down your oesophagus into your stomach. This keeps your airways clean.

Chemicals in smoke paralyse the cilia. The mucus now flows into your lungs, making it hard to breathe and often causes infection – **bronchitis**. Smokers have to cough this mucus up, which can damage the lungs further.

d) How do cilia keep the lungs clean?

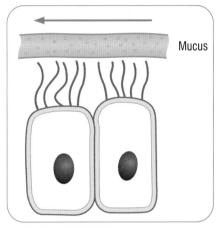

A ciliated cell

How does carbon monoxide harm the body?

Oxygen is transported around your body by the red blood cells. The oxygen is carried by binding to haemoglobin. Carbon monoxide also binds to haemoglobin. If this happens, the red blood cell cannot carry oxygen. So less oxygen is carried around your body.

e) What is the role of haemoglobin in your body?

Discuss the reasons for banning smoking in public places.

TEST YOURSELF!

1 Match the contents of a cigarette to their harmful effect.

Content of cigarettes:	Harmful effect:
Tar	Addictive and makes the heart beat faster
Nicotine	Lowers the oxygen carrying capacity of the blood
Carbon monoxide	Contains chemicals which cause cancer

2 Why do smokers often cough badly when they first wake in the morning?

3 Smoking wastes money. If someone smokes 30 cigarettes at a cost of £5.50 a day, how much will they spend in a year?

2.7   How does drinking alcohol affect us?

Most adults in this country drink alcohol, but this does not mean it is harmless. Alcohol contains the drug **ethanol**, which affects the nervous system. It is a depressant – it slows down your body's reactions.

Even in small quantities, drinking alcohol can change your behaviour. Most people feel relaxed and happy, but some become aggressive and depressed.

a) Why do many adults drink alcohol?
b) What is the name of the chemical in alcohol that causes its effect on the body?

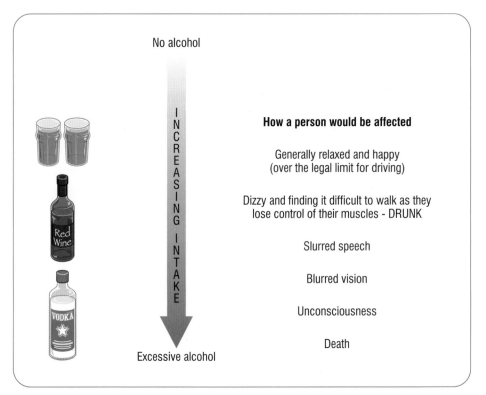

No alcohol

INCREASING INTAKE

How a person would be affected

Generally relaxed and happy
(over the legal limit for driving)

Dizzy and finding it difficult to walk as they lose control of their muscles - DRUNK

Slurred speech

Blurred vision

Unconsciousness

Death

Excessive alcohol

What happens when a person increases their intake of alcohol

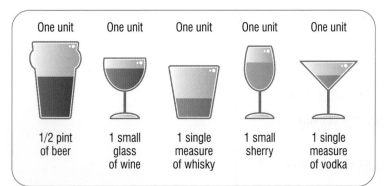

One unit	One unit	One unit	One unit	One unit
1/2 pint of beer	1 small glass of wine	1 single measure of whisky	1 small sherry	1 single measure of vodka

What is one unit of alcohol?

How does alcohol affect your body?

When you drink alcohol, it is absorbed into your bloodstream in your intestines. It then travels to your brain, where it affects your nervous system. Alcohol can affect the body for several hours – it takes about an hour for the body to break down one unit of alcohol.

c) How many small glasses of wine (125 ml) are equivalent to two pints of beer?

Why is drinking large amounts of alcohol dangerous?

Heavy drinking over a long period of time can cause stomach ulcers, heart disease and brain and liver damage.

The liver is responsible for breaking down alcohol in your body. It breaks down the poisonous ethanol into harmless waste products that are then excreted from the body.

The livers of heavy drinkers become scarred. Healthy cells are replaced with fat or fibrous tissue. The liver performs less efficiently and it takes much longer for alcohol and other toxins to be broken down.

This condition is known as **sclerosis** of the liver. This disease can be fatal.

d) What happens to alcohol when it reaches the liver?

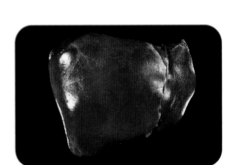

A diseased liver. Compare this with the healthy liver below.

A healthy liver

Alcohol tolerance

When people drink alcohol regularly they need greater and greater amounts to have the same effect on their body. This is because their body has developed a tolerance to ethanol.

If they carry on drinking, they may become addicted. They become dependent on alcohol and feel they cannot survive without a drink. These people are called alcoholics. Often alcoholics do not realise they are addicted.

Organisations such as Alcoholics Anonymous help people overcome their addiction.

e) What is an alcoholic?

TEST YOURSELF!

1 Copy and complete the following sentences using these words:

   nervous   relaxed   depressant   ethanol

   Alcohol is called a _____, because it slows down your body's reactions. The drug in alcohol is called _____. It affects your _____ system. This usually leaves the drinker feeling _____ and happy.

2 Explain why many heavy drinkers suffer from sclerosis of the liver.

3 Explain why driving a car under the influence of alcohol is extremely dangerous.

4 How might a paramedic make a judgement about how much alcohol a patient has drunk?

2.8   Genetically inherited disorders

Most diseases occur when microorganisms enter our body. These include measles and 'flu. Diseases such as cancer occur when our body goes wrong.

Some illnesses, though, are passed on from parents to their children in their genes. These are called **genetically inherited disorders**. Examples include cystic fibrosis and haemophilia.

Genetic counsellors work out the chance of a couple's child being born with an inherited disorder.

a) What is an inherited disorder?

Cystic fibrosis

This affects about one child in every 2000. It is caused by a 'faulty' gene. Cystic fibrosis is caused by a recessive allele (represented by **c**). A person will only suffer from the disease if both their copies of the gene are 'faulty' (**cc**). (See pages 54–55.)

A genetic counsellor discusses inherited disorders with a couple planning to have a baby

* **Symptoms**

  Thick sticky mucus is produced. This blocks the air passages, making it difficult to breathe. Mucus in the lungs allows germs to grow, causing chest infections. Excess mucus in the pancreas stops digestive juices being released. The child finds it difficult to absorb food.

* **Treating cystic fibrosis**

  Physiotherapy helps the person cough up the mucus.
  Antibiotics treat infection.

Each infection damages the lungs further. The child becomes more ill. At the moment there is no cure.

People can be carriers of cystic fibrosis without knowing (they have one copy of the faulty gene – **Cc**). They are healthy, but can pass the disorder on to their children.

This diagram shows how two carriers of cystic fibrosis can produce a child who suffers from the disease.

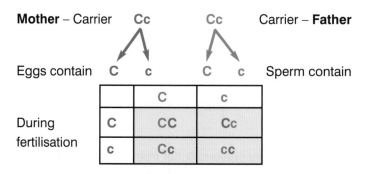

	C	c
C	CC	Cc
c	Cc	cc

Children would be born in the ratio: 1CC   :   2Cc   :   1cc

1 normal : 2 carriers : 1 cystic fibrosis

b) What are carriers?

Haemophilia

Haemophilia is a **sex-linked** disorder – it only affects males. Men have one X chromosome and one Y chromosome. As the Y chromosome is shorter, several genes are missing.

Haemophilia is caused by a recessive allele carried on the X chromosome (represented by X_h). A man has only one copy of this gene, so if the 'faulty' allele is present, he will suffer from haemophilia.

- **Symptoms**

  Blood does not clot properly. Even small cuts can be dangerous, because they keep bleeding and the person can lose so much blood that they die. Small knocks can cause internal bleeding, resulting in huge bruises.

- **Treating haemophilia**

  Regular injections of Factor 8. This chemical is normally present in the blood and is needed for clotting. Haemophiliacs cannot produce this chemical.

Females can be carriers of the disease ($X_H X_h$), but they never suffer from the disease, because fertilised eggs with the genes $X_h X_h$ never develop into a baby. The diagram below shows how females can pass this disorder on to their male children.

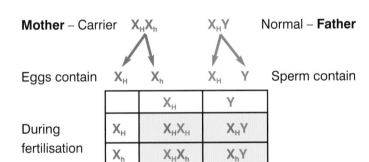

This diagram shows how females can pass the haemophilia disorder on to their children.
H = healthy clotting gene (dominant)
h = 'faulty' clotting gene (recessive)

Children would be born in the ratio: $1X_H X_H$: $1X_H X_h$: $1X_H Y$: $1X_h Y$

1 normal : 1 carrier : 1 normal : 1 haemophiliac
female   female   male   male

TEST YOURSELF!

1 Copy and complete the following sentences using these words:

cystic fibrosis   recessive   haemophilia
symptoms   carriers

Two examples of inherited disorders are _____ and _____. Both are caused by _____ alleles. _____ have one copy of the faulty gene and have no _____ of the disease.

2 a) Why is Factor 8 important for the body?

   b) Can males be carriers of haemophilia? Explain your answer.

2.9　Staying healthy

How Can You Help?

Smokers are 6 times more likely to die prematurely than non-smokers. As well as putting their own lives in danger, they are risking yours. Breathing in other people's smoke (passive smoking) significantly increases your risk of developing lung cancer and heart disease. Tobacco smoke seriously affects people with asthma (3.4 million live in the UK).

Smoking during pregnancy causes complications, and babies are often born with a low birth weight. Smoking considerably increases the risk of sudden infant death syndrome. It is estimated that smoking results in the death of 100 babies a year. 17 000 children under 5 are admitted to hospital for respiratory problems as a result of breathing in their parent's smoke.

Activities

The Government have recently decided to ban smoking in all enclosed public places. But not everyone agrees this is a good thing. Write a PowerPoint presentation explaining why you think smoking should or should not be banned in public places.

 Discuss your ideas as a group, then have a class vote on this issue.

This small child is suffering from passive smoking

How Can We Prevent Another Epidemic?

SARS is a serious respiratory disease which killed nearly 800 people in China in 2002/2003. To try and prevent its spread, the government:

1　Measured the body temperature of passengers at airport terminals.

2　Confined people suffering with SARS to their homes for 10 days, for monitoring and treatment.

3　Suggested that people in affected areas wore protective masks.

4　Made the disease symptoms widely known.

5　Advised ill and elderly people to avoid crowded places.

Activities

a)　When do you think the government gave out these guidelines? (Use the graph.)

b)　Explain how the 5 steps above managed to prevent the disease spreading.

c)　Why is it important, if an epidemic occurs, that all countries of the world are alerted?

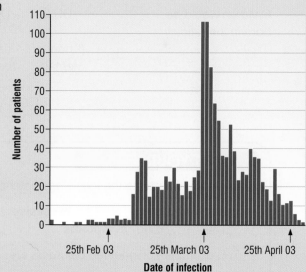

This graph shows the number of people in the Tai Po district of Hong Kong who were infected with the SARS virus

Why Should You Maintain A Healthy Body Weight?

Being overweight has very serious effects on your health. Many obese people die prematurely. Being overweight increases your risk of suffering from:

- High blood pressure
- High cholesterol
- Diabetes
- Coronary heart disease
- Stroke
- Respiratory problems
- Cancer of the breast, colon and uterus.

Activity

Design a leaflet, aimed at children, to encourage them to eat healthily and exercise regularly. Draw their attention to problems that may arise if they don't.

An overweight 'couch potato'

What happens if your blood doesn't clot?

About 6000 men in the UK suffer from the inherited disorder **haemophilia**. They are missing an essential factor (either Factor VIII or Factor IX) needed for blood to clot. This makes it very difficult for them to stop bleeding.

Bleeding from everyday cuts and grazes can usually be controlled with plasters and bandages. However, internal bleeding is much harder to control. People with severe haemophilia can suffer from bleeding into joints, which can cause permanent disability.

Treatment for bleeding involves injections of the missing blood factor. These are usually given after an injury has occurred. Severe sufferers need injections several times a week.

Activity

Write an A4-sized fact sheet to inform people about haemophilia. Include: who is affected, the symptoms, and the treatments available for this disease.

Use the Internet to gather extra information on this subject and how current research might be used in the treatment of genetic disorders.

IS THIS 'COOL'?

Activities

 Discuss the following:

a) Why do people take drugs?

b) What risks are involved in drug-taking?

c) Photographs like the one above are used by the Government and health professionals to try to shock young people and stop them from damaging their health or even dying as a result of taking drugs. Do campaigns like this work?

d) How would you inform people of the dangers?

SUMMARY QUESTIONS

1

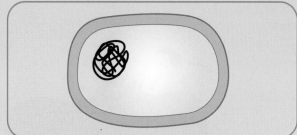

a) What type of microorganism is shown above?

b) Name 2 diseases caused by this type of microorganism.

c) What are the 2 ways that this type of microorganism causes disease?

2 Elliot falls over and cuts his knee. Explain why a scab will form using these key words:

platelets   clot   fibres   scab

3

This is the label from a cigarette packet. Explain why smokers can suffer from:

a) A 'smoker's cough'.

b) Shortness of breath.

c) Lung cancer.

4 Match the following ways diseases can be spread with methods of prevention:

Ways to spread disease	Prevented by
Sexual intercourse	Using a handerchief
Droplet infection	Avoiding contact
Sharing needles	Using a condom
Touching infected people	Using sterilised needles

5 In the following groups, which word is the odd one out? Why?

a) tobacco; alcohol; heroin

b) virus; bacteria; dog; fungi

c) red blood cells; neurones; lymphocytes

d) emphysema; heart disease; measles

6 Are the following statements true? If not, explain why.

a) Drinking large amounts of alcohol has no long-term effect on your health.

b) Addicts suffer withdrawal symptoms when they stop taking the drug.

c) Anti-depressants help relieve depression.

d) Smoking is not addictive.

7 Rearrange the sentences below to describe correctly how a virus replicates.

a) New viruses are made.

b) Cell bursts, releasing the new viruses.

c) A virus invades a cell.

d) 'Tells' the nucleus to copy its genes.

8 Choose the food from the picture which best matches each description below:

Cereal   Apple   Pasta   Burger

a) This food is rich in vitamins.

b) You would eat this food a few hours before running a marathon.

c) You may wish to reduce this type of food in your diet if you are trying to lose weight.

d) This food adds bulk to your food to help remove waste from the body.

9 Huntington's chorea is an example of an inherited disorder. It is a dominant disorder (H).

a) What combinations of genes would a normal person have?

b) What are the two combinations of genes that a sufferer could have?

c) A man (Hh) and a woman (hh) want to know how likely it is that their children will suffer with Huntington's chorea. Draw out a genetic cross diagram to explain the likelihood.

EXAM-STYLE QUESTIONS

1   The following information can be found on the labels of spreads available in the supermarket.

Nutrient	Amount in g per 100g of spread		
	Spread X	Spread Y	Spread Z
Protein	Trace	0.3	0.5
Carbohydrate	Trace	0.5	Trace
Fat	29	44.9	73.8
Of which saturates	12	19.5	54
Of which unsaturated	17	25.4	19.8

a) i)   Which spread would a nutritionist in a hospital advise for his patient who has recently had a heart attack?   (1)
    ii) What information in the table did you use to make your decision?   (1)
    iii) How will the nutritionist explain why this is the best choice?   (3)
    iv) Which spread is most likely to have come from an animal source? Explain your choice.   (2)

b) The nutritionist also advised the person to stop smoking. What chemical in cigarette smoke would be most dangerous to this person. Explain your answer.   (3)

2   A drugs counsellor needs to know how drugs work.

a) For each of the statements choose two drugs from the list that match that statement.
    alcohol   amphetamines   barbiturates   cocaine heroin   nicotine

Statements	Drug
Stimulant – speeds up the nervous system	1. 2.
Depressant – slows down the nervous system	1. 2.

(4)

b) The counsellor is advising a patient who is addicted to a drug and is suffering withdrawal symptoms. Explain the meaning of the words:
    i)   addicted   (1)
    ii) drug   (1)
    iii) withdrawal symptoms.   (1)

3   A technician in a hospital laboratory was examining some blood under the microscope. The following diagram shows the cells he found in the blood.

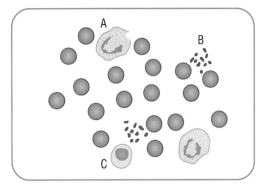

a) Which part of the blood (A, B or C):

    i)   helps the blood to clot   (1)
    ii) produces antibodies to destroy bacteria   (1)
    iii) engulfs and digests bacteria.   (1)

b) Explain how the cells identified in part a) ii) work.   (3)

c) Describe how blood clots and prevents further infection.   (3)

4   Many people smoke cigarettes despite the health risks.

a) What chemical found in cigarette smoke causes lung cancer?   (1)

b) The graphs show some information about smoking and lung cancer.

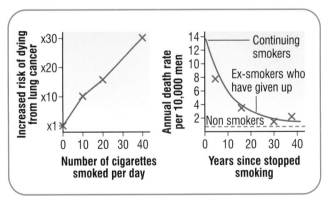

Use the information in the graphs to give advice to someone who smokes 40 cigarettes a day,   (3)

3.1

What can doctors prescribe to help us feel better?

1 What is an antibiotic?
2 What kind of drugs make us feel better?

When you feel ill, doctors can prescribe drugs to make you feel better. Some drugs work by killing the pathogen that has made you ill. Others work by relieving the symptoms of an illness, like cough medicines and pain killers.

Penicillin

Penicillin is an **antibiotic**. These are drugs that kill bacteria but do not damage the cells in your body. They have no effect on viruses or fungi.

This is Penicillium growing on an orange!

Penicillin was discovered by accident! Alexander Fleming was growing bacteria on agar plates. One day he forgot to seal one of the plates, leaving it open. When he returned he found mould (called *Penicillium notatum*) growing.

He noticed that where the mould was growing the bacteria were killed. The substance that killed the bacteria was extracted and named penicillin.

a) How do antibiotic drugs work?
b) Where might the fungus that produces penicillin grow in your house?

There are several different types of antibiotic. Each kills different species of bacteria. To identify the type of bacteria that is making you ill, doctors often send blood and stool samples to the hospital.

Scientists working in public health laboratories will grow the bacteria in the samples on agar plates. They then treat the plates with different antibiotics, to see which is the most effective. You would then be prescribed this drug.

c) How can you tell from the plate if the bacteria have been killed by an antibiotic?

You can investigate the growth of bacteria in Unit 3. (See page 266–269.)

The photo on the left is of an agar plate showing bacteria being killed when in contact with penicillin. Notice the 'halo' around the disc. We say that the growth of bacteria is 'inhibited' in that area. It is called the '**zone of inhibition**'.

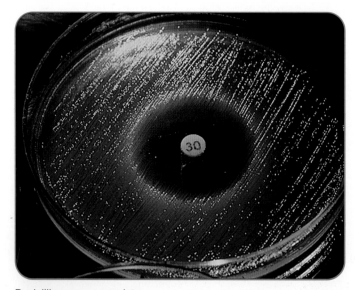

Penicillin on an agar plate

Aspirin

Aspirin is often taken to relieve headaches. Headaches are caused when capillaries in the brain become inflamed. This swelling slows the blood flow around the brain. Aspirins are **anti-inflammatory**. They reduce the swelling – this in turn stops the pain.

d) What type of drug is aspirin?

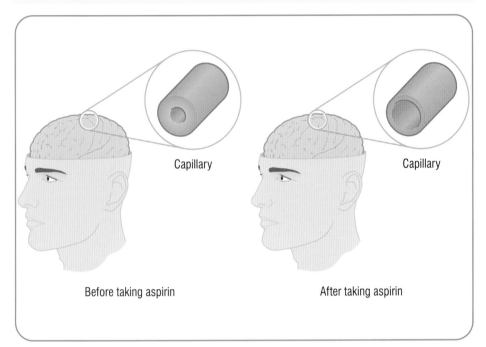

Capillary   Capillary

Before taking aspirin   After taking aspirin

Action of aspirin

Paracetamol

This drug is used as a painkiller. Like aspirin, it treats the symptoms of a disease, but does not kill pathogens.

When you hurt yourself, the body releases a hormone-like substance called prostaglandin. This makes you feel pain. Paracetamol reduces the production of this chemical, decreasing the pain that you feel.

TEST YOURSELF!

1   Copy and complete the following sentences using these words:

anti-inflammatory   bacteria   penicillin   symptoms

Aspirin is an _____. It is a chemical drug that can relieve

_____ like headaches. The drug _____ is an antibiotic. It is

able to kill _____.

2   Tonsillitis is a bacterial infection. If you have it:
    a) How can taking antibiotics make you better?
    b) How can taking aspirin help relieve the symptoms?

3   Carry out research to find out why some bacteria are becoming resistant to antibiotics.

3.2

Protecting ourselves from harmful pathogens

LEARNING OBJECTIVE

1 How can you protect yourself from disease?

You come into contact with potentially harmful microorganisms every day. However, there are several ways you can protect yourself from disease.

Personal hygiene

Follow these simple steps to stay healthy:

- Wash your hands – before meals, before preparing food and after going to the toilet. Be careful to scrub under your nails, as bacteria grow well there.
- Have a bath or shower daily – especially in hot weather, as microorganisms thrive in these conditions.
- Clean your teeth twice a day – to stop plaque building up. Remember to change your toothbrush every 3 months, as bacteria can breed there.

a) In the photo below how do the women's clothing stop them contaminating the food?

Antiseptics

When you cut or graze your skin you should clean it with an **antiseptic**. These are chemicals that kill microorganisms but do not damage your skin.

This photo shows women working in the food preparation industry. They have to wear special clothing such as a hair net, white coat and gloves.

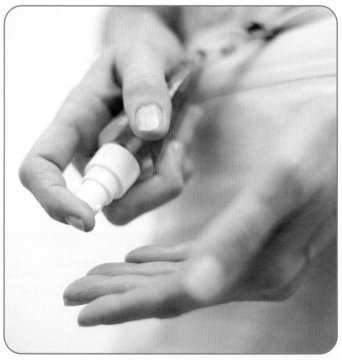

People working in the medical professions often carry a bottle of antiseptic gel. They rub it into their hands between seeing patients, to stop infections spreading.

b) What other professionals should use antiseptic soap or gels to stop contamination?

Disinfectants

Disinfectants are also chemicals that kill microorganisms. They are much stronger than antiseptics, which means they are more effective. However, they can damage skin cells, so you must never use them on your skin.

Disinfectants are widely used in kitchens and toilets both at home and in places like restaurants and hospitals.

c) Why should disinfectants be clearly labelled with the symbol?

Sterilisation

This technique kills all microorganisms. **Sterile** objects have no microorganisms on them.

Objects are usually sterilised with heat or radiation, although chemicals can be used. Some people use chemical tablets to sterilise babies' bottles.

A hospital's operating theatre equipment is sterilised in an autoclave. This heats the equipment to 120°C, killing all microorganisms.

d) Why is it important that surgical equipment is sterile?

Chemicals that are irritant will have this symbol

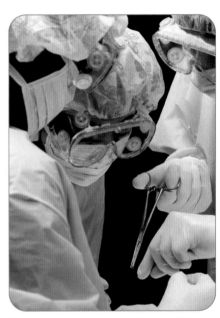
The surgical equipment being used here will have been sterilised in an autoclave

TEST YOURSELF!

1 Copy and complete the following sentences using these words:

heating   skin   harmful   disinfectants   microorganisms

Antiseptics kill _____ but do not damage your _____. However _____ are stronger chemicals. They kill more microorganisms but are _____ to our body. Most things are sterilised by _____ to very high temperatures.

2 Why would you not want to wash your hands with a soap containing disinfectant?

3 Look at the picture of the surgeon.
   a) What type of protective clothing is she wearing?
   b) How does this protect the patient from infection?

4 Imagine you are the manager of a restaurant. Write a set of rules for your employees to ensure good hygiene in the kitchen.

3.3   Immunisation

Immunisation is a way of protecting you against some diseases caused by microorganisms. If you are immunised, and come into contact with these microorganisms, your body will be able to fight them off without getting ill. This is called **immunity**.

Are your immunisations up to date? Look at the table below:

Child's age	Disease immunised against
2, 3 and 4 months	Polio, diphtheria, tetanus, whooping cough, Hib meningitis and meningitis C
About 13 months	Measles, mumps and rubella – MMR
3–5 years	MMR, polio, diphtheria, tetanus and whooping cough
10–14 years	Tuberculosis
13–18 years	Polio, diphtheria and tetanus

a) What is meant by the term 'immunity'?

How do immunisations work?

Most **vaccines** contain dead microorganisms or microorganisms that have been weakened so that they can no longer cause disease. The microorganisms do not make you ill, but still trigger your white blood cells (lymphocytes) to make antibodies. (See pages 64–65.)

The antibodies destroy the microorganisms. Some remain in your body. These will fight off the microorganism quickly if it enters your body again, preventing it causing disease. You are now immune.

Polio

Polio is a disease that affects your nervous system. It can damage your nerves and lead to permanent paralysis of parts of your body. In very severe cases, it can cause death. The polio vaccine is not always injected but can be given by mouth – often on a sugar lump, as it doesn't taste very nice!

Tuberculosis (TB)

You may recently have been injected with the BCG vaccine. This protects you against tuberculosis (TB). TB is a disease which affects your lungs and causes breathing problems. In very severe cases it can cause death.

b) Explain how a vaccine works.

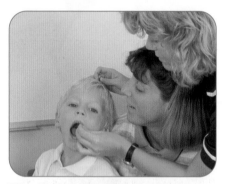

This child is being given the polio vaccine

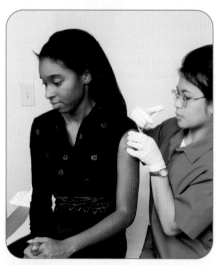

The BCG vaccine is injected into the arm

Measles, mumps and rubella

Just after their first birthday, children are given an immunisation called MMR. This single injection protects them against measles, mumps and rubella.

As well as being unpleasant, measles and mumps can cause permanent damage. In some cases, measles can cause deafness, and mumps can make men infertile. In extreme cases, both diseases can be fatal.

Rubella is generally less unpleasant. However, if a woman gets the disease when she is pregnant, the unborn baby may be born deaf or blind. In some cases it can even die.

This child is suffering from mumps

c) Why should children have the MMR immunisation?

How do we know immunisations are working?

During the period 1971–2000, the population of the UK increased. The BCG and measles injections were both given to large numbers of the population during this time. Despite the population increasing, the number of cases of these diseases decreased.

d) Explain why the number of cases of TB and measles fell during the period 1971–2000.

 Discuss the advantages and disadvantages of immunisations. Use the table as a starting point:

Advantages	Disadvantages
Many lives are saved	Injections may hurt
People don't suffer from nasty diseases	May get a temperature
Side effects of disease may last for years e.g. paralysis/deafness	BCG leaves a scar

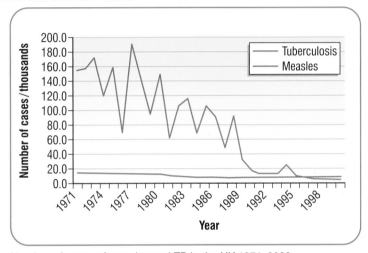

Number of cases of measles and TB in the UK 1971–2000

You can find more information on immunisation on page 92.

TEST YOURSELF!

1 Copy and complete the following sentences using these words:

vaccines   immunity   diseases   microorganisms

The spread of infectious _____ can be prevented by the use of

_____. These work by introducing dead or weakened _____ into

the body. Your body builds up a defence to this infection – this is known

as _____.

2 Which diseases would a 15-year-old have been immunised against?

3 A few members of the population cannot have immunisations, due to other medical conditions. Explain why mass immunisation in a country helps to prevent these people from getting an infectious disease.

3.4

How do X-rays diagnose medical conditions?

LEARNING OBJECTIVES

1 What is an X-ray?
2 How are X-ray images formed?
3 How can we use X-rays to identify some illnesses?

You may have had an **X-ray**, perhaps to identify a broken bone. Have you ever asked yourself how an image of the inside of your body is made?

X-rays were discovered over 100 years ago. Their use in medicine was quickly appreciated, but the dangers of X-rays were not. Many of the early researchers working with X-rays developed forms of cancer.

Doctors and dentists use X-rays to see inside the body of a patient, without the need for an operation. This removes the chance of a patient developing an infection.

a) Why do doctors take X-ray images?

What are X-rays?

X-rays are high energy **waves**. They are just a small part of a large family of waves known as the **electromagnetic spectrum**. (See pages 242–243.)

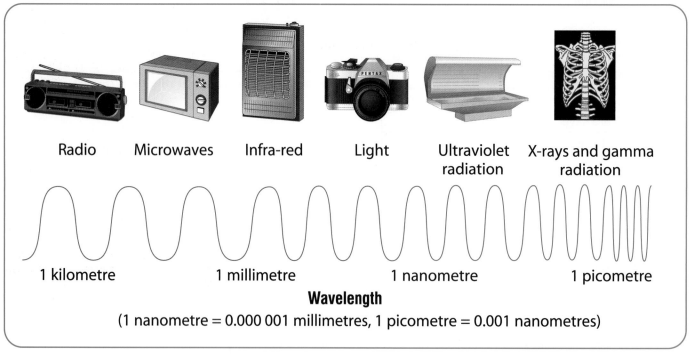

The electromagnetic spectrum

Ultra-violet (UV) waves have been linked with skin cancer. They damage your cells if you spend too long in the sun without using suntan lotion. X-rays are higher energy waves than UV, and therefore cause even more damage to living cells.

b) What is an X-ray?
c) Which waves in the electromagnetic spectrum can cause cancer?

How are X-ray images produced?

- Photographic film is placed behind the part of the patient being investigated.
- This part of the patient is exposed to X-rays.
- X-rays penetrate through soft tissues like skin and muscle. They are absorbed by denser structures, such as bones and teeth.
- The X-rays that penetrate through the patient expose the film.
- The image is then developed. Regions of the film that were exposed to X-rays show up black. Areas of film that were not exposed to X-rays, because they were absorbed, are white.
- We call these images 'shadow pictures'.

d) Name some parts of the body which absorb X-rays.

How can we protect ourselves from the dangers of X-rays?

X-rays are known to cause cancer. However, the risk to your health of having a few X-rays is tiny.

Radiographers take X-rays as part of their job. They are at risk of receiving high doses of this **radiation**. It is important that they protect themselves from this danger.

Lead (because it is very dense) absorbs X-rays, so a lead screen is placed between the radiographer and the patient. Radiographers also wear film badges. These measure the dose of radiation received.

e) How do radiographers protect themselves from X-radiation?

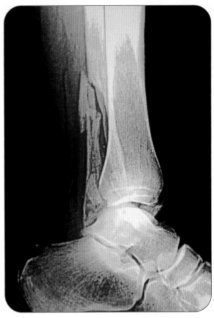

X-ray image of a broken leg

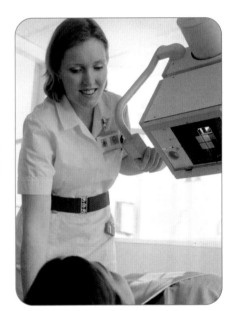

This radiographer wears a film badge to monitor her exposure to radiation. You can find out how it works on page 89.

TEST YOURSELF!

1 Copy and complete the following sentences using these words:

soft   waves   dense   inside

X-rays are high energy _____. They are used to make images of the

_____ of the body. Only _____ parts of the body can be imaged, as

X-rays will pass through _____ tissues.

2 Small children can have X-rays taken sitting on their parent's lap. Why does the parent need to wear a lead apron?

3 Explain why X-ray images are known as 'shadow pictures'. (Hint – think about how shadows are made using light.)

3.5   What is radioactivity?

1 What is radioactivity?
2 Why is ionising radiation dangerous?

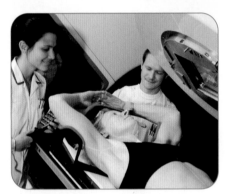

Medical use of radioactivity

Before you study this page, read about what's inside atoms on page 154.

Some atoms have an unstable nucleus. They throw out particles. This process is known as **radioactivity**.

Radioactivity can cause cancer, but we can also use it to treat cancer. There are many other medical uses. Most hospitals have a nuclear physics department to manufacture and control these substances.

What is emitted from the nucleus?

Three types of **ionising radiation** can be emitted. These are called alpha, beta and gamma radiation.

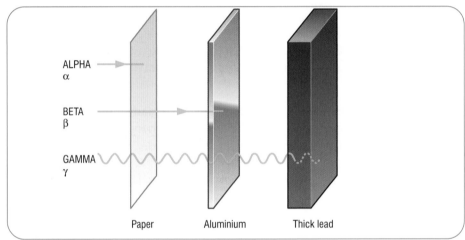

Diagram showing alpha, beta and gamma absorption

a) What is radioactivity?
b) What are the 3 types of ionising radiation called?

Each type of radiation has different properties. Scientists need to understand these properties when deciding which type of radiation to use for a particular job.

Type of radiation	What is it?	What stops the radiation?	Ionisation power (damage caused)	Detected by
Alpha particles (α)	2 protons and 2 neutrons (a helium nucleus)	A sheet of paper; About 20 cm of air	Very high	Photographic film *or*
Beta particles (β)	A fast-moving electron	5 mm aluminium; About 2 m of air	Medium	Geiger–Muller (G-M) tube
Gamma rays (γ)	An electromagnetic wave	Thick lead; Very thick concrete	Low	

c) Which type of radiation is not made from particles?

The dangers of ionising radiation

You have looked briefly at some of the dangers involved with radioactive materials in Unit 1. (See page 18.)

Any exposure to ionising radiation is potentially harmful, and can lead to cancer. The amount of radiation you have been exposed to is known as your **dose**.

The greater the received dose, the greater the damage to your body. It is therefore very important, when working with radioactive substances, to minimise your exposure. There are several ways of doing this:

- Ensuring that substances are handled safely.
- Using shielding around the radioactive substances.
- Keeping exposure times low.

Wearing a film badge will monitor your exposure to radiation. So you will know if you have had too much. It won't stop radiation getting to your body, though!

d) How can you ensure that people who work with radioactive substances receive as low a dose of radiation as possible?

How does a film badge work?

All types of ionising radiation expose photographic film, making it 'fogged'.

Look at the picture showing the inside of a film badge. The region of the badge covered in plastic detects beta particles and gamma rays. The area covered by aluminium detects only gamma rays, because the aluminium shield absorbs beta particles.

Once worn, the film badges are sent to be developed. The dose a worker has received can be judged from how 'fogged' the film has become.

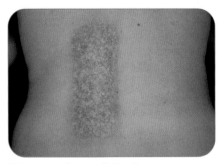
This person has radiation burns.

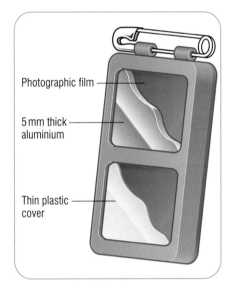
Photographic film

5 mm thick aluminium

Thin plastic cover

The inside of a film badge

TEST YOURSELF!

1   Copy and complete the sentences using these words:

   alpha   cancer   dose   gamma

   Three types of ionising radiation exist. The most ionising (damaging) is

   _____. The most penetrating radiation is _____. The higher the radiation

   ____ received, the greater the risk of _____.

2   How can you measure a radiation dose?

3   A worker is accidentally exposed to alpha particles at very short range (10 cm). Explain why the film badge does not detect this radiation.

4   Why are some people concerned about transporting radioactive substances by road?

3.6 Uses of ionising radiation

LEARNING OBJECTIVES

1 How can radioactivity be used in medicine?
2 What is radiotherapy?

Radioactive materials have many uses in medicine:

- Identifying some medical disorders.
- Treating certain illnesses.
- Sterilising medical equipment.

a) What are three medical uses for radioactivity?

Radioactive tracers

The movement of ionising radiation through your body can be tracked. This can be used to detect problems inside the body without operating on a patient. These substances are known as **tracers**.

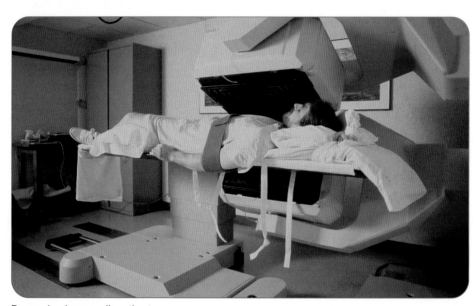

Person having a radioactive trace

Gamma camera image of thyroid uptake of iodine–131

Tracers are swallowed, or injected into the patient. They emit low-energy gamma rays. This type of radiation causes the least damage to a patient's cells. However, it is penetrating enough to escape from the body.

The radiation is detected outside the body using a **gamma camera**. This device produces an image of the gamma radiation received.

Tracers can be used in a number of ways:

- Detecting cancerous tumours.
- Monitoring blood flow around the body.
- Checking organs are working properly (e.g. to see if your kidneys are removing waste as expected).

b) What is a medical tracer?
c) How can medical tracers be used?

Radiotherapy

Some types of cancer can be treated using radioactive substances. This treatment is known as **radiotherapy**.

Most cancers are treated using gamma radiation. This is placed outside the body, and aimed at the tumour.

However, some cancers are treated by placing a radioactive substance (usually a beta-emitter) inside the tumour. This is known as an **implant**.

In both cases, high doses of ionising radiation are directed at the cancerous tissue. This kills the cancerous cells, but also damages healthy cells around the cancer. This treatment can leave the patient feeling very ill.

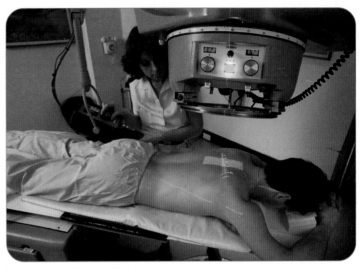
A person receiving radiotherapy

d) What is radiotherapy?
e) How does radiotherapy treat a cancerous tumour?

Sterilising medical equipment

Hospitals treat some medical equipment with high doses of radiation to ensure that it is sterile. Gamma rays are used. They can penetrate through sealed packaging to the equipment inside, killing any microorganisms which may be present.

f) Why are alpha or beta particles not used to sterilise medical equipment?

Gamma rays are sometimes used to sterilise medical equipment

TEST YOURSELF!

1 Match the word to the description:

Word:	Description:
Radiotherapy	Using gamma radiation to kill bacteria
Sterilising	Using ionising radiation to detect problems in the body
Tracer	Treating medical disorders using radioactivity

2 Why is it important that substances used as tracers do not stay radioactive for long periods of time?

3 Why does radiotherapy leave a patient feeling ill after the treatment?

4 Do some research to find out why iodine-131 is used to treat disorders of the thyroid gland.

3.7   Preventing disease

Are vaccines effective?

Whooping cough is a disease which can cause long bouts of coughing and choking. This can make it hard to breathe. It can be fatal to babies younger than 1 year old.

Children are now routinely vaccinated against whooping cough.

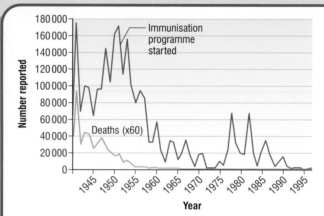

Graph showing the number of cases of whooping cough in the UK in the years 1940–1997. The graph also shows the number of deaths from this disease

Activities

a) Look at the graph opposite. In which year was the immunisation programme started?

b) What effect has the vaccine had on the number of cases of whooping cough?

c) How many deaths from whooping cough have occurred since 1980?

d) Between 1972 and 1973, the vaccine was linked with Sudden Infant Death Syndrome. This link was later proved to be wrong. A lot of parents did not vaccinate their children in these years. What was the effect on the number of cases of whooping cough after this time?

e) Suggest why the number of deaths from whooping cough were decreasing even before the vaccination programme was started?

Are autism and the MMR vaccine linked?

A study was carried out in California to research a possible link between the MMR vaccine and autism. The data collected on the vaccination rate and the number of cases of autism between 1980 and 1994 are shown in the table.

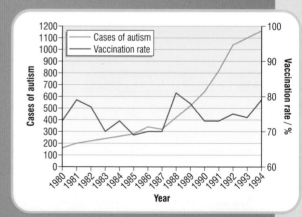

Activities

a) Describe how the number of children diagnosed with autism has varied between 1980 and 1994.

b) Describe how the rate of vaccination has varied between 1980 and 1994.

c) Explain whether or not these data support the hypothesis that children given the MMR vaccine are more likely to develop autism.

d) Fears over the possible link with autism have led to some parents in the UK not giving their children the MMR vaccine. Explain why there have been recent outbreaks of mumps and measles in British schools.

 Discuss whether you would give babies of your own the MMR vaccine.

MRSA – the killer bug

Since penicillin was discovered, bacterial infections have been treated with antibiotics. This has saved millions of lives worldwide.

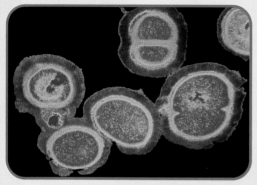

MRSA bacteria

MRSA is a bacterium that is resistant to many antibiotics. It is therefore very difficult to treat, and can be fatal. It is a particular problem in hospitals, because seriously ill patients are more likely to pick up this infection.

However, the spread of MRSA can be prevented through good hygiene practices. (See page 29.)

Activity

Write a set of rules for medical staff, to stop the spread of MRSA in hospital wards.

A life sentence

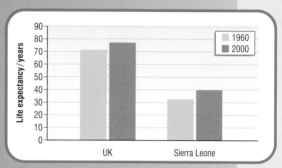

Graph comparing life expectancy in the UK and Sierra Leone in 1960 and 2000

Sierra Leone is a small country in Africa. Life expectancy there is around half that in the UK.

Activity

Think about why life expectancy in the UK increased between 1960 and 2000. Write a letter to your local MP explaining what could be done to improve the life expectancy of the citizens of Sierra Leone.

A plane loading up with supplies for the disaster region

Dealing with disaster

After the 2004 Asian tsunami, Médecins Sans Frontières (MSF) sent over 200 staff and more than 2000 tonnes of supplies to the region. Some of their main targets were to provide medical provision and clean water to prevent disease claiming the lives of many survivors. Immunisations, medical care and treatment were administered. Wells and water supplies were treated, toilets built, and basic human hygiene equipment provided, like soap and clean towels. Largely through the work of MSF, no outbreaks of the life-threatening diseases cholera, measles, dengue fever and malaria occurred.

Activity

Write a short report explaining how each of the activities carried out by Médecins Sans Frontières helped prevent the outbreak of any life-threatening diseases after the Asian tsunami.

SUMMARY QUESTIONS

1 a) Match the following drugs to their uses:

Drug:	Uses:
Aspirin	Kills bacteria
Penicillin	Pain killer
Paracetamol	Anti-inflammatory and pain killer

  b) Which of the above drugs kills the pathogen that causes the disease?

  c) How does an anti-inflammatory drug work?

2 Which type of ionising radiation (alpha, beta or gamma) would you link with each of these statements?

  a) A fast moving electron.

  b) Not made from particles.

  c) Could not be used as a tracer.

  d) Used to sterilise medical equipment.

  e) The most ionising radiation.

  f) Can be absorbed only by very thick lead or concrete.

3 Describe how you could reduce the risk of catching a disease or developing an infection in each situation below:

  a) Injecting yourself with insulin.

  b) Eating chicken which was cooked the day before.

  c) Preparing food for customers on a work surface.

  d) Grazing your knee in a muddy field playing sport.

  e) Going on holiday to a country where typhoid is common.

4 Rearrange the sentences below to explain how immunisations work.

  a) The antibodies destroy the microorganisms.

  b) These will fight the microorganism off quickly if it enters your body again, preventing it causing disease.

  c) Vaccines contain dead or weakened microorganisms.

  d) Some antibodies remain in your body.

  c) The microorganisms do not make you ill, but still trigger your white blood cells to make antibodies.

5

  a) What information does the above graph show?

  b) Why is it important for radiographers to minimise their exposure to X-rays?

  c) A patient suffers a major injury, and requires several X-rays. Explain why this is less damaging to the patient than operating on the patient many times.

6

Look at the picture of the dentist above.

  a) State four items of protective clothing the dentist wears.

  b) Explain the purpose of these pieces of clothing.

  c) Which, if any, of the items protect the patient as well as the dentist?

EXAM-STYLE QUESTIONS

1 Staff working in a hospital use the methods listed below to prevent the spread of infection.

antiseptics   disinfectant   immunisation   sterilisation

a) i) Which method would be used on the hands between seeing each patient? (1)
   ii) Which method would be used on the equipment used in the operating theatre? (1)
   iii) Which method would be used to clean the operating table? (1)

b) A student has a viral infection that is painful. Which medicine could she take to make her feel better? (1)

   amoxycyllin   asprin   paracetamol   penicillin

2 Graph A shows the level of antibodies produced the first time a child comes into contact with a disease and graph B shows what happens when they come into contact with the disease again.

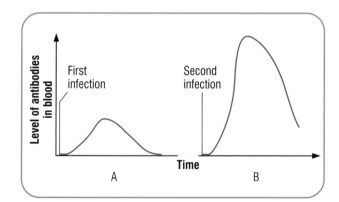

a) Using the graphs explain why a child usually gets Chickenpox once in its life. (4)

b) Read the following information about childhood vaccinations.

"A vaccination gives your child a tiny dose of the microbe which causes the disease. This enables his body to develop its own natural defence system that will protect him from the disease. Diseases such as polio have been wiped out in this country thanks to the national immunisation programme. Polio is still present in other parts of the world. In order to eradicate a disease at least 95% of the population needs to be immunised against it. Since its introduction in 1988 the MMR vaccine has had its critics. Some claim that some children have suffered severe medical conditions as a result of the vaccine. No evidence has been found to support the links between MMR and severe medical conditions."

i) What does a vaccine contain? (1)
ii) What does MMR stand for? (1)
iii) What are the advantages and disadvantages of being vaccinated against a disease? (4)

c) The graph shows the uptake of MMR (how many children have been vaccinated) since 1990.

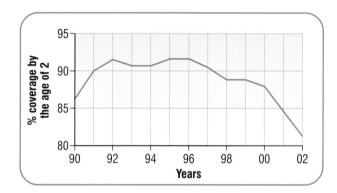

i) What is the trend shown on the graph? (1)
ii) Suggest a reason for this trend. (1)

3 A student was suffering from a painful hip. He had an X-ray but the cause of the pain was not shown. He then went for an MRI scan which showed inflammation of the tissue in the joint.

a) i) What is an X-ray? (1)
   ii) How are X-rays detected? (1)
   iii) Why was the inflammation not shown on the X-ray? (2)

b) i) A second student had cancer. What treatment would he receive for the cancer? (1)
   ii) How does this treatment work? (2)

2 | Countryside and Environmental Management

In this section you will learn about:

Agriculture and farming

- What photosynthesis is.
- What plants need to grow.
- Intensive and organic farming.

Useful organisms

- Products made from living things.
- Food and drink made using microorganisms.
- How organisms can be altered to produce more useful substances.

Managing the environment

- Elements, compounds and mixtures.
- Processing raw materials.
- Extracting metals.

Energy sources

- Generating electricity.
- Renewable and non-renewable energy resources.
- Environmental impact of industrial activity.

This section is tested by examination

Dog breeder

"I need to be able to breed dogs selectively, to produce Huskies with the best characteristics."

Research chemist

"Understanding about elements, mixtures and compounds helps me to develop new materials."

Environmental scientist

"My job is to monitor pollution levels, to ensure the environment is protected."

Career opportunities

Organic farmer

"I have to be aware of all the criteria I must meet to sell my produce as organic."

Brewer

"Creating the best conditions for yeast to grow produces good-quality beer."

Worker in a nuclear power station

"By using my knowledge of electricity generation, I am helping to provide power for the country."

4.1 Photosynthesis

Plants are called **producers** because they make their own food. They convert simple materials found in their environment into sugar. This process is called **photosynthesis**.

a) What is a producer?
b) What is photosynthesis?

Photosynthesis takes place inside the plant's chloroplasts. (See page 33 to revise plant cells.) This mainly occurs in the leaf, though a small amount happens in the stem. Photosynthesis is summarised in the equation below:

$$\text{carbon dioxide} + \text{water} \xrightarrow[\text{chlorophyll}]{\text{light energy trapped in}} \text{sugar} + \text{oxygen}$$
$$6CO_2 + 6H_2O \longrightarrow C_6H_{12}O_6 + 6O_2$$

How do gases get into and out of a plant?

On the underside of the leaf there are tiny holes. These are called **stomata**. They allow gases to diffuse through into the leaf:

• Carbon dioxide diffuses **in**.
• Oxygen and water vapour diffuse **out**.

Stomata are opened and closed by guard cells. They normally open during the day and close at night.

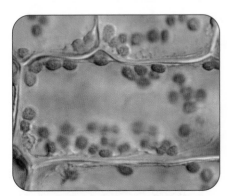

Chloroplasts in water plants

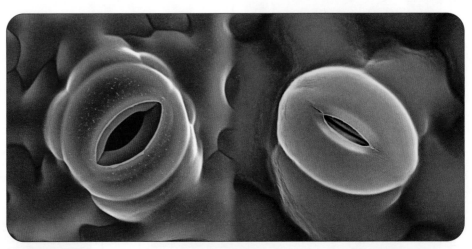

Stomata in leaves

c) Why do stomata close in hot dry weather?

How does water get into a plant?

Water moves by osmosis into the root hair cells. It is then transported around the plant in vessels called **xylem**. As water evaporates from the leaves, more is drawn up through the plant. This is called **transpiration**. It is a bit like sucking on a straw!

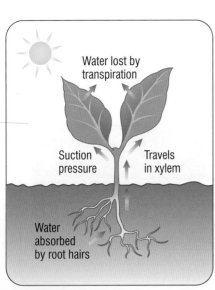

Transpiration in plants

Where do plants get their energy from?

Leaves are green because they contain the pigment **chlorophyll**. It traps light energy from the Sun. This energy is needed for the plant to convert carbon dioxide and water into glucose. Oxygen is the waste product that is made. This replaces the oxygen taken from the air when we breathe or burn things. So without plants, you wouldn't be able to breathe.

d) Why is chlorophyll essential for photosynthesis?

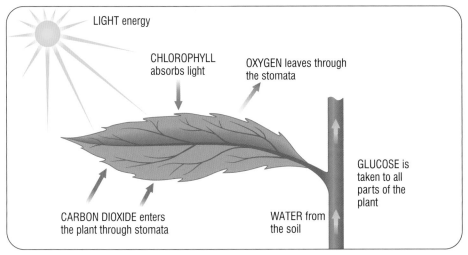

LIGHT energy

CHLOROPHYLL absorbs light

OXYGEN leaves through the stomata

GLUCOSE is taken to all parts of the plant

CARBON DIOXIDE enters the plant through stomata

WATER from the soil

This diagram represents the process of photosynthesis

Four factors affect the rate of photosynthesis:

- Light intensity.
- Concentration of carbon dioxide.
- Availability of water.
- Surrounding temperature.

It is essential for plant-growers using huge industrial-size greenhouses to monitor these factors. They can make sure the rate of photosynthesis is high by changing conditions. The faster photosynthesis occurs, the more glucose is made, so the more the plant grows.

An industrial-sized greenhouse

TEST YOURSELF!

1 Copy and complete the following sentences using these words:

carbon   glucose   light   photosynthesis   producers   water

Plants are _____. They make their own food by _____.

They use _____ dioxide and _____ to make _____ and oxygen using _____ energy.

2 Why doesn't photosynthesis happen at night?

3 Why do plants have to respire?

4 If we cut down all the trees in the world, why would we struggle to breathe?

5 What are the ideal conditions for plants to photosynthesise?

4.2 What helps a plant grow big and strong?

LEARNING OBJECTIVE

1 Which minerals do plants need for healthy growth?

In order to grow, plants need to photosynthesise. Some of the glucose made is used in respiration to release energy. Some is stored. The rest is converted into cellulose, which is needed to make plant cell walls, and proteins needed for growth and repair.

a) Name some ways that glucose is used in a plant.

For healthy growth, plants need four important minerals:

- **Nitrates** (contain nitrogen) – for healthy growth.
- **Phosphates** (contain phosphorus) – for healthy roots.
- **Potassium** – for healthy leaves and flowers.
- **Magnesium** – for making chlorophyll.

Plants get the minerals they need from the soil. However, lots of soils lack all the minerals required. Farmers need to recognise mineral deficiency symptoms in plants. Then they can add appropriate chemicals to provide the missing minerals. Look at the photos below to see what happens when minerals are lacking.

A nitrate-deficient plant – older leaves are yellowed, growth is stunted

A plant suffering from phosphorus deficiency – younger leaves have a purple tinge, poor root growth

Plant with potassium deficiency – has yellow leaves, with dead areas on them

Magnesium deficiency – leaves turn pale and then yellow

b) How could you tell the difference between a plant lacking magnesium and a plant lacking phosphorus?

Why are nitrates needed for healthy plant growth?

Nitrates are involved in making DNA and amino acids. The amino acids join together to form proteins. Proteins are needed for cell growth.

c) What is the role of nitrates in plant growth?

Why do plants lacking magnesium have yellow leaves?

Plants are green because they contain chlorophyll. The chlorophyll molecule contains magnesium. So if a plant is lacking magnesium it won't be able to make as much chlorophyll as it needs. Fewer chlorophyll molecules will result in pale or yellow leaves.

d) What is the role of magnesium in plant growth?

Why do plants need phosphorus and potassium for healthy growth?

Phosphorus is involved in making DNA. It is also used to make cell membranes and enzymes involved in photosynthesis.

Potassium is needed to transfer minerals across the cell membrane and into the cell. It also helps enzymes to work in the processes of photosynthesis and respiration.

Why do farmers use fertilisers?

NPK is a common fertiliser. It contains three of the essential minerals needed for healthy plant growth.

When crops are harvested, minerals are removed from the ground. These would normally be replaced when the plant dies or material like leaves are shed. So fertilisers are used routinely to replace minerals that are lacking in the soil.

e) What do you think the letters NPK stand for?

NPK fertiliser used by farmers

A farmer spreading fertiliser

> ### DID YOU KNOW?
>
> Plants need 16 nutrients for healthy growth. These include boron, calcium, molybdenum, manganese, copper, iron and zinc. Quite a diet!

TEST YOURSELF!

1 Match the nutrient with the effect it would have on a plant if it was missing:

Nutrient:	Effect of deficiency:
Magnesium	Poor root growth and purple leaves
Phosphorus	Stunted growth and yellow leaves
Potassium	Yellow leaves with dead spots
Nitrogen	Pale leaves

2 If a farmer didn't want to use chemical fertilisers, what else could be spread on the fields?

3 Why is it hard for farmers to work out exactly which minerals a plant is lacking?

4 How do you think a farmer could monitor soil mineral levels?

4.3   Intensive farming

1 What is intensive farming?
2 Which chemicals are used in intensive farming?

Intensive farming is the type of farming which produces as much food as possible, by making the best use of land, plants and animals. Controlled environments and a number of different chemicals are used to achieve this. This makes the food produced as cheap as possible.

a) What is meant by intensive farming?

Chemicals can be applied to both plants and animals to ensure that they grow as fast as possible. They can also stop diseases from spreading.

How can you make a plant grow as fast as possible?

Harvesting intensively farmed wheat

Name of chemical additive	Effect on the crop
Artificial fertiliser	Gives a plant the nutrients it needs to grow effectively
Pesticide	Kills insects which may eat the crop
Herbicide	Kills other plants (weeds) which would compete with the crop for water, nutrients and space
Fungicide	Kills fungi which can damage the crop

b) Why do intensive farmers add chemicals to crops?

c) What are the four chemical additives used to ensure crops grow as effectively as possible?

How can you make an animal grow as fast as possible?

Intensively farmed animals are kept in a strictly controlled environment. The conditions are chosen to make the animals grow more quickly.

Examples of intensively farmed animals include chickens, pigs, sheep and cattle.

Intensively farmed chickens

Factor controlled	Reason for use
Food supply	High protein diet for rapid increase in body mass
Temperature	Environment kept warm. Animals waste less energy heating their own bodies
Space	Restricted movement. Animals do not waste energy moving around
Antibiotics	These are given to animals to prevent the spread of disease
Safety of enclosure	Animals are kept safe from predators

d) Why are animals kept in a controlled environment?
e) What 5 factors can you control to make an animal grow as quickly as possible?

TEST YOURSELF!

1 Copy and complete the following sentences using these words:

chemicals   controlled   intensive

In _____ farming you try to make as much food as possible from the land available. This involves adding _____ to crops and keeping animals in a _____ environment.

2 What are the advantages of intensive farming?

3 Why are antibiotics given to healthy animals?

4 Free range eggs are much more expensive than eggs from a battery farm. Explain why, giving as many reasons as you can.

4.4 Organic farming

LEARNING OBJECTIVES

1 What is organic farming?
2 How is organic farming used?

Organic farming uses natural methods of producing crops and rearing animals. Artificial chemicals are not used, and animals are allowed to roam as freely as possible. Many people believe food grown in this way is healthier and tastes better.

a) What is meant by organic farming?

How can crops be grown effectively without using chemicals?

- Nutrients are added to the soil by adding manure or compost.
- Crops are rotated, because different crops take different nutrients from the soil.
- Leguminous plants like clover are planted, because they add nitrates to the soil.

Organic food takes longer to produce than the same amount of food produced using intensive farming techniques. It requires more land, crop yields tend to be smaller and more crops are lost to pests. Therefore it is often more expensive.

How can you control pests without using pesticides?

All crop pests have natural predators. Farmers can exploit this relationship to kill pests. This is called **biological control**. Predators (normally other insects) are grown in large numbers. They are then released onto the crops, where they eat the pests.

Ladybird eating aphids

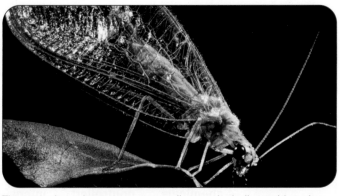

The green lacewing eats many small pests, including spider mites and mealybugs

Sometimes microorganisms are used to kill the pests. This works by the microorganism infecting the pest with a disease. The fungus *Entomophaga maimaiga* is used to kill gypsy moths. These are responsible for destroying acres of forest.

Organic farmers also use selective breeding techniques to produce new varieties of crops that are more resistant to pests and disease.

b) Name two examples of predators used as a biological control.

How can you control weeds without using herbicides?

On a small scale, weeds are removed by hand. This is time-consuming, and is not practical on a large scale.

Machines have been developed to help weed large areas of crop without damaging the crop itself. This method works well on crops which are grown in rows, such as vegetables.

A weeding machine like this one helps farmers pull out weeds quickly

c) How do organic farmers control weed growth?

How are animals reared organically?

- **Diet:** organic food is fed to the animals.
- **Space:** animals are allowed to roam as freely as possible.
- **Drugs:** animals are not given artificial growth hormones or antibiotics (unless they are ill). So they tend to grow more slowly and may suffer from more diseases than intensively farmed animals.
- **Security:** animals are usually kept indoors at night, for safety from predators.

d) Give two reasons why organically reared animals grow more slowly than intensively farmed animals.

TEST YOURSELF!

1 Copy and complete the following sentences using these words:

   artificial   healthier   longer   natural

   Organic farming uses _____ methods. This means that the food takes

   _____ to produce than intensive farming. No _____ chemicals are used.

   Some people think that organic food tastes better and is _____ for you.

2 Why do biological control methods take longer to kill pests than using pesticides?

3 In a table, compare the differences between how an animal is reared organically and intensively.

4 Explain why biological control works better in a controlled environment, such as a greenhouse.

4.5   The intensive farming debate

Activity

Read through the information and write a balanced view
(using arguments for and against) of these two types of farming.

Discuss which you would choose with your group.

Who lives in a hedge?

Inhabitants
of a hedge

To make the most of their land, many intensive farmers remove hedgerows to create larger fields. This creates more space for growing crops. The fields are also much easier to farm, as large machinery can be used.

Hedges are the homes for hundreds of plants and animals. A few of the most common animal species are shown in the cartoon.

As well as destroying the habitats of many organisms, removing hedges causes soil erosion. The hedges act as natural wind blocks. Once hedges are removed, when the fields are barren during winter, soil can be blown or washed away.

Activity

Your head teacher has proposed to cut down the hedges surrounding the school playing fields to allow more space for sports activities. Write a letter to your head teacher, explaining why this decision would be damaging to the environment.

Can organic farms feed the world's population?

The world's population is currently 6.5 billion people. Nearly 1 billion of these people are undernourished, almost all in less developed countries (LDCs). By 2050, the population will increase to more than 9 billion.

The majority of farming in LDCs is small-scale, organic farming. In the developed world, most farming is intensive.

Activities

a) Why do you think most farming in LDCs is organic?

b) Explain why many LDCs are trying to introduce intensive farming techniques.

c) What resources would LDCs require to convert from organic to intensive farming?

d) In the UK the opposite is happening – intensive farms are converting to organic farms. Explain why this is happening.

How do pesticides kill birds?

DDT was widely used as a very effective pesticide. Only very small amounts are needed to kill an insect. As well as saving many people from starvation by killing crop pests, it has also been used to kill the mosquitoes that spread malaria.

However, it also killed large numbers of wildlife. DDT is dangerous and does not decompose easily. It is not broken down by plants or animals, and therefore passes along food chains until it reaches fatal levels. So it is now banned in many countries.

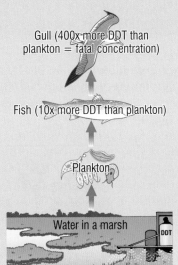

Gull (400x more DDT than plankton = fatal concentration)

Fish (10x more DDT than plankton)

Plankton

Water in a marsh

DDT

Activity

Design an A5 flyer which can be handed out in the street to make people aware of potential dangers of spraying plants with insecticides in their gardens.

Be careful using fertilisers!

Be careful using fertiliser

When large amounts of fertiliser are used by farmers, lots may be wasted. When it rains, it drains away from the soil into ponds, lakes and rivers.

The fertiliser increases the growth of water plants. Algae grow rapidly, quickly covering the surface. This stops light reaching the lower plants. When these and the algae die, they are broken down by microorganisms. The decaying process uses up lots of oxygen from the water. This makes it increasingly difficult for animals to survive and many fish die. This is called **eutrophication**.

If high levels of nitrates enter our drinking water, it can damage our health. Bacteria change the nitrates to nitrites. These can stick to red blood cells, stopping them carrying oxygen.

Activity

Design a poster to make farmers aware of the potential problems caused by fertilisers.

You might include a cartoon strip or a flow diagram to explain how eutrophication occurs.

SUMMARY QUESTIONS

1 Use these words to help answer the following questions:

**carbon dioxide   chlorophyll   glucose
stomata   oxygen   roots   water**

a) Write the equation for photosynthesis.

b) Where is light energy trapped?

c) What are the 2 products of photosynthesis?

d) Which substance is used by the plant to produce energy for growth?

e) Describe how carbon dioxide and water enter a plant.

2

Paul decides that this plant is unhealthy.

a) Describe the features which help Paul reach this conclusion.

b) Paul thinks this plant may suffer from a lack of water. Is he correct?

c) What do you think is wrong with this plant?

d) How can Paul solve the problem?

3 Match the chemicals with their use:

Chemical	Use
Herbicide	Adds minerals to the soil
Fungicide	Kills pests
Pesticide	Kills weeds
Fertiliser	Kills fungi

4 Look at this picture:

a) Is this animal intensively or organically reared?

b) Give reasons for your answer to a).

c) Why do farmers keep animals in this way?

5 Dave wants to set up an organic farm. He knows he must not use chemicals.

How could he deal with these problems without using chemicals?

a) His fields contain lots of weeds.

b) His soil is lacking in minerals.

c) His tomatoes are covered in aphids.

6 Lacewing insects can be used to control greenhouse pests.

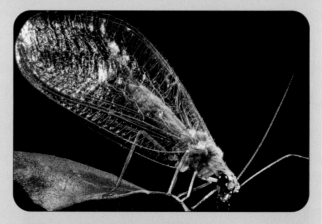

a) What is this technique called?

b) How does this technique work?

c) Why are the insects bought as eggs or pupae, not fully grown?

d) Why would this technique not be as successful if used on pests in a field?

EXAM-STYLE QUESTIONS

1 Large greenhouses are used to grow crops of tomato plants. To increase the yield the grower needs to increase the rate of glucose production.

a) i) Copy and complete the following word equation to describe how the tomato plants make glucose.

.... + ... ➤ glucose + ...

(3)

ii) What is this process called? (1)
iii) Give two ways that the grower could increase the rate of this process and so grow more tomatoes. (2)

b) The grower planted two tomato plants (P and Q) at the same time. They were grown in different fertilisers, the contents of which are shown in the following table.

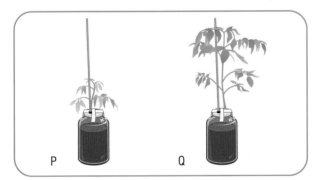

Type of fertiliser present	Percentage of elements		
	Nitrogen	Phosphorus	Potassium
Fertiliser X	30	10	10
Fertiliser Y	3	12	6

i) Suggest which fertiliser was used to grow plant Q. (1)
ii) Explain your choice. (2)

c) The pictures show leaves from two different tomato plants A and B.

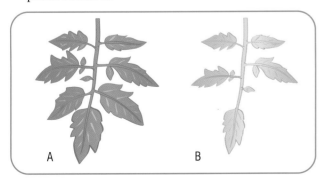

i) What differences can you see between the leaves in the pictures? (2)
ii) Leaf B is suffering from a condition called Chlorosis caused by a lack of chlorophyll. Suggest what could be added to the soil to treat this condition. (1)

2 The diagram shows how nitrates can be cycled on a farm. Use the diagram to answer the following questions.

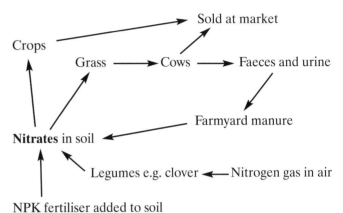

a) i) What do plants and animals need nitrates for? (1)
ii) Suggest how the nitrates could be lost from this cycle. (2)

b) Explain how the nitrates can be put back into the soil:
i) on an organic farm (2)
ii) on an intensive farm. (1)

c) The farmer's crop of corn was attacked by aphids. The yield decreased and he did not make as much money when they were sold at the market.

How could the farmer improve his yield:
i) by organic methods (2)
ii) by intensive methods? (1)

3 a) Chicken is a very popular food in the UK. Many chickens are now farmed intensively. Give two advantages and two disadvantages of farming them in this way. (4)

b) The chickens are raised in a controlled environment.
i) Name three factors which may be controlled. (3)
ii) Explain how each of the factors you have mentioned will increase the growth of the chickens. (3)

5.1

What products can we make using organisms?

The most obvious product we get from plants and animals is food. This is what most agriculture and horticulture businesses concentrate on. A huge variety of food is produced, coming from a range of sources.

Yeast and bacteria are also involved in making food and drink products like beer and cheese. However, many other products are also made from living organisms.

a) Name 5 food products made from plants.
b) Name 5 food products made from animals.

Fabrics

Fabrics are made from both animals and plants. Leather and suede goods are made from animal skins. Fur coats used to be made from animals like mink, though many are now made synthetically.

Cotton is picked from cotton plants

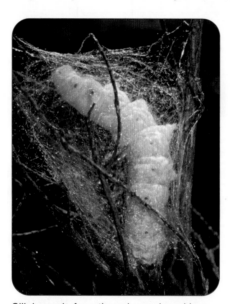

Silk is made from threads produced by silk worms

Sheep are shorn to remove their winter coat. This is used to make woollen clothing like jumpers.

DID YOU KNOW?

The tiny cochineal beetle lives on cactus plants. The females eat the red berries and concentrate the colour in their bodies. The beetles are killed with hot water, then dried in the sun. They are then crushed into powder. This red dye is used to colour food products like sweets and ice cream, and make-up, especially lipstick!

c) Why do some people choose not to wear leather?

Dyeing fabrics

Many fabrics are dyed to make clothing and soft furnishings, like curtains and sofa covers. Originally, all dyes had a plant or animal origin.

To make denim-coloured jeans, cotton is dyed with an indigo dye obtained from the woad plant. Fabrics can be dyed yellow using turmeric dye, made from the root of the turmeric plant.

Medicine

Nearly half of the medicines used by doctors today are based on plant extracts that have come from the rainforests. Rainforest plants provide the basic ingredients of anaesthetics, contraceptives, cancer drugs and hundreds more.

Scientists believe that the rainforests may still hold the cures for many more diseases. As more and more forests are being cut down, though, the chance of finding these drugs is being reduced.

Many ingredients for medicines and cancer drugs come from the rainforests

Drugs derived from the rosy periwinkle have helped to increase the number of children who survive leukaemia from less than 20% to over 80%

d) What other materials do we get from the rainforest?

Microorganisms are also important in the pharmaceutical industry. A fungus is used to make penicillin, and bacteria are involved in making insulin.

TEST YOURSELF!

1 Copy and complete the following table with an example of where the product can be obtained:

Product	Organism
Wooden chair	
Bacon	
Pasta	
Silk	
Leather	
Yellow dye	
Penicillin	

2 Name as many products as you can that can be obtained from a cow.

3 Name as many products as you can that can be obtained from an apple tree.

4 Although clothing made of nylon doesn't come from an animal directly, explain how animals were once involved in making nylon. (Hint – nylon is made from oil.)

5.2 Making bread, beer and wine

LEARNING OBJECTIVES

1 How is bread made?
2 How do we brew beer?
3 How is wine produced?

In Unit 1 (page 26) you looked at the work of a brewery. Yeast is an important microorganism in brewing and in bread making.

Yeast is a type of fungus. It is very useful in food production. Yeast is needed to make bread, beer and wine. These three products are made using a chemical reaction called **fermentation**. Fermentation is an example of anaerobic respiration – the yeast respires without oxygen. The chemical equation for fermentation is:

$$\text{glucose} \rightarrow \text{ethanol (alcohol)} + \text{carbon dioxide}$$
$$C_6H_{12}O_6 \rightarrow 2C_2H_5OH + 2CO_2$$

Enzymes speed up the process of fermentation. These enzymes are found in yeast.

a) How is fermentation different from aerobic respiration?
b) What is the common name for ethanol?

What are the ideal conditions for yeast to work?

There needs to be a good supply of glucose and no oxygen present for yeast enzymes to carry out fermentation. The enzymes work best at a temperature between 15°C and 25°C.

c) Why must there be no oxygen for fermentation to take place?

How do you make bread?

Microscopic image of yeast

Bread rising in a baking tin

Bread is made using the fermentation reaction. A baker mixes together flour, water, sugar and yeast to make dough. The dough is then left in a warm place to rise. Enzymes in the yeast change the sugar into ethanol and carbon dioxide. As the gas is trapped inside the dough it makes it rise. The dough is then baked. In the oven, the ethanol evaporates. The bubbles of gas expand, making the bread rise further.

d) Why is dough not put in the fridge to rise?

How do you make beer?

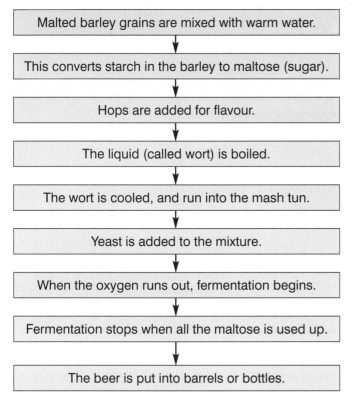

| Malted barley grains are mixed with warm water. |
| This converts starch in the barley to maltose (sugar). |
| Hops are added for flavour. |
| The liquid (called wort) is boiled. |
| The wort is cooled, and run into the mash tun. |
| Yeast is added to the mixture. |
| When the oxygen runs out, fermentation begins. |
| Fermentation stops when all the maltose is used up. |
| The beer is put into barrels or bottles. |

This is how beer is made

A 'mash tun', where fermentation occurs in a brewery

e) Why does fermentation stop after a period of time?

How do you make wine?

Wine is made in a very similar way to beer. Grapes are crushed and yeast added. Yeast changes the sugar in grapes into alcohol. When the fermentation process is complete, the wine is bottled.

Why are some wines red and others white?

TEST YOURSELF!

1 Copy and complete the following sentences using these words:

alcoholic   **bread**   **carbon dioxide**   **fermentation**   **fungus**

Yeast is a _____. It is very important in the production of food and

_____ drinks. During _____, glucose is converted into ethanol

and _____. Yeast is involved in making beer and _____.

2 Jewish people do not eat yeast at Passover. They still eat bread, but it has to be made without yeast. How would it be different from normal bread?

3 Vodka is made from potatoes. Yeast is involved in fermenting the potato sugars. Write a standard procedure to explain how vodka could be made?

4 During step 7 of brewing beer (above), why does the oxygen in the mash tun get used up?

5.3 Using microorganisms to make cheese and yoghurt

LEARNING OBJECTIVE

1 How are microorganisms used to make cheese and yoghurt?

There are hundreds of types of cheese. Cheese is made from the curdled milk of many animals. The flow chart shows simply how cheese is produced.

Milk

Bacteria added to convert lactose (milk sugar) into lactic acid

Rennet added. Rennet contains the enzyme, rennin, which changes a milk protein into casein (curd)

Milk curdles and separates into curds and whey

Whey (mainly water) is drained off

Curds (milk solids – fats and proteins) are pressed to make the cheese solid

Cheese left to ripen to improve its flavour and consistency

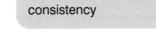

How cheese is made

a) What 2 substances have to be added to milk to turn it into cheese?
b) Why is the whey removed?

Apart from using milk from different animals, we can make different styles and flavours of cheese using different species of bacteria and moulds. Cheeses like stilton have mould growing throughout the cheese. Others like camembert have mould on the outer skin.

Stilton cheese has mould growing throughout it

How is yoghurt made?

Yoghurt is another product which is made from milk. Commercially, cows milk is used, but any milk can be turned into yoghurt.

A mixture of bacteria is added to boiled milk. The milk is kept warm for several hours. During this time the bacteria multiply and ferment lactose into lactic acid. The lactic acid curdles the milk into yoghurt. It also restrains the growth of harmful bacteria. This increases the time that yoghurt can be kept and eaten safely.

Yoghurts that have not been pasteurised (heated) to kill the bacteria used to make them are known as 'live' yoghurts.

c) What are the useful properties of lactic acid in yoghurt production?

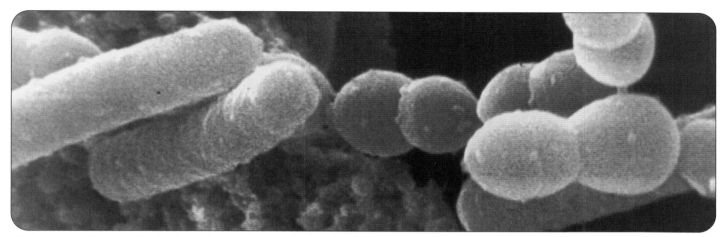

Streptococcus thermophilus (red) and *Lactobacillus bulgaricus* (blue) are both used in yoghurt production

Fermentation of milk

Bacteria are used to ferment milk in both cheese and yoghurt production. In both cases, lactose is converted into lactic acid. It is the acid that gives these products their characteristic tangy taste.

d) What conditions must exist for bacteria to ferment sugar?

TEST YOURSELF!

1 Copy and complete the following sentences using these words:

> **bacteria   curdles   ferment   lactose   yoghurt**

We use _____ to _____ milk in cheese and _____

production. The bacteria change _____ into lactic acid. This

_____ the milk.

2 Why are live yoghurts safe to eat, even though they contain bacteria?

3 Both cheese and yoghurt are made from milk. How are the processes different?

4 Why can you eat pasteurised food for a longer period of time than non-pasteurised food?

5.4 Selective breeding

LEARNING OBJECTIVES

1 What is selective breeding?
2 How are cows selectively bred?
3 How is selective breeding used to grow wheat?

Farmers often select the animals they keep or plants they grow by their characteristics. These characteristics are of benefit to the farmer. For example, they choose sheep that produce lots of wool or chickens that lay lots of eggs.

To ensure that they maintain their desired stock of plants or animals, farmers choose which plants or animals should mate. This is called **selective breeding**.

a) What characteristics would a horse trainer selectively breed for?

Choosing the best cow

The type of cow a farmer desires depends on the produce they sell. Beef farmers need cows that can quickly turn grass and feed into meat, whereas dairy farmers need cows that have high milk yields.

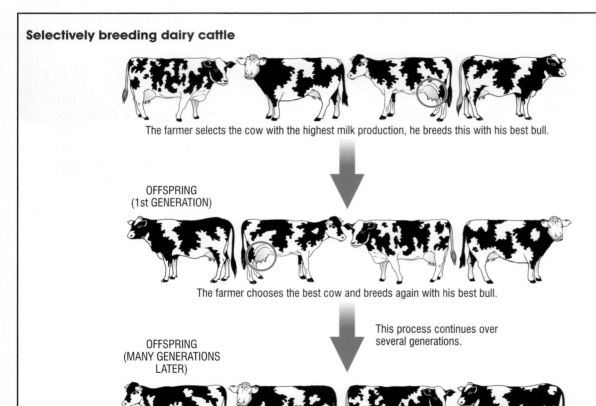

Selectively breeding dairy cattle

The farmer selects the cow with the highest milk production, he breeds this with his best bull.

OFFSPRING (1st GENERATION)

The farmer chooses the best cow and breeds again with his best bull.

This process continues over several generations.

OFFSPRING (MANY GENERATIONS LATER)

All cows have the desired characteristic of high milk production.

b) How does the farmer choose which of the offspring to breed?

c) Why does it take several years of selective breeding to produce a herd of cattle with the desired characteristics?

Selectively breeding wheat

Wheat is a very important plant in the agricultural industry. It is turned into flour, which has a wide number of uses, such as making bread. Selective breeding by farmers has changed what wheat looks like, as the table and figure show:

Wild wheat plants	Modern wheat plants
Ears are small and have few seeds	Ears are large and have many seeds
Stalks are brittle and ears often fall off	Stalks are stronger, so ears stay on
Ears ripen at different times	Ears ripen at the same time
Stalks grow to different heights	Stalks grow to the same height

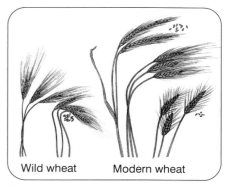

Wild wheat　　　Modern wheat

Effect of selective breeding of wheat

d) How do the features of modern wheat make it easier to harvest?

Through selective breeding, as well as producing high yields, many modern crops have high resistance to disease.

Problems of selective breeding

Selective breeding reduces the number of genes (the **gene pool**) from which a species is created. This means that, if a new disease arises, an organism may not exist that contains the gene for resistance to this disease. This could result in a species becoming extinct. Selective breeding reduces variation.

DID YOU KNOW?

Pedigree dogs are selectively bred. They have the desired characteristics of their breed, but suffer from many health problems. They have a much lower life expectancy than cross-breeds.

TEST YOURSELF!

1 Copy and complete the table with the characteristics a farmer may choose to breed:

Organism	Characteristics
Sheep	
Chicken	
Cow	
Wheat	
Apple tree	

2 What are the disadvantages of selective breeding?

3 A farmer wants to grow large tasty strawberries. One species of strawberry is large and tasteless. Another species produces very small but very sweet and juicy strawberries. Draw a diagram to show how a farmer can selectively breed for the large and tasty characteristics.

5.5   What is genetic engineering?

Farmers use selective breeding to produce animals with desired characteristics. This is a slow process and is not very accurate. Farmers were not originally aware that in this process they were changing the organism's genes.

Scientists now have a much greater understanding of genetics. They are able to alter an organism's genes to produce the desired characteristics. This is called **genetic engineering** (or **genetic modification**). It can happen in one generation.

a) What is genetic engineering?
b) Name 2 advantages of genetic engineering over selective breeding.

Genetically modified cotton has a high cotton yield and pest resistance

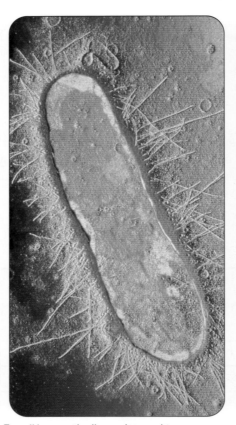

E. coli is genetically engineered to produce insulin

The Glo-Fish, which is genetically engineered to glow when it comes into contact with environmental pollution

What happens to a plant or animal during genetic engineering?

Genes from another organism (foreign genes) are put into plant or animal cells at a very early stage in their development. As the organism develops, it will display the characteristics of the foreign genes.

c) Why are the genes inserted into the plant or animal cells called foreign genes?

Making frost-resistant plants

Frost-resistant tomatoes are an example of a genetically modified crop. Scientists isolated a gene in flounder (a type of fish) and put it into a tomato. This gene codes for an antifreeze chemical which enables the fish to survive in very cold water.

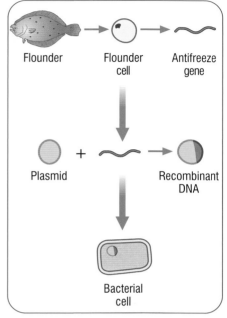

Flounder   Flounder cell   Antifreeze gene

Plasmid   +   Recombinant DNA

Bacterial cell

First steps in producing genetically engineered frost-resistant tomatoes

A useful gene is removed from the nucleus of a donor cell.

↓

The foreign gene is then put into a circular piece of DNA called a **plasmid**. This is now known as a piece of **recombinant DNA**.

↓

The recombinant DNA is put into a bacterial cell.

↓

The bacteria reproduce lots of times, producing lots of copies of the recombinant DNA.

↓

Plant cells are infected with the bacteria. The foreign gene becomes integrated with the DNA of the plant cells.

↓

The plants cells are placed in a growing medium to grow into plants. These plants will have the desired characteristics.

Process of how tomatoes and other crops are genetically modified

Animals are genetically modified in a similar way, by inserting the required genes into an embryo. This technique is used in sheep. They can be genetically modified to produce pharmaceutical agents in their milk.

d) Why is it an advantage for farmers to grow frost-resistant tomatoes?

A ripe tomato

TEST YOURSELF!

1 Copy and complete the following sentences using these words:

chemicals   foreign   resistant   characteristics   genetic

It is possible to insert_____ genes into organisms to change

their_____. This is called _____ engineering. Plants can be

produced which are _____ to disease. Microorganisms can be

engineered to produce useful_____.

2 Name 2 examples of genetically modified:
a) Plants.
b) Animals.

3 Why must the foreign genes used in genetic engineering be inserted into an embryo, and not into a more developed organism?

5.6   A closer look at genetic engineering

Genetically engineered bacteria can treat diseases

Genes that code for the production of useful chemicals are inserted into bacteria. The bacteria are then placed in a warm fermentation tank which contains nutrients. The bacteria reproduce, producing millions of identical copies of the gene and the substance it codes for.

The useful substances are separated from the bacteria and used to treat diseases. Without these medicines many people could die.

Substances produced in this way include insulin, growth hormones, vaccines, Factor VIII and antibiotics.

A fermenter

Activity

Many people believe that genetic engineering is unethical and wrong. Produce a leaflet to try and convince them that genetic engineering is a valuable scientific tool. Explain how genetic engineering is used to treat patients suffering from a range of diseases. From your own research, include a diagram to show how bacteria can produce insulin.

Genetic engineering may cure many diseases!

Gene therapy

It is possible that inherited disorders like haemophilia may be cured by replacing defective genes with normal ones.

How can the genes be put into the DNA of millions of body cells? This is still being researched. Possibly, viruses will be used. Their disease-causing genes will be removed and replaced with the disease-curing gene. When the viruses attack the body cells, the new gene will be placed into the human's DNA.

New treatments

Mice and other laboratory animals can be injected with genes that make them develop diseases like cystic fibrosis and cancer. Possible treatments for these diseases can then be studied and trialled before using on humans.

Mice have a role in genetic engineering

Activity

People have very strong views about animal testing. Some religious groups are against interfering with the human body. What do you think? Using this information and any more you research, produce a PowerPoint presentation explaining why you are for or against the use of genetic engineering in medicine.

Genetically modified crops could feed the world!

Genetically modified (GM) crops were first sold in 1996. However their safety, and the possibility of them damaging the environment, is still being debated.

Each year the world's population increases by more than 80 million people. To feed this number of people by traditional farming methods, all usable soils in the world would have to be ploughed. This would destroy many habitats. Crops can be genetically modified to give a higher yield than a traditional variety. This could feed the world without destroying large areas of the environment.

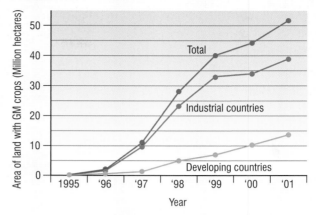

Number of GM crops worldwide from 1995 to 2001

Activity

a) Why are more GM crops grown in industrialised countries?

b) Why has the growth of GM farming slowed down in the industrialised world?

c) If tropical fruits like bananas could be genetically engineered to live in cool climates, how would this harm the economy of poorer countries?

d) Most people prefer seedless grapes. Other fruits could be genetically engineered not to contain seeds. However, these plants could cross-pollinate with wild plants. What effect could this have on the native plants in an environment?

Would you like to be cloned?

When microorganisms reproduce, they produce identical copies of themselves – **clones**. This is exploited when bacteria are used to make useful chemicals, and to produce several copies of genes for use in GM plants. When you take plant cuttings, this is also an example of cloning. Most people happily accept this, but there are very mixed opinions about cloning animals.

Dolly was the first mammal to be cloned. She died prematurely.

Only 700 mountain gorillas are left. Scientists could clone more.

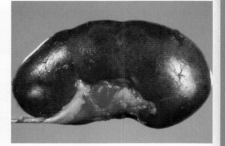
You would not reject a cloned copy of your kidney.

Activity

Human cells are already being cloned, and are used for research.

a) Do you agree with human cloning? Make a list of all the possible advantages and disadvantages.

b) Should there be strict guidelines for cloning?

 Discuss your views in your group.

SUMMARY QUESTIONS

1 Name 3 useful products we can get from each of the following:

a) Plants.

b) Animals.

c) Microorganisms.

2 Use these words to answer the questions:

**carbon dioxide   respiration   ethanol
glucose**

a) Write the equation for fermentation.

b) What is the proper name for alcohol?

c) The bubbles of which gas make bread rise?

d) If oxygen is present fermentation cannot occur. What process would happen instead?

3 Match the animal to their desired characteristics for farming.

Animal	Characteristic
Pig	High milk yield
Goat	High egg yield
Sheep	Lean meat
Chicken	Thick fleecy coat

4 The following sentences explain how farmers may selectively breed their crops. Rearrange them into the correct order:

a) Offspring grow.

b) Farmer chooses crops with the best characteristics.

c) Farmer then chooses the offspring which have the best characteristics.

d) These crops are then cross-pollinated.

e) These are then bred. This process is repeated for many years.

5 A hill farmer wants to breed sheep selectively so that they produce more wool. Draw a simple cartoon to explain how he would do this.

6 The Flavr Svr tomato is genetically engineered to stay firm for longer.

a) Why is this an advantage for tomato sellers?

b) How are the genes in this tomato's nucleus different from that of a normal tomato?

c) Why is this process quicker than selective breeding?

d) What other features might a tomato grower choose to improve?

7 Microorganisms are used in the production of some foods.

a) Name 2 food products that are made using bacteria.

b) Name 2 food products that are made using yeast.

c) Beer and bread are made in similar ways. Why does bread not contain alcohol?

8 You can make alcohol in the lab at school using this simple equipment (but not for drinking!):

**conical flask   yeast   sugar solution
bung containing one-way valve**

a) Draw a diagram to show how you would set up your equipment.

b) Why might you want to sit the conical flask in a beaker of warm water?

c) Explain how alcohol will be produced using this apparatus.

d) What is the purpose of the one-way valve?

EXAM-STYLE QUESTIONS

1   The following passage explains how yoghurt is made. Read the passage and answer the questions.

"A mixture of bacteria is added to boiled milk. The milk is kept warm for several hours. During this time the bacteria multiply and ferment lactose into lactic acid. The lactic acid curdles the milk into yoghurt. It also restrains the growth of harmful bacteria. This increases the time that yoghurt can be kept and eaten safely."

a) Suggest why:

   i)   the milk is boiled to start with   (1)
   ii) the milk is kept warm   (1)
   iii) the growth of harmful bacteria is prevented.   (1)

b) When making yoghurt commercially great care must be taken to ensure it does not become infected with harmful microorganisms. What precautions should the people making the yoghurt take?   (3)

2   Microorganisms are used in the wine industry to make wine.

a) Which microorganism is used to make wine?   (1)

b) A student's parents were making wine at home. They used the following apparatus.

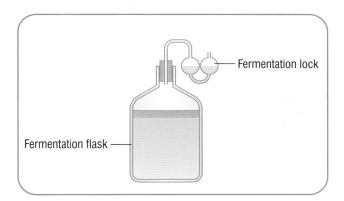

Fermentation lock

Fermentation flask

   i)   The fermentation lock is to stop any air getting into the flask. Why is this necessary?   (1)
   ii) Why does there need to be a tube in the bung?   (1)

   iii) Copy and complete the equation for this reaction.

   .... ➤ alcohol + ...   (2)

c) Describe an experiment the student could do to investigate how temperature affects the growth of microorganisms.   (3)

3   A farmer went to the market to buy a cow.

Characteristics of cows		
Feature	Cow A	Cow B
Growth rate	medium	fast
Udder size (in cms)	4.3	2.9
Total body mass (in lbs)	890	1390
Meat: fat ratio	medium	large

a) i) Which cow would you choose if you were a dairy farmer selling milk? Give a reason for your answer.   (1)

   ii) Which cow would you choose if you were a beef farmer selling meat? Give two reasons for your choice.   (2)

b) Explain how you could use selective breeding to improve the beef production of your cows.   (4)

4   Scientists are now able to alter an organism's genes to produce specific characteristics. The diagram shows the stages in producing genetically modified animals.

The required gene is cut from the DNA using a restriction enzyme

▼

Fertilised eggs are taken from a donor animal and the gene is injected into the egg nucleus

▼

The fertilised eggs are put into a surrogate mother animal

▼

Baby animals are tested for the presence of the gene

a) i)   What is a gene?   (1)
   ii) Where in the donor cell will the gene be removed from?   (1)
   iii) What type of cell is the DNA injected into?   (1)
   iv) Why is this type of cell used?   (1)

b) Pigs can be genetically modified so that they can be bred to provide organs for humans.

   i)   What are the economic arguments in favour of this?   (2)
   ii) Why do some people find this unacceptable?   (2)

123

6.1 Elements, compounds and mixtures

Materials scientists work with thousands of types of materials. To make things easier, they describe materials as elements, compounds or mixtures.

Elements

Atoms are the building blocks for all materials. Materials made of only one type of atom are called **elements**. The **Periodic Table** is a list of all the different elements.

1	2											3	4	5	6	7	0
																	4 **He** helium 2
7 **Li** lithium 3	9 **Be** beryllium 4											11 **B** boron 5	12 **C** carbon 6	14 **N** nitrogen 7	16 **O** oxygen 8	19 **F** fluorine 9	20 **Ne** neon 10
23 **Na** sodium 11	24 **Mg** magnesium 12											27 **Al** aluminium 13	28 **Si** silicon 14	31 **P** phosphorus 15	32 **S** sulfur 16	35.5 **Cl** chlorine 17	40 **Ar** argon 18
39 **K** potassium 19	40 **Ca** calcium 20	45 **Sc** scandium 21	48 **Ti** titanium 22	51 **V** vanadium 23	52 **Cr** chromium 24	55 **Mn** manganese 25	56 **Fe** iron 26	59 **Co** cobalt 27	59 **Ni** nickel 28	63.5 **Cu** copper 29	65 **Zn** zinc 30	70 **Ga** gallium 31	73 **Ge** germanium 32	75 **As** arsenic 33	79 **Se** selenium 34	80 **Br** bromine 35	84 **Kr** krypton 36
85 **Rb** rubidium 37	88 **Sr** strontium 38	89 **Y** yttrium 39	91 **Zr** zirconium 40	93 **Nb** niobium 41	96 **Mo** molybdenum 42	[98] **Tc** technetium 43	101 **Ru** ruthenium 44	103 **Rh** rhodium 45	106 **Pd** palladium 46	108 **Ag** silver 47	112 **Cd** cadmium 48	115 **In** indium 49	119 **Sn** tin 50	122 **Sb** antimony 51	128 **Te** tellurium 52	127 **I** iodine 53	131 **Xe** xenon 54
133 **Cs** caesium 55	137 **Ba** barium 56	139 **La*** lanthanum 57	178 **Hf** hafnium 72	181 **Ta** tantalum 73	184 **W** tungsten 74	186 **Re** rhenium 75	190 **Os** osmium 76	192 **Ir** iridium 77	195 **Pt** platinum 78	197 **Au** gold 79	201 **Hg** mercury 80	204 **Tl** thallium 81	207 **Pb** lead 82	209 **Bi** bismuth 83	[209] **Po** polonium 84	[210] **At** astatine 85	[222] **Rn** radon 86
[223] **Fr** francium 87	[226] **Ra** radium 88	[227] **Ac*** actinium 89	[261] **Rf** rutherfordium 104	[262] **Db** dubnium 105	[266] **Sg** seaborgium 106	[264] **Bh** bohrium 107	[277] **Hs** hassium 108	[268] **Mt** meitnerium 109	[271] **Ds** darmstadtium 110	[272] **Rg** roentgenium 111							

Key

relative atomic mass
atomic symbol
name
atomic (proton) number

1 **H** hydrogen 1

Elements with atomic numbers 112–116 have been reported but not fully authenticated

* The Lanthanides (atomic numbers 58 –71) and the Actinides (atomic numbers 90–103) have been omitted.
Cu and **Cl** have not been rounded to the nearest whole number.

Periodic Table

Look at the Periodic Table shown above. You can probably see some materials you have already heard of, like iron, oxygen, gold and tin.

These all contain one type of atom. They are all elements.

a) Can you name the elements in the pictures above?

Compounds

Most chemicals you have used in science lessons are **compounds**. Compounds all have these two features:

- They contain more than one element.
- The different elements are **bonded** (chemically attached) to each other.

The chemical **bonds** in compounds hold the atoms together tightly. This makes it difficult to separate a compound back into its elements.

b) Do you know which elements are in the compounds shown on the right?

Mixtures

Most of the materials you see every day are **mixtures**. There are two key things you need to know about mixtures:

- They contain more than one type of substance.
- The different substances are not bonded to each other.

Because the different substances are not bonded together, they are easier to separate.

You can look at mixtures in more detail in Chapter 11.

Salt and water are both compounds

There are lots of different substances in these mixtures

TEST YOURSELF!

1 Copy and complete the following sentences using these words:

compounds   atoms   contain   substances   elements

All substances are made of _____. Substances made up of only one type of atom are called _____. Substances which _____ more than one type of element bonded together are called _____. In mixtures, different _____ are not bonded to each other.

2 Look at the following diagrams. Use the descriptions on this spread to decide which is an element, a compound or a mixture.

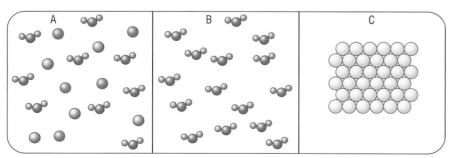

Element, compound or mixture?

KEY FACTS

- Elements are made of only one type of atom.
- Compounds contain more than one type of atom, bonded together.
- Mixtures contain more than one type of substance, not bonded together.

6.2

Materials we take from the environment

LEARNING OBJECTIVES

1 Which materials can we use straight from the Earth?
2 Which materials do we have to separate before use?
3 How do we separate mixtures like crude oil and rock salt?

As well as being decorative, gold is used in electronics

KEY FACTS

- Gold, marble, limestone and sulfur can all be used straight from the ground.

- Crude oil is a mixture of hydrocarbons. We can separate hydrocarbons by fractional distillation.

- Pure salt can be extracted from rock salt by adding water and filtering out the rock.

We all depend on the materials we can find in our environment. However, some materials are harder to get at than others.

Straight from the ground

Since ancient times, **gold** has always been highly valued because of its attractive appearance. Gold does not easily react with other substances. This is why it stays shiny for years.

a) Is gold an element, a compound or a mixture?

Limestone and **marble** are very important construction materials. Both are made mainly from calcium carbonate – a very important compound. They can be either blasted or cut out of the ground.

Marble in the construction industry

Sulfur is another useful material taken straight from the ground. It is important for producing acids and fertilisers.

b) Which sulfur-containing acid have you used in the lab?

All mixed up

Crude oil is a mixture of chemicals called **hydrocarbons**.

A hydrocarbon is a compound containing only hydrogen and carbon.

Petrol and **natural gas** are important examples of hydrocarbon fuels. We also use hydrocarbons to make plastics, paints and some medicines. We can separate the hydrocarbons in crude oil because they have different boiling points.

Separating crude oil like this is called **fractional distillation**.

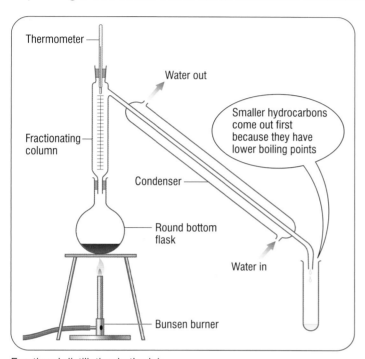

Fractional distillation in the lab

Fractional distillation in industry

Salt from rock salt

We mine huge amounts of salt from the ground. This type of salt is called **rock salt**.

Rock salt is a mixture of salt (sodium chloride) and, yes, rock. Rock salt can be easily separated by adding water to the mixture. The salt dissolves. Then we can remove the bits of insoluble rock by filtering.

A wall of salt in a salt mine

TEST YOURSELF!

1 a) Name one material we use straight from the Earth and one material we need to separate.

  b) Describe two uses for each material you named in a).

2 Look at the picture of gold contacts used in electronics on the previous page. Why do you think gold is more useful here than a metal like iron?

3 How are we able to separate the hydrocarbons in crude oil?

4 Describe how you would get a pure sample of salt from rock salt in your school laboratory.

6.3

Chemical shorthand

1 What are the chemical symbols for some important elements?

2 What does a chemical formula tell us?

3 How do we write chemical equations?

Do you like NaCl and CH_3COOH on your chips? What about sodium chloride and ethanoic acid? Don't worry – you're not being poisoned! Those are just the chemical shorthand and names for salt and vinegar.

Chemists often use **symbols** when writing about chemicals. It's not supposed to be a code to make it more complicated – it's just a way of speeding up the writing! The same symbols are used by scientists all over the world.

Mad scientist!

The symbols for most elements are easy to work out. C for carbon, O for oxygen and H for hydrogen are some of the easiest. Some symbols just have to be learned, though.

These are the most important elements you need to know the symbols for:

Non-metals		Metals	
Element	Chemical symbol	Element	Chemical symbol
Argon	Ar	Aluminium	Al
Bromine	Br	Calcium	Ca
Carbon	C	Gold	Au
Chlorine	Cl	Iron	Fe
Hydrogen	H	Lead	Pb
Nitrogen	N	Magnesium	Mg
Oxygen	O	Potassium	K
Phosphorus	P	Silver	Ag
Silicon	Si	Sodium	Na
Sulfur	S	Zinc	Zn

a) Can you find all these elements on the periodic table on page 124? Which ones do you think are given symbols from their old Latin names?

As well as knowing the symbols for elements, you need to be able to put them together to show compounds. We call this a **chemical formula**.

Sometimes, we need numbers to help us describe a substance. A small number after a symbol tells us how many atoms there are in a compound.

Let's look at water as an example:

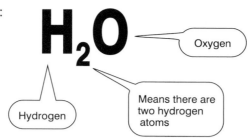

The 'chemical shorthand' for water

Water's formula is H_2O. This tells us it contains hydrogen and oxygen. The number 2 tells us there are two hydrogen atoms attached to the oxygen atom. (Notice that we don't bother writing 1 after a symbol. If there is no number there, we just assume there is one atom.)

You need to know the chemical formulas of these other common compounds:

Compound	Formula
Carbon dioxide	CO_2
Ethanol	C_2H_5OH
Hydrogen chloride	HCl
Methane	CH_4
Ammonia	NH_3

b) Can you describe carbon dioxide in the same way we just described water?

Putting it into practice

In the next spread, we will look at metal **ores**. Most need to be chemically processed in order to get the metal from the ore.

Iron oxide is a metal ore. We react it with carbon monoxide to produce pure iron. This is the chemical **equation**, using words and using symbols:

$$\text{iron oxide} + \text{carbon monoxide} \rightarrow \text{carbon dioxide} + \text{iron}$$
$$Fe_2O_3 + 3\,CO \rightarrow 3\,CO_2 + 2\,Fe$$

Did you notice that some of the numbers are in different places now? A full-sized number in front of a formula tells us how much of the whole chemical there is. So for any number of iron oxide particles we have, we need three times as many carbon monoxide particles to react with it.

KEY FACTS

- We use symbols to represent atoms of the chemical elements.

- Small numbers after a symbol tell us the numbers of each atom in a substance.

- Full-sized numbers in front of a formula tell us how much of each substance is used or made in a reaction.

TEST YOURSELF!

1 Write out the names of the elements on the previous page. Now, close the book and test yourself on their symbols. No cheating!

2 a) Which elements are in ethanol?
b) How much is there of each?

3 Which of the following is the symbol for potassium chloride?
A. PCl
B. KCl
C. KCL

129

6.4 Getting useful metals from the Earth

LEARNING OBJECTIVES

1 What is an ore?
2 Which common metals do we get from ores?
3 How can we use reducing agents to get metals from ores?

Metals are vital in our modern society. Without metals, we wouldn't have electronics, or most machines.

Most metals exist in the Earth's crust as compounds called **ores**. An ore is a rock containing a useful amount of metal. Ores contain enough metal to make it worth spending the money to extract it. We need to be able to separate the metal from the other elements in the ore.

Rocks rich in iron ore

Many ores contain oxides, compounds of the metal plus oxygen. We can remove oxygen from a compound with a **reducing agent**.

A reducing agent has to be more **reactive** than the metal in the oxide. Being more reactive means it is able to 'pull' the oxygen away from the metal. We say that the metal oxide has been **reduced**.

Scientists use a **reactivity series** to work out which reducing agent they use with which ore. A reactivity series is just a list of elements in order of how reactive they are:

Magnesium	More reactive
Aluminium	
Carbon	
Zinc	
Iron	
Tin	
Lead	
Copper	
Gold	Less reactive

Reactivity series

Look at the reactivity series above. Carbon is more reactive than iron or lead. This means we can use carbon as a reducing agent for iron and lead ores.

Producing iron from iron ore

Iron is a very important metal. We use it to make steel. Most iron comes from an ore called haematite. This contains iron oxide (Fe_2O_3).

Haematite is crushed and put into a huge tower called a **blast furnace**. Carbon (in the form of coke made from coal) is also added. The temperature in the furnace is around 1500°C.

Hot air is blasted through the furnace, and the following chemical reaction happens:

$$C \quad + \quad O_2 \quad \rightarrow \quad CO_2$$
carbon   oxygen   carbon dioxide

Then the carbon dioxide reacts with more coke to produce carbon monoxide:

$$C \quad + \quad CO_2 \quad \rightarrow \quad 2\,CO$$
carbon   carbon dioxide   carbon monoxide

The carbon monoxide then reduces the iron oxide:

$$3\,CO \quad + \quad Fe_2O_3 \quad \rightarrow \quad 3\,CO_2 \quad + \quad 2\,Fe$$
carbon monoxide   iron oxide   carbon dioxide   **iron**

Limestone is also added to remove impurities. This forms a substance called **slag**.

Extracting lead from its ore

Lead is used in car batteries, roofs and making solder.

Lead is easier to extract than iron, because it is easier to reduce lead oxide than iron oxide.

Coke is added to lead oxide. This reduces the lead and makes carbon monoxide:

$$PbO \quad + \quad C \quad \rightarrow \quad Pb \quad + \quad CO$$
lead oxide   carbon   **lead**   carbon monoxide

The carbon monoxide also reduces some of the lead oxide:

$$PbO \quad + \quad CO \quad \rightarrow \quad Pb \quad + \quad CO_2$$
lead oxide   carbon monoxide   **lead**   carbon dioxide

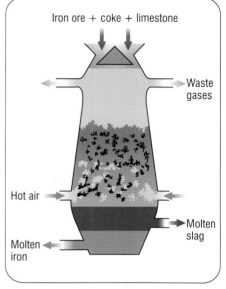

Iron ore + coke + limestone

Waste gases

Hot air

Molten iron

Molten slag

Diagram of a blast furnace

KEY FACTS

- Reducing agents remove oxygen from ores.

- Reducing agents have to be more reactive than the metal in the oxide.

- Iron is produced from its ore in a blast furnace.

- Iron oxide and lead oxide are reduced by carbon and carbon monoxide.

TEST YOURSELF!

1 What is iron's main ore called?

2 What are the two reducing agents mentioned on these two pages?

3 Why could you not use carbon to reduce aluminium oxide into aluminium?

4 What waste products come out of a blast furnace?

6.5 Advantages and disadvantages of using natural resources

LEARNING OBJECTIVES

1 How do mined materials benefit society?
2 What are the drawbacks of mining and quarrying?
3 How can mining be managed sustainably?

Mining and quarrying affect all of us. Everyone relies upon items made from metals, every day. We use electronics; we use cars, buses and trains. Our water reaches us through metal pipes; our electricity reaches us through metal wires.

We are constantly using other mined materials too. Our homes are made from brick, concrete and steel. We put salt from salt mines on our food. We use plastics made from oil that was extracted from the ground.

Without the products from the mining industry, life would be very different. This is an example of an open-cast mine.

As well as the consumer benefits, society benefits from mining in other ways. More than 100 000 jobs in the UK are related to the mining and quarrying industries.

What are the problems with mining?

Mining activity damages the environment. Environmentalists argue that mines and quarries damage the appearance of the landscape. Then there is the noise and dust that affects the nearby area. Also, mining activity increases traffic near the mine. This leads to more air pollution.

Transporting mined materials

a) Which air pollutants are created by traffic?

Air pollution isn't just caused by the dust and traffic. Processing ores pollutes the air as well. Metals like iron and lead produce carbon dioxide when they are purified. Lead, in particular, is very poisonous. Sulfur dioxide gas is also produced when metal sulfide ores are heated. This causes acid rain.

In some mines, rain can cause toxic chemicals to wash into rivers and lakes. This causes even more environmental damage.

There can be social drawbacks with mines as well. The material being mined runs out, eventually. This means that mines don't stay open forever. This can cause problems in communities relying on mines for employment.

Managing mines responsibly

The Planning and Compulsory Purchase Act (2004) set out new rules for developing land into mines. Any development plans now need to be assessed for **sustainability**. Sustainable development is using resources in a way that finds a balance between human and environmental needs.

Sites which will cause the least environmental damage are preferred. Plans are discussed with all the people it will affect before a mine is started. Also, the after-effects of the mine on the community are considered.

KEY FACTS

- Humans benefit from the products, services and jobs provided by mining.

- The environment can be damaged by mining operations.

- Managing mining sustainably reduces long-term environmental damage.

TEST YOURSELF!

1 Which materials mined from the ground are most important to your everyday life? Why?

2 What are:
   a) The potential social benefits of opening a mine?
   b) The social costs of opening a mine?

3 Describe three ways mining can damage the environment.

4 How can we manage mining sustainably?

6.6   Extracting metals from the Earth

The Great American Gold Rush

Gold used to be a lot easier to find than it is today! In 1799, a farmer's son in North Carolina, USA, found a large yellow rock whilst hiding in the creek instead of going to church. He used it as a doorstop until 1802, when the family realised what he had found. A gold nugget the size of a grapefruit! By the middle of the 1800s, lots of gold was being found in California. Solid gold nuggets were just sitting at the bottom of rivers waiting to be picked up. Thousands of people travelled across the country to join the 'gold rush'. They would 'pan for gold' in streams and rivers. Unfortunately, not everybody got there. The Nevada deserts were hot and dry – hundreds died because they hadn't prepared for the journey.

19th Century prospectors
panning for gold

Activity

Research the following:

a) Why were gold rush prospectors called 49ers?

b) Where else in the world is gold mined from?

These days, gold mining can cause environmental problems. Nearly 80 tonnes of waste is produced for every 30 grams of gold that is found.

  Discuss the advantages and disadvantages of gold mining.

Early iron

Iron was being used by the Egyptians from as early as 4000 BC, but only in small amounts. It was difficult to heat it strongly enough to melt it and 'cast' it into shapes.

China was the first country to make cast iron, in 800 BC. Iron didn't reach the UK for another three hundred years.

The iron that comes out of a blast furnace still isn't completely pure. It's a brittle form of the metal called pig iron.

An early ironworks in Wales. The furnace is at the centre of the picture.

Activity

Research the following:

a) Where was the first blast furnace made?

b) Is any iron ore mined in the UK today?

c) What needs to be taken into account when choosing a location for a mine? It's more complicated than just being near a source of ore.

Jobs in the mining industry

There are almost a hundred different types of jobs in mining. Here are some of them:

Geologist – explores for ores and works out where to mine.

Geophysicist – uses sophisticated equipment to detect metal ores underground.

Sampler – collects samples or ore for testing.

Driller – drills holes in the rock to get samples for geologists.

Blaster – packs explosives into holes, making sure everything is safe before blasting.

Crusher operator – runs the machinery that pulverises the ore.

Environmental technician – makes sure environmental rules are followed.

Mining engineer – decides on the best way to get the ore out of the ground.

Activity

Find out more about each job – what skills or qualifications are needed?

SUMMARY QUESTIONS

1   Why can't you find water in the periodic table?

2   What are the chemical symbols for these elements?
   a) Sulfur.   d) Sodium.
   b) Chlorine.   e) Silver.
   c) Potassium.

3   What are the names of these compounds?
   a) CH_4.
   b) CO.

4   What are the differences between:
   a) A compound and a mixture?
   b) An element and a compound?

5   Sort these materials into things we use straight from the ground and things we need to separate using chemical reactions:
   a) Iron.   d) Aluminium.
   b) Limestone.   e) Marble.
   c) Lead.   f) Sulfur.

6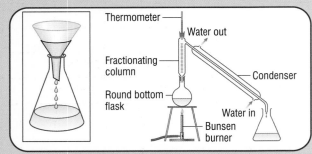

Laboratory filtration and laboratory fractional distillation

Which of these methods would you use to:
   a) Separate the hydrocarbons in crude oil?
   b) Separate salt from rock salt?

7   Explain why lead and iron are both important to society.

8   Which needs a higher temperature to extract it from its ore – iron or lead?

9   What reducing agent is used to extract lead from its ore?

10 When deciding whether to build a mine...
   a) What could be the environmental problems?
   b) What might the local benefits be?

EXAM-STYLE QUESTIONS

1   A student was clearing out her medicine cabinet. The diagram shows some of the things she found in it.

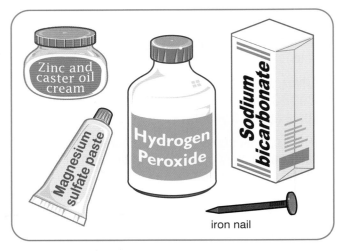

iron nail

a) i)   Copy the table below and write each item under its correct heading.

Element	Compound	Mixture

(3)

   ii) Which of the above items cannot be separated into anything simpler?   (1)
   iii) What is the difference between a compound and a mixture?   (2)

b) Magnesium sulphate has the formula $MgSO_4$

   What elements does it contain?   (3)

2   Lots of chemical substances we use are extracted from the ground.

   a) i)   Name two substances found in the ground as elements.   (2)
      ii) Name two substances that are compounds, which are used straight from the ground.   (2)

   b) Other substances obtained from the ground have to be separated before use. Sodium chloride is obtained from rock salt. Rock salt also contains sand. Describe how you could find out how much sodium chloride there is in 25g of rock salt.   (4)

3 Many metals are obtained from the earth.

a) Copy and complete the sentence below using words from the list.

carbon   lead   ores   oxygen   oxidising   reducing

Most metals are found as ………… Many of these are an oxide, a compound of the metal with ………… A ………………..agent is used to separate the oxide from the metal, an example is …………………… (4)

b) Iron can be extracted from a mineral called haematite in a blast furnace.

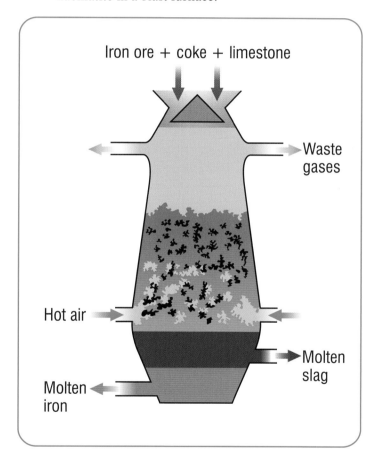

Iron ore + coke + limestone

Waste gases

Hot air

Molten iron

Molten slag

Use the diagram of a blast furnace to help you explain:

   i) why coke is added   (2)
   ii) why limestone is added   (1)
   iii) why air is added.   (2)

4 The local council have written to you to tell you that they want to open a new limestone quarry in your area.

a) How might this affect you? Give two possible advantages and two possible disadvantages. (4)

b) The formula for limestone is $CaCO_3$.
   i) Is limestone a compound or a mixture? Explain your choice. (2)
   ii) What are the elements present in limestone? (3)

5 Crude oil has many uses in industry. Crude oil is a mixture of chemicals called hydrocarbons.

a) i) What elements do hydrocarbons contain? (2)
   ii) What is the name of the method used to separate crude oil into its fractions? (2)

b) The table shows some information about the fractions obtained from crude oil.

Fraction	Boiling point in °C (approximate)	Number of carbon atoms per molecule (approximately)
Petrol	40 – 75	4 – 12
Kerosene	150–240	7 – 14
Lubricating oil	250 – 350	20–70
Bitumen	Above 350	Above 70

   i) Which fraction would be separated first when crude oil is heated? (1)
   ii) Give two reasons for your answer. (2)

7.1 Finding fossil fuels

We need a source of energy to change things or to make things happen. Fossil fuels are examples of **primary energy resources**. They are valuable because they are concentrated sources of energy. The stored chemical energy is released by burning them, when they react with the oxygen in air.

As you can see below, solid lumps of **coal** burn with an orange-yellow flame.

Crude oil is a very thick dark liquid.

Natural gas burns very well, with a blue-ish flame.

These pie-charts show how the UK's use of different energy resources to make electricity has changed from 1990 to 2003:

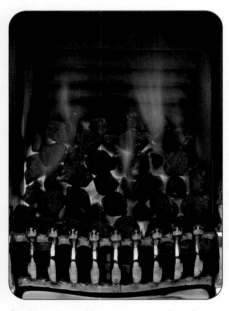

Coal burning with an orange-yellow flame

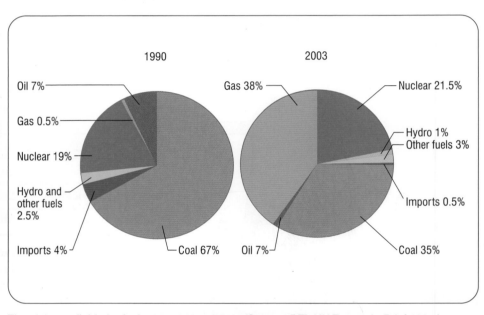

Electricity available by fuel type, 1990 to 2003. (Source: DTI, UK Energy in Brief 2004.)

The charts show that in the UK we used to burn a lot of coal to make our electricity, but this has decreased recently.

Since the discovery of natural gas deposits underneath the bed of the North Sea, they have become a major source of energy for us.

Our use of oil has decreased, partly because of its cost and partly because of the increased availability of natural gas as an alternative.

a) Look at the pie-charts carefully. What were the 3 most important energy resources for us in 2003?

Why have fossil fuels got energy in them?

Coal, oil and natural gas are all called **fossil fuels**. That's because they have been made over millions of years from plants and animals.

Coal is formed from the remains of plants that grew about 300 million years ago.

Oil and **gas** are formed from tiny sea creatures and plants that lived about 150 million years ago.

The energy for these living plants and animals came from the Sun. It was stored in them as chemical energy. This energy has stayed there until now, even though the living things have become fossils.

A Carboniferous swamp – where the formation of coal started about 300 million years ago

Fossil fuels contain a lot of chemical energy. When we burn them, that energy is released as heat which we can use to make electricity. Look at this energy transfer diagram for these changes:

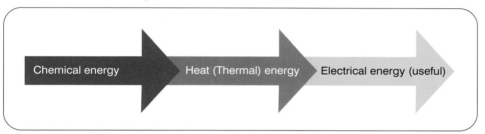

Chemical energy → Heat (Thermal) energy → Electrical energy (useful)

Energy transfer diagram

TEST YOURSELF!

1 Copy and complete this table:

Fuel	Description	When it formed
Coal		
Oil		
Natural gas		

2 Look again at the pie-charts. Which energy resources are increasing in use – and which are decreasing?

3 Do some extra research – find out how the plants and animals that form coal and oil became fossils. Draw flow charts to explain how it happened.

DID YOU KNOW?

Fossil fuels took between 100 000 000 and 300 000 000 years to form – that's why we won't be able to replace them when they run out.

7.2   Tour of a power station

This photo shows a coal power station. It burns about 250 tonnes of crushed coal an hour.

A power station

Most power stations generate electricity by burning a **fuel** to boil water. The steam this makes is used to spin a **turbine**, which turns a **generator** that makes electricity.

Generating electricity from a primary energy source, like coal, is not a very **efficient** process. A lot of energy is wasted. This means that electricity is expensive.

Look at the photo above and diagram below of a power station.

You can tell from the steam leaving the cooling towers that a lot of energy is wasted as heat. Most power stations waste about 60% of the **chemical energy** from their fuels.

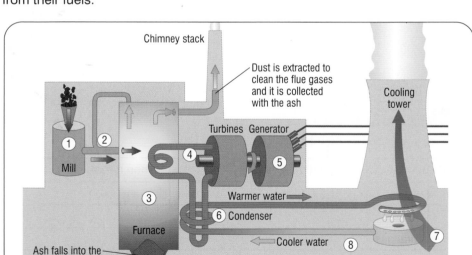

Main parts of a coal power station

The diagram shows the main parts of a coal power station.

a) Write a list or draw a flow chart showing what happens at the 8 marked points in the power station.

Inside the power station

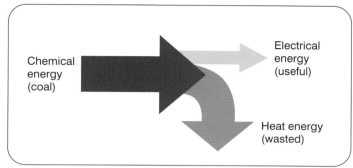

This energy transfer diagram shows the main energy transfers that happen in a power station

How does the chemical energy from the fossil fuels change into electricity and heat? We'll have to take a look inside to see.

The furnace

This is where the crushed coal is burned, releasing a lot of its **chemical energy** as heat.

The heat exchanger

Water-filled pipes pass through the furnace. The water in the pipes boils and leaves as steam.

b) Draw energy transfer diagrams for the burning of the coal and the heating of the water.

The generator

The steam makes large **turbine** blades spin, which turn a **generator** (dynamo), producing electricity.

The cooling towers

The steam has lost a lot of its energy in the turbine. Now it cools even more in these huge towers, before returning to the furnace for more heating.

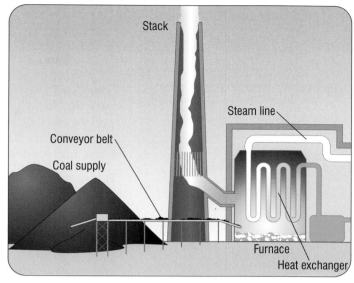

Energy from coal

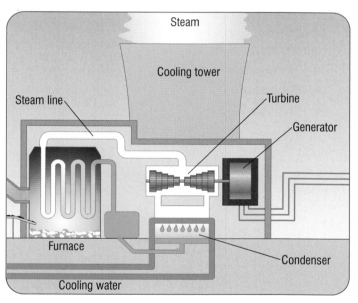

From heat into electricity

TEST YOURSELF!

1 Copy and complete the following sentences using these words:

generator   chemical   water   turbines

In a coal power station, the _____ energy from the coal is released in the furnace, where _____ is heated into steam. This makes _____ spin a _____, making electricity.

2 Why are coal power stations only about 40% efficient? How is so much energy lost?

3 Compare a coal power station with one that burns either oil or natural gas. How are they different and how are they similar?

7.3 Problems with fossil fuels

Fossil fuels take millions of years to form. This means that we can never replace the ones that we are burning now. We say that they are **non-renewable**. This also means that there is only a limited amount of fossil fuel in the Earth's crust.

Fossil fuel reserves will not last forever

This graph shows how much longer the different fossil fuels are expected to last:

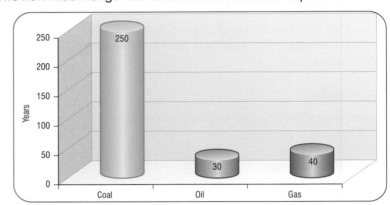

How long will fossil fuels last?

a) Use the graph to work out roughly when we will run out of each fossil fuel.

Oil is not just a fuel

An extra problem is that **crude oil** is used for making many important chemicals. These include plastics and medicines. As we run out of oil, we will also need to find alternative ways to make these.

b) Using the picture below, make a list of as many things as you can that are made from parts of crude oil.

Things that are made from oil

Pollution effects of fossil fuels

Another problem with burning fuels is the pollution caused by the gases that are made. Most fossil fuels are not very pure, but even the cleanest fuels cause pollution.

The complete **combustion** (burning) of a clean fuel can be described by this **word equation**:

fuel + oxygen → carbon dioxide + water (+ *heat*)

So, even the cleanest fuel produces carbon dioxide (CO_2). This isn't poisonous, but it does add to the **greenhouse effect** (see below).

Dirtier fuels, like most of them really are, make a range of nasty **pollutants** when they burn. This table lists some of these and their effects:

Gas	Effect
Carbon soot	Can cause breathing problems and cancers
Carbon monoxide	Can cause permanent damage to the nervous system
Sulfur dioxide	Dissolves to form acid rain; Causes breathing problems
Nitrogen oxides	Can lead to lung damage; Dissolves to form acid rain

The greenhouse effect

The carbon dioxide made when fuels burn helps heat from the Sun get trapped in our atmosphere. Because this heat can't escape, the atmosphere gets warmer and warmer. This is just like a greenhouse staying warm by trapping the Sun's heat.

c) If the atmosphere gets warmer, what might happen to:
   i) the polar ice caps and ii) the deserts?

Until recently, scientists were still arguing about whether global warming was really happening. Now most people agree it is.

However, some are still arguing over the causes!

> ### DID YOU KNOW?
> Efforts to reduce CO_2 levels have to be coordinated across the world. The UK, along with many other countries, has agreed to reduce the amount produced in future years.

The greenhouse effect

> ### TEST YOURSELF!
>
> **1** Copy and complete the following sentences using these words:
>
> **acid   dioxide   carbon   greenhouse   nitrogen**
>
> All fuels produce _____ dioxide when they burn, but some also produce sulfur _____ and _____ oxides. These gases add to problems like ____ rain and the _____ effect, as well as causing health problems for people.
>
> **2** Summarise the main reasons why scientists are working on alternatives to fossil fuels.
>
> **3** Look back at page 154. Compare the amount of each fuel we use with how long they have left to last. Which type do we need to find replacements for first?

7.4 The nuclear alternative

We saw on pages 142–143 that there are a lot of problems with fossil fuels. In the 1950s, scientists designed a type of power station that could run on **nuclear energy** instead.

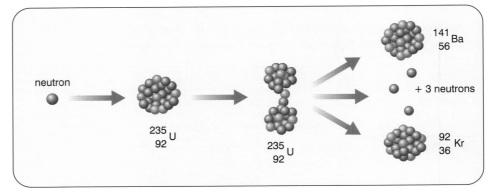

Nuclear fission of uranium

Nuclear power stations work in a very similar way to coal power stations.

The main difference is that the heat comes from a nuclear **fission** reaction. Large and unstable **uranium** atoms split apart and give off lots of energy.

Compare this flow diagram of how a nuclear power station works with the coal power station on page 140:

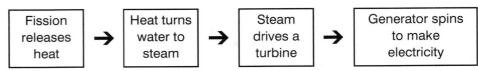

Flow diagram showing how a nuclear power station works

Uranium holds so much energy that 1 g can supply enough energy to boil more than 2000 kettles. It releases **ten thousand** times as much energy as the same mass of coal.

a) What is the name of the type of energy stored in each uranium atom?

In 1999, a quarter of the UK's energy was generated in nuclear power stations. By 2003, this had dropped to a fifth. Let's look at the reasons behind these numbers:

Why is nuclear power a good idea?

- Electricity from nuclear power costs about the same as coal, so it isn't very expensive to make.
- It does not cause smoke pollution. As it doesn't give off carbon dioxide, it does not add to the greenhouse effect.
- Nuclear power is a reliable source of energy. The amount of electricity produced is easily controlled.
- It makes large amounts of electricity from small amounts of fuel.
- It doesn't create much waste.

A nuclear power station

So why don't we use nuclear power more?

- If it goes wrong, a nuclear power station accident can affect millions of people. This means that lots of money has to be spent on safety.
- The waste that is produced is very dangerous. It is radioactive, which means that it can cause illnesses, including cancers. The waste takes many hundreds of years to become safe, and so has to be buried very carefully.
- Uranium is not a renewable resource. Once we have dug it all up, we won't be able to make any more.

b) Draw up a table summarising the advantages and disadvantages of using nuclear power.

Nuclear fuel can be recycled (well, nearly!)

One of the best things about nuclear fuels is that 95% of the used-up **fuel rods** can be used again. Chemical reactions are used to separate the waste from pure uranium, which we can then use again.

This makes nuclear fuels a lot more efficient and brings down the cost. It also means that we have to get rid of much less of the dangerous radioactive waste.

Is there a future for nuclear power?

If our use of nuclear power continues to decrease as it is, in 15 years, only a twentieth of our electricity will be made from nuclear fuels. However, some scientists argue that new safe nuclear reactors are needed to supply the electricity we need. What do you think?

> ### KEY FACTS
> Nuclear power is a very clean, efficient and reliable source of energy.
>
> When it does go wrong, it is a disaster – try looking up **Chernobyl**, **Three Mile Island** or **Windscale** for examples.

TEST YOURSELF!

1 Copy and complete these sentences, using only the words **more** or **less**:

Nuclear fuel is about the same price as coal, but it releases much ____ energy. Coal is much ____ efficient than nuclear fuel, but it is much ____ dangerous. Nuclear fuel causes ____ pollution than fossil fuels, but its waste is much ____ dangerous.

2 The percentage of our electricity generated from nuclear power has dropped since 1999. Why do you think this is?

3 How much of our electricity do you think will be made in nuclear power stations by 2020? Explain your reasons.

7.5 Renewable energy resources

You have now seen the problems with fossil and nuclear fuels. That's why scientists have been working hard to find other ways of making enough electricity. In particular, we need resources that won't run out. We call these **renewable** energy resources.

These pages introduce five of the main renewable energy resources. Before you look at them, it is best to know a bit about the **units** that we use to measure electrical **power** in.

Power units

- A 100-watt light bulb uses 100 joules of energy every second.
- 1 kilowatt (kW) is the power required by ten 100-watt light bulbs, or a typical electric fire.
- In Britain, most homes use an average of 1.5 kW – or 1500 watts.

Bigger units for power

- 1 million watts = 1 megawatt (MW)
- 1000 megawatts = 1 gigawatt (GW)
- 1000 gigawatts = 1 terawatt (TW)

The peak electricity demand for the UK is 48 GW (48 000 MW).

a) A coal power station produces about 1000 MW (1 GW). How many watts is this?

Now you can compare the energy resources below to this.

Wind power

A 1994 report suggested the UK's offshore wind resource is almost enough to meet the whole of the UK's electricity needs.

Large turbine blades spin when it is windy

Wind turbines provide electricity when we need it most – it is windier at night and in the winter! But each turbine produces less than 1 MW.

Hydro-electric power (HEP)

Most hydroelectric power stations in the UK have only small outputs.

Water spins turbines inside a river dam

A large station of 100 MW would be able to supply about 70 000 households.

Solar power

Photo-voltaic panels covering a roof area of about 16 square metres could supply the electricity needs of one household.

Solar cells convert sunlight straight into electricity

It isn't sunny all the time. So a 'back-up' supply of some sort would be needed for cloudy weather!

Wave and tidal power

Only small tidal installations currently exist in the UK. Medium-sized schemes could probably supply around 33 000 households.

The flow of water generates electricity

Britain's first commercial wave-powered station will be built on Islay, off Scotland. It will have a capacity of 500 kW.

Biomass

These stations can burn poultry litter. They use a mixture of straw, wood chippings and poultry droppings.

Plant or animal matter is burned as a fuel

Three biomass stations combined produce 64.7 MW. The total output of these stations could supply about 43 000 households.

GET IT RIGHT!

Exam questions usually want you to compare the different energy resources by thinking about their advantages and disadvantages. Make sure you know these.

DID YOU KNOW?

Another type of biomass is alcohol, which can be distilled from sugar cane and used to power cars!

b) Make a table showing the advantages and disadvantages of each of these renewable energy resources. Which type do you think we should make more use of in the UK?

TEST YOURSELF!

1 Solar panels are the least powerful of the five resources described here and HEP is the most powerful. List all five resources in order from least to most powerful.

2 Which of these renewable resources do you think causes the most pollution? Why?

3 One type of energy resource not described here is geothermal. Why do you think there are no geothermal power stations in the UK?

4 Which of the energy resources described above do you think is the most efficient (the least wasteful)? Explain your answer.

7.6   Energy resources

Global warming?

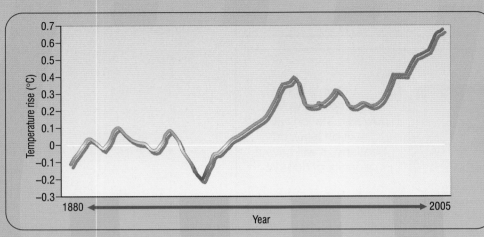

It's getting warmer

The Upsala Glacier in 1928 (Source: www.bbc.co.uk)

The Upsala Glacier in 2004 (Source: www.bbc.co.uk)

Scientists and politicians are still arguing about whether the warming up of our atmosphere is being caused by human activity. What they can't argue about is that the atmosphere is definitely warming up.

One piece of evidence for global warming is how fast the world's glaciers are now melting. The photos below show Argentina's Upsala Glacier. Once it was the biggest glacier in South America, but it is now disappearing at a rate of 200 metres per year.

Some scientists argue that this fast melting must be caused by our warming up of the atmosphere. Other scientists say it is because of changes in the way the glaciers are flowing, or how the Earth's crust underneath is moving.

 Discuss what other environments on the Earth will be affected by global warming? How do you think they will change? How will this affect us?

The Kyoto Protocol

The Kyoto Protocol is an international agreement that was signed in 1997. It sets targets for industrialised countries to cut down the amount of greenhouse gases produced.

These gases are considered at least partly responsible for global warming:

Greenhouse gases

Carbon dioxide (CO_2)
Methane (CH_4)
Hydrofluorocarbons (HFCs)
Perfluorocarbons (PFCs)
Sulfur hexafluoride (SF_6)

What are the targets?

Most industrialised countries have agreed to cut their emissions by 5% by 2012.

Each country that signed the protocol set its own target:

- European countries aimed to cut emissions by 8% and Japan by 5%.
- Some countries with low emissions were allowed to increase them.
- Russia didn't sign the agreement at first, but eventually did in 2004.

 Discuss why you think the USA didn't sign the Kyoto Protocol?

Activity

Research why some countries were allowed to increase their emissions.

Saving in Stechford

Cascades Leisure Centre, Stechford

Birmingham City Council was looking for alternatives to electric heating for some of its multi-storey homes in the Stechford area of the city.

Because of how the homes had been built, they were difficult to heat in the winter. The owners were cold, even though they paid high electricity bills.

The heating system of the Cascades Leisure Centre next door also needed a lot of repairs and improvements. The council decided to install a combined heat and power (CHP) system. The new boilers that they put in could make 180 kW of electricity to power the Leisure Centre. The boilers also make 350 kW of heat, some of which is now used to heat the homes next door through underground pipes.

Because of this new CHP boiler system, CO_2 emissions were reduced by 1900 tonnes a year and the heating costs for the home owners were reduced by about £15 each week.

(Source: The Combined Heat and Power Association)

Activities

a) Describe the energy transfers in this Combined Heat and Power system.

b) What are the two main reasons why this CHP scheme reduced the amount of carbon dioxide that was produced so much?

Renewable energy use in the UK

Look at this diagram: It shows how much of different types of renewable energy resources we used in the UK in 2003.

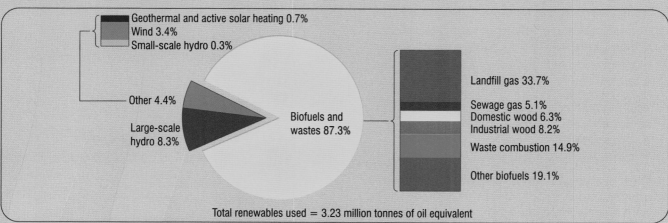

Pie chart showing renewable energy use in the UK in 2003

Activities

a) List the renewable resources we used in order, starting with the highest amount first.

b) Why do you think we use so much more biofuel than any other renewable resource?

149

SUMMARY QUESTIONS

1 Copy and complete the following sentences about energy resources using these words:

nuclear, heat, coal, fossil, carbon dioxide, global, energy, millions, oil, chemical, combustion, dangerous, electricity, natural gas, non-renewable, renewable

The three fossil fuels are called ____, ___ and ____ ___. They take _____ of years to form and can never be replaced once we have used them all. They are called ___ _____.

Fossil fuels store _____ energy in them. When they burn, this energy is released as ____. A scientific word for burning is _____.

Power stations make _____. The most common ones either burn _____ fuels or use a _____ fuel like uranium. Fossil fuel power stations produce a lot of _____ _____ gas, which helps cause _____ warming. Nuclear power stations are cleaner, but the wastes they produce are very _____.

Resources like solar power and biomass are _____ – we can keep replacing them, so they will never run out. Unfortunately, they don't yet provide enough _____.

2 a) List as many energy resources as you can.
   b) For each resource, say whether it is renewable or non-renewable.
   c) Identify which of the resources use energy that originally comes from the Sun and which don't.

3 Explain the differences between these three words:
   • Renewable.
   • Reusable.
   • Recyclable.

4 Some scientists work to develop new alternative energy resources. Other scientists are trying to find ways to recycle more plastics.
   Use your knowledge of how much oil we have left to explain why these are both important areas for scientists.

5 Draw energy transfer diagrams for:
   a) A wind turbine.
   b) A solar cell.
   c) A hydro-electric (HEP) station.
   d) A nuclear power station.

A

B

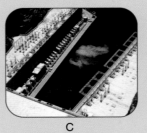
C

D

6 Every year, some scientists advise the government that we should start to build more nuclear power stations.
   a) Why do we need more power stations?
   b) Why should we build nuclear power stations instead of coal or oil power stations?
   c) What are the main arguments against building more nuclear power stations?

7 One group of alternative energy resources is called biofuels.
   a) Explain what is meant by 'biofuel'?
   b) How do these three types of biofuel provide energy:
      • Landfill gas?
      • Wood?
      • Sugar cane alcohol?
   c) Explain why these are all renewable.
   d) What sort of pollution do these biofuels cause?

8 Two environmental problems linked to power stations are acid rain and the greenhouse effect.
   a) Explain each of these problems.
   b) How are they both linked to power stations?

EXAM-STYLE QUESTIONS

1   Electricity is very important in our daily lives. The pie chart shows the fuels used to generate electricity in 2003.

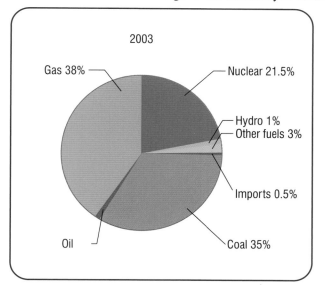

2003

Gas 38%

Nuclear 21.5%

Hydro 1%
Other fuels 3%

Imports 0.5%

Oil

Coal 35%

a) Calculate the percentage that is supplied by oil. (2)
b) Name two fossil fuels shown in the chart. (2)
c) Give an example of a renewable energy resource shown in the chart. (1)
d) Suggest another renewable energy resource that might make up the 3% 'other fuels'. (1)
e) How is the energy available in oil released? (1)

2   Scientists have been trying to make effective use of other energy supplies, e.g. renewable energy resources.

The picture shows a renewable energy resource.

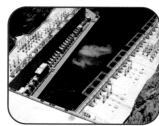

a) i)   What is this resource called?
(1)

ii) Explain how this method generates electricity. Use the diagram below to help you. (4)

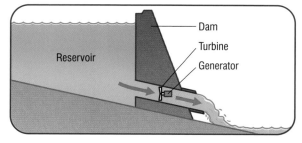

Dam

Turbine

Reservoir

Generator

b) Give three disadvantages of using this method. (3)

3   A research scientist found the following gases in the air.

a) i)   List the gases from the table that could have been released from burning fossil fuels. (3)

Gases that could be present in air
Oxygen
Nitrogen
Argon
Carbon dioxide
Carbon monoxide
Neon
Methane
Helium
Hydrogen
Sulphur dioxide
Nitrogen oxides

ii) A gas engineer will check boilers and heaters in houses regularly to make sure they are not releasing one of the above gases which could be poisonous. Which one? (1)
iii) Which two of the above gases are the most important contributors to acid rain? (2)

b) An alternative to using fossil fuels to generate electricity could be nuclear fuels.
i)   Name a nuclear fuel. (1)
ii) What are the main problems involved with using nuclear fuel to generate electricity? (3)

4   a) Copy and complete the word equation to show the burning of a fossil fuel.

fossil fuel + ………….➤carbon dioxide + ……….+ heat
(2)

b) Explain why the release of carbon dioxide is a danger to our environment. (3)

c) 74% of our electricity is generated using fossil fuels. Apart from the pollution issue, why is this a cause for concern amongst scientists? (2)

d) i)   Fossil fuels are described as non-renewable. What does this mean? (1)
ii) Give one example of a non-renewable fuel (1)

e) Coal is an example of a fossil fuel. 1.8 tonnes of coal contain 62.2 million kilojoules of energy. Calculate the energy available in 1 tonne of coal. (2)

3 | The Home Environment

In this section you will learn about:

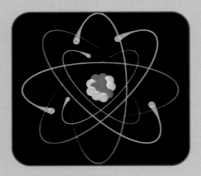

Structure and bonding

- Atomic structure.
- Properties of materials.
- Chemical bonding.

Construction materials

- Limestone as a construction material.
- Building with cement and concrete.
- The importance of metals.
- Ceramics, composites and polymers.

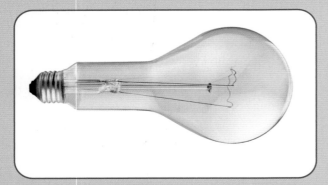

Using energy

- Choosing the right energy source.
- Home electricity usage and cost.
- Fuses and circuit-breakers.
- Heat transfer and efficiency.

Useful mixtures

- Solutions and solvents.
- Different types of mixtures.
- Mixtures in domestic products.
- Separating mixtures.

This section is tested by examination

Materials scientist

"I have to understand the properties of existing materials so I can develop new ones."

Construction engineer

"I need to use materials safely and efficiently in buildings."

Electrician

"Understanding electrical power helps me wire up your home."

Career opportunities

Architect

"I need to know about heat transfer so I can design efficient homes."

Consumer scientist

"My knowledge of mixtures helps me develop new products for your supermarket."

Pharmacologist

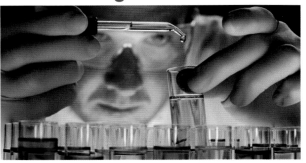

"I have to be able to choose the right solvents to use when I am working on a new drug."

8.1

Small building blocks

LEARNING OBJECTIVES

1 What are protons, neutrons and electrons?
2 Where do we find these particles in any atom?
3 How do atoms of one element differ from those of another element?

Atoms are the stuff of life, the universe and everything!

The ancient Greeks were the first to think that everything might be made up of atoms. Atoms are very, very small. In fact, if you laid about 1 billion in a line they would be as long as this full stop.

About a hundred years ago, we discovered that the atom is made up of even smaller particles.

Look at the picture below, it shows an atom of helium.

You can see that there are two types of particle in the centre or **nucleus**. These are called **protons** and **neutrons**. The particles whizzing around the outside are called **electrons**.

The particles have different charges and masses. The protons are positive. The neutrons are neutral and the electrons are negative.

- The nucleus is small and very dense as the protons and neutrons are the heavy particles in an atom. We give them a relative mass of 1.
- The smaller electrons have hardly any mass and whiz around the nucleus in shells.

a) How many protons are in the helium atom shown below?
b) Look at the picture of the lithium atom below. How many protons are in this atom?

The helium and lithium atoms have different numbers of protons because they are different **elements**.

- The number of protons an atom has tells you what element that atom is.

So if an atom has 3 protons, it has to be a lithium atom.

If you look at the **Periodic Table** on page 124, you will see that next to every element there are two numbers.

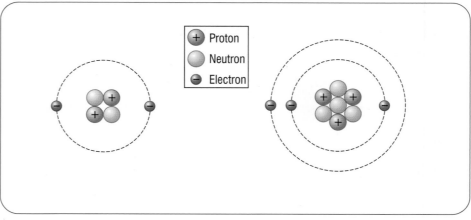

Helium atom   Lithium atom

The bottom number tells you the number of protons in an atom of that element. This is called the **atomic number**, for example:

$$_6C \qquad _2He \qquad _{10}Ne$$

Obviously, protons are too small to count. Instead, we use the Periodic Table.

c) Use the Periodic Table to find the atomic numbers of; iron, chlorine, sodium and gold.

The top number is called the **mass number**. This tells you the number of protons plus neutrons in an atom. Look at the lithium atom on the previous page. It has 3 protons and 4 neutrons so its mass number is 7.

So, why is knowing about atoms so important to us?

By knowing the structure of an atom, you can predict how an element will behave. For example, will it conduct heat? Or, will it react with other substances?

I'M NOT SURE WHAT WE HAVE HERE

JUST COUNT THE PROTONS

KEY FACTS

Particle	Where is it?	Charge	Mass
Proton	Nucleus	Positive	1
Neutron	Nucleus	Neutral	1
Electron	Outside nucleus	Negative	Hardly anything

- All atoms of the same element have the same number of protons.
- The atomic number of an element is the number of protons its atoms contain.
- The mass number tells us the number of protons plus neutrons.

DID YOU KNOW?

Atoms may be small, but they can release huge amounts of energy. When some nuclei are hit with a neutron, they will split and release energy. If this is controlled, then you have nuclear power. If it is an uncontrolled chain reaction, then it is a nuclear bomb!!!

TEST YOURSELF!

1 Copy and complete the following sentences using these words:

nucleus three positive one negative outside protons atomic

Atoms contain _____ types of particles. Neutrons are neutral and

are found in the _____. Protons, which have a _____ charge,

can also be found in the nucleus. Protons and neutrons have a relative

mass of _____. Electrons have a _____ charge and are located

_____ the nucleus in orbits. All atoms of the same element have the

same number of _____. This is shown on the Periodic Table by the

_____ number.

2 a) Why is the nucleus the most dense part of an atom?
  b) An atom contains 9 protons. What type of atom is it?
  c) If an atom is neutral in charge and contains 5 protons, how many electrons will it have?

8.2

Bigger building blocks

1 What is the difference between:

- an atom
- a molecule, and
- an ion?

Incredibly, there are only 92 types of **atoms** that exist naturally. The other 20 or so have been created by humans. All the types of atom are listed in the Periodic Table on page 124.

Everything around you, even your own body, is made up from these atoms. In diagrams we represent atoms as circles.

Usually we represent the different atoms with symbols. This makes it a lot easier for scientists from different countries to communicate with each other.

a) Look at the diagram below. Which three elements are shown?

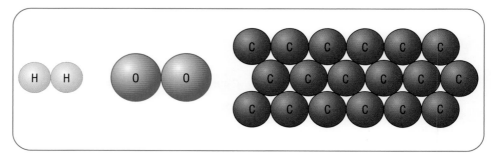

Some examples of atoms

Atoms are like building blocks. They can join together with **chemical bonds** to form **molecules**.

- A molecule is 2 or more atoms that are chemically joined.

The atoms in a molecule can be the same, like the oxygen that is in the air. Or they can be made up from different types of atom, like water.

- A compound is made by 2 or more **different** types of atoms that are chemically joined.

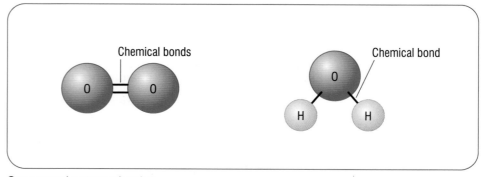

Oxygen and water molecules

b) Look at the pictures of oxygen and water molecules above. Which shows a molecule of an element, and which a compound?

Look around you. How many different materials can you see? All of these are made from atoms (usually in molecules). Some molecules have been discovered by accident. Silly putty was discovered by scientists trying to make artificial silicon!

Sometimes atoms can get a positive or negative charge. This is because they can gain or lose electrons. (See page 162.) Remember, an electron has a negative charge, so...

...if an atom gains an electron it will become *negatively* charged by 1.

...if an atom loses an electron it will become *positively* charged by 1.
We call these charged particles **ions**.

c) If an atom gained 2 electrons, what would the charge on the ion be?
d) If an atom lost 3 electrons, what would the charge on the ion be?

Some ions produce great colours when put in a Bunsen flame. If you needed to identify an unknown substance, this may be an experiment you could do.

Using flame tests to identify chemicals is a type of **qualitative analysis**. (See page 270 in Unit 3.)

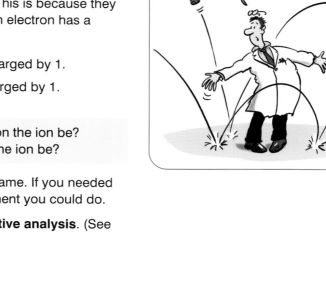

Look at the photo opposite. A bright red flame shows that lithium ions are present.

Lithium burns with a bright red flame

DID YOU KNOW?
Aspartame, the sweetener in Diet Coke, was an accidental discovery. A chemist got some on his hands in the lab. He noticed the sweet taste when he licked his finger to turn a page. Luckily aspartame was not toxic!

TEST YOURSELF!

1 Copy and complete the following sentences using these words:

joined   ion   two   atoms

Everything is made up of small particles called _____. A molecule is

_____ or more atoms that are chemically_____. If an atom or a

molecule becomes charged it is called an _____.

2 Why is water a compound?

3 When an atom loses one of its electrons, does it become negatively or positively charged?

KEY FACTS
- All elements contain only one type of atom.

- A molecule is two or more atoms that are chemically bonded.

- If an atom or molecule becomes charged, it forms an ion.

8.3

What's the difference between metals and non-metals?

LEARNING OBJECTIVES

1 What are the properties of metals and non-metals?
2 How are the properties of a substance linked to its chemical bonding?

We can group the elements in the periodic table into **metals** and **non-metals**. Metals and non-metals have different properties. The table below shows some of the common properties:

Metals	Non-metals
Have high **melting points** and **boiling points**	Have low melting and boiling points
Are usually strong, dense and shiny	Are less dense than metals and dull in appearance
Can be shaped and bent	Are brittle
Conduct heat and electricity well	Don't conduct heat and electricity well

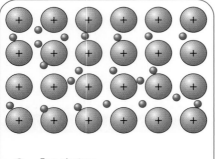

● Free electron

⊕ Positively charged metal ion

The bonding in a metal

a) You have a sample of 'element X'. You need to find out if it is a metal or a non-metal. What tests could you do on it?

One simple test is to see if a substance conducts electricity. Why are metals good **conductors** of electricity?

Look at the diagram on the left. Can you see the 'free electrons'? These free electrons are able to move through the metal structure. This allows the metal to conduct electricity and heat.

In fact, the properties of many substances are linked to how they bond or chemically join, and to the forces in and between their particles.

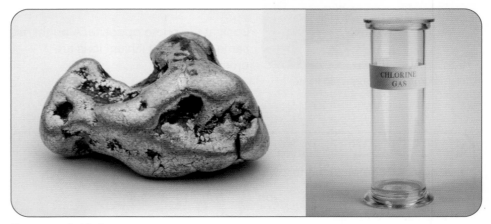

Copper and chlorine

b) Look at the two substances above. What differences in appearance can you see between them?

The properties of these elements can be linked to the way that the particles within them are arranged. Copper ions (charged particles) are arranged in **giant structures** with the ions packed as closely as possible.

Non-metallic elements like chlorine bond in a different way to metals. They contain strong **covalent bonds**. (See page 160.) These strong bonds join the atoms within each individual molecule. However, **the forces between the molecules are weak.** This means that they will have a **low boiling point**.

Carbon breaks the rule that 'non-metals do not conduct electricity well'. In the form of graphite, it does contain free electrons, so it is a good conductor of electricity.

c) Look at the diagram on the right. It is of the same elements as the photo on the previous page. Describe how the structures are different.

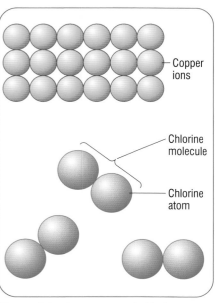

The particles in copper and chlorine

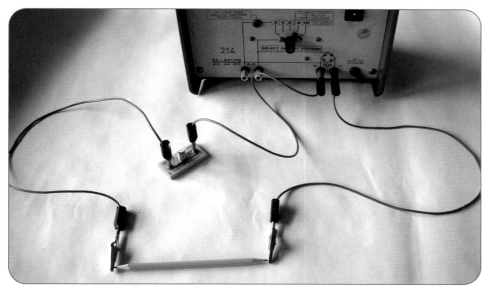

The 'lead' in pencils is actually graphite (a form of carbon). It isn't a metal, but it still conducts electricity.

Some metals are magnetic. Iron is one of the three magnetic elements.

d) Find out the other two magnetic elements. They are on the right of iron in the Periodic Table.

TEST YOURSELF!

1 Copy and complete the following sentences using these words:

heat   dull   high   non-metals   conductors

Elements can be divided into metals and _____. Metallic elements typically have _____ melting and boiling points. They are good conductors of electricity and _____. Non-metallic elements typically are _____ in appearance. They are also poor _____ of heat and electricity.

2 Identify these substances as metals or non-metals:
   a) A shiny material that conducts electricity well.
   b) A brittle material that is dull and doesn't conduct heat well.

3 Explain why the structure of a metal can explain its density.

8.4

Covalent molecules – electron *sharing*

1 What is covalent bonding?
2 Why do small, covalent molecules have low boiling points?

On pages 158–159, you saw how metals atoms are bonded together. Other molecules are held together in different ways.

Covalent bonding occurs when atoms share electrons with each other. This makes them more stable. **Covalent** molecules usually only contain non-metal atoms.

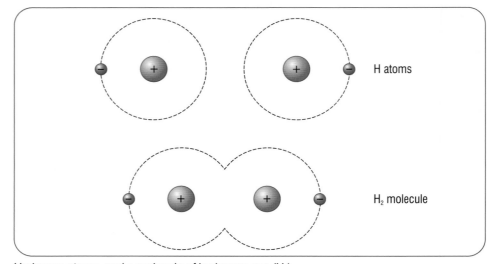

Hydrogen atoms, and a molecule of hydrogen gas (H_2)

Nitrogen helps keep the crisps fresh, because it doesn't react with them

a) What is the chemical formula of a hydrogen molecule?

Have you ever seen 'Packaged in a protective atmosphere' printed on a packet of crisps? Nitrogen is pumped into the packet before it is sealed. Nitrogen helps keep the crisps fresh, because it doesn't react with them.

Nitrogen gas is made up of covalent molecules, and you're surrounded by them right now! Nitrogen makes up 78% of the Earth's atmosphere. Its covalent bonds are hard to break. This is what makes it unreactive.

Some more covalent substances:

Name of substance	Structure of covalent molecule
Water	
Oxygen	
Methane	
Chlorine	
Ethanol	

Properties of covalent molecules

Covalent molecules like hydrogen and oxygen gas share some properties. Despite the fact that their atoms are bonded strongly to each other within their molecules, the forces between the individual small molecules are weak. This gives them low melting and boiling points.

Oxygen boils at $-183°C$ and hydrogen boils at $-253°C$. This is why most small covalent molecules are liquids or gases at room temperature ($20°C$).

b) Water is also a covalent molecule. The forces between its molecules are stronger than those in hydrogen and oxygen. How can you tell?

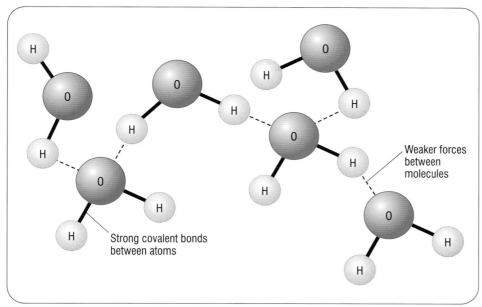

Water molecules

KEY FACTS

● In covalent molecules, the atoms of non-metals share electrons with each other.

● Covalent molecules include water, oxygen, nitrogen, hydrogen and ethanol.

● Covalent bonds are strong.

● The forces **between** covalent molecules are weak. This is why they have low boiling and melting points.

TEST YOURSELF!

1 Copy and complete the following sentences using these words:

   hydrogen   stable   water   share   covalent   oxygen

   When atoms _____ electrons with each other _____ molecules are formed. They do this to become more _____. Examples of covalent molecules are _____, _____ and _____.

2 Why is nitrogen unreactive?

3 Why do covalent molecules have low melting and boiling points?

4 Research the melting and boiling points of the molecules in the table on the left. Can you work out why the values for chlorine and oxygen are the lowest?

8.5   Ionic compounds – electron *transfer*

Ionic compounds are an important group of substances used by chemists.

Electrons orbit atoms in different layers (like an onion skin). Atoms are much more stable if the outermost layer of electrons is completely full. To get to this state, they can do two things. Sometimes they can share electrons, as in covalent bonds between non-metal atoms. However, if we have a metal and a non-metal atom, the metal gives away electrons and the non-metal accepts electrons. This produces **ionic compounds**.

a) Are electrons positively or negatively charged?

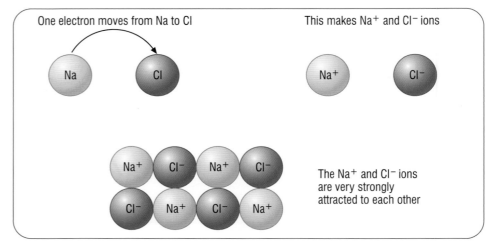

One electron moves from Na to Cl

This makes Na^+ and Cl^- ions

The Na^+ and Cl^- ions are very strongly attracted to each other

Na and Cl atoms and Na^+ and Cl^- ions

Sodium is more stable if it has one less electron. Chlorine needs an extra one to be stable. So, a sodium atom can give an electron to a chlorine atom. When this happens, the atoms become **ions** with opposite charges. The opposite charges make the ions stick together very strongly. This is an **ionic bond**.

Some more ionic compounds:

Name of ionic compound	Part of the giant ionic structure
Iron sulfide	Fe^{2+} S^{2-} Fe^{2+} S^{2-} / S^{2-} Fe^{2+} S^{2-} Fe^{2+}
Magnesium oxide	Mg^{2+} O^{2-} Mg^{2+} O^{2-} / O^{2-} Mg^{2+} O^{2-} Mg^{2+}
Lithium fluoride	Li^+ F^- Li^+ F^- Li^+ F^- / F^- Li^+ F^- Li^+ F^- Li^+ / Li^+ F^- Li^+ F^- Li^+ F^-

Properties of ionic compounds

All ionic compounds form crystals. This is because the differently charged ions line up neatly with each other. These crystals are basically lumps of positive and negative charges all stuck together in regular patterns. They form **giant structures** containing millions of ions.

Pulling the charged ions apart needs a huge amount of energy. This gives ionic compounds very high melting and boiling points.

For example, sodium chloride (the salt that goes on food) has a melting point of 801°C. If you wanted to boil salt, you would need a temperature of 1465°C!

b) How could you get the ions in sodium chloride to separate at room temperature?

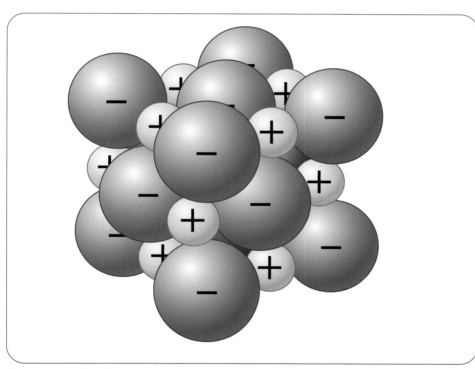

The structure of sodium chloride – the strong electrostatic forces of attraction operate in all directions

DID YOU KNOW?

Table salt is made from sodium and chlorine. On their own, these elements are deadly. Sodium would burst into flames if you put it in your mouth. Chlorine would poison you – you'd be dead in seconds!

GET IT RIGHT!

Be able to tell the difference between ionic and covalent compounds. If a metal is in the formula, it's probably ionic.

KEY FACTS

- Ionic compounds are formed when atoms give and take electrons.

- Strong forces exist between the ions, holding their giant structures together.

- The strong forces mean that ionic compounds have high melting and boiling points.

TEST YOURSELF!

1 Copy and complete the following sentences using these words:

> stable   sodium chloride   transfer   crystals
> ions   iron sulfide   magnesium oxide

Atoms of a metal _____ one or more electrons to atoms of non-metals

to form _____. They do this to become more _____. Examples of

ionic compounds are _____, _____ and _____. Solid

ionic compounds form _____.

2 Why do the ions in ionic compounds stick together?

3 Why do ionic compounds have such high melting points?

8.6 Giant covalent structures

Some of the most fascinating molecules chemists use are giant covalent structures. They're called **giant structures** (or macromolecules) because they're so huge compared with other molecules. Still, the atoms they are made of are the same size as regular atoms.

Giant structures can be ionic or covalent. Look back to the diagram of sodium chloride on the last page. This is an example of a giant ionic structure. All the atoms are held together very tightly. Like ionic crystals, giant covalent structures have very high melting points.

a) Why to the ions stick together in ionic structures?
b) Why do the atoms stick together in covalent structures?

Giant structures of carbon atoms

Carbon can make some very interesting giant structures. You might have one of them with you right now!

Graphite (the 'lead' in pencils) is made of millions of sheets of carbon atoms. The atoms are covalently bonded to make hexagons.

The bonds in each sheet are strong covalent bonds, but the forces between the sheets are weaker. This is why graphite rubs off onto the paper when you write with a pencil.

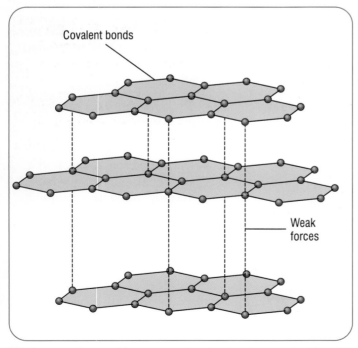

3D diagram of a graphite macromolecule, showing covalent bonds between the carbons in each sheet and weaker bonds between the sheets

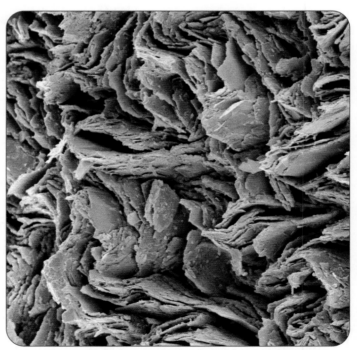

A close up of a pencil tip. Can you see the sheets of graphite?

Diamond is another giant structure made of carbon atoms. They are arranged in a different way to graphite.

In diamond, all the bonds between carbons are very strong. They are all covalent bonds This is why diamond is such a hard substance.

Intense heat and pressure deep under the Earth's crust cause carbon atoms to make diamond. This takes between 1 and 3 billion years!

These days, we can make diamonds artificially.

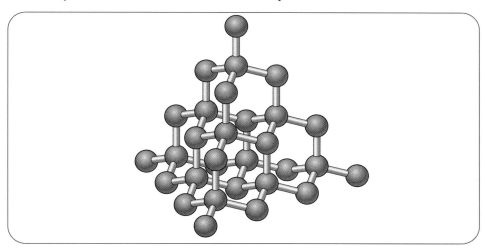

Strong covalent bonds hold a diamond together

Silica

Another important substance with a giant covalent structure is silica. Its chemical name is silicon dioxide. It is the main part of sand. You are surrounded by it – even if you don't live near the seaside. We use sand to make mortar and concrete. (See pages 174–175.)

c) Name another material we make from sand.

The formula of silica is SiO_2. However, it definitely does not exist as small '3-atom' molecules. The melting point of silica is over 1500°C! It has a giant covalent structure, like diamond's.

DID YOU KNOW?

The Cullinan diamond.

The Cullinan is one of the biggest diamonds ever found. It weighs 112 g (about the same as an apple) and is part of the Crown Jewels.

KEY FACTS

● Giant structures contain millions of atoms.

● Strong bonds between the atoms give giant covalent structures high melting points.

● Graphite and diamond both have giant covalent structures.

TEST YOURSELF!

1 Copy and complete the following sentences using these words:

high   ionic   bonds   covalent   diamond   graphite

Giant structures can be either _____ or _____. The atoms are

all held together by very strong _____. Examples of giant structures

are _____ and _____. Giant structures have _____ melting

points.

2 Look at the diagram of a diamond molecule above. How many bonds come from each carbon atom?

3 How is graphite different from diamond?

4 Name one giant covalent and one giant ionic structure.

8.7   Bucky balls!

Bucky balls

In the 1980s, scientists discovered a new form of carbon. Each molecule contained 60 carbon atoms. They didn't know much about it apart from that!

The mystery chemical can be found in soot from a candle

After making lots of models, they still couldn't work out what the new chemical looked like. Then someone in the team saw an unusual piece of architecture. It was a dome made by the architect, Buckminster Fuller. Fuller made ball-shaped buildings like the one in the picture below. He used patterns of hexagons and pentagons, the same as a football.

They knew that a molecule with 60 carbon atoms wouldn't be very stable. If it was flat, the edges would quickly react with other chemicals. For some reason, though, this molecule was very stable. They thought the edges must somehow be curled up.

What is the mystery molecule?

Activity

Research the following:

a) Find out more about bucky balls and their uses on the internet.

b) How are bucky balls connected to HIV and deep space?

c) What are 'bucky babies', 'bucky onions' and 'bucky bunnies'?

One of Buckminster Fuller's domes

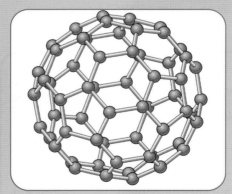

A 'bucky ball'

The scientists realised that the mystery molecule was actually football-shaped!

Now, they had to think of a name for their new discovery. Because of its shape, names like ballene or soccerene were suggested. They just didn't sound right.

In the end, they decided to name it after the dome buildings it looked like. And so, 'buckminsterfullerene' was born (bucky balls for short!).

Ernest Rutherford and the chocolate chip cookies

Scientists' ideas about the structure of atoms have changed a lot over the years. About a hundred years ago, the scientific community thought atoms looked like the picture below:

Some scientists called it the 'plum pudding' model, because it reminded them of a fruitcake.

You can think of this as the 'chocolate chip cookie' model. It was thought that electrons sat in a 'soup' of positive charge, like chocolate chips surrounded by cookie.

a) At the time, only electrons had been discovered. What are the missing two particles called?

A scientist called Ernest Rutherford wasn't sure if this was right. He designed an experiment to give him more information about the structure of atoms.

Rutherford and his co-workers used a very thin piece of gold leaf. They then fired thousands of tiny particles at it from a radioactive source.

b) What precautions should Rutherford have taken when working with radioactive material?

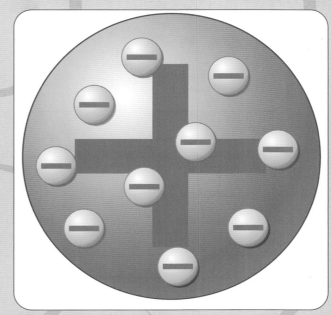

An early idea of atomic structure

If atoms really did look like chocolate chip cookies, most of these particles should have gone through, like the top picture below. In fact, some of the particles bounced off the atoms, like the bottom picture.

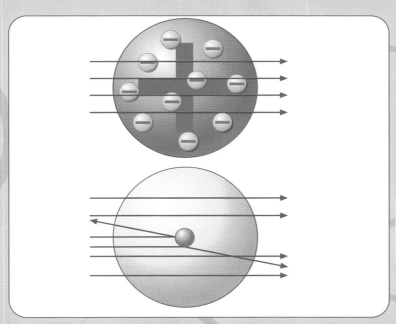

Was the chocolate chip cookie model correct?

This led Rutherford to the conclusion that the chocolate chip cookie model was wrong. He decided that particles were bouncing back because the positive bit was all in the same place. Rutherford had just discovered the nucleus of the atom!

c) If the particles Rutherford used were positively charged, what charge was probably on the nucleus that repelled them?

d) Which part of the atom did Rutherford still not know about?

Activity

Imagine you were in Rutherford's position. Write a letter to the rest of the scientific community, describing what you have found out.

SUMMARY QUESTIONS

1

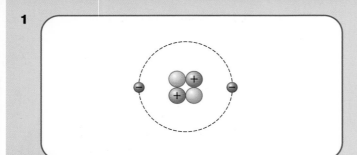

Diagram of a helium atom

Identify the protons, neutrons and electrons in this diagram.

2 Copy and complete this table:

Name of particle	Mass	Charge	Where is it?
Proton			
Neutron			
Electron			

3 What is the difference between an atom and an ion?

4 Are all molecules compounds? Explain your answer.

5 If an atom loses two electrons, what is the charge of the ion?

6 Which type of bonding involves:

a) Sharing electrons?

b) Giving and accepting electrons?

7 Which has a higher melting point – water or salt? Why?

8 Why is diamond so hard?

9 Why is graphite suitable for writing with?

10 How many protons, neutrons and electrons do the following atoms have?

a) Helium, with an atomic number of 2 and a mass number of 4.

b) Sodium, with an atomic number of 11 and a mass number of 23.

c) Phosphorus, with an atomic number of 15 and a mass number of 31.

11 Look at the chemical structures of diamond, graphite, sodium chloride and water below. What differences can you see between:

a) Diamond and graphite?

b) Graphite and sodium chloride?

c) Diamond and water?

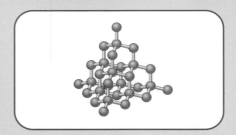

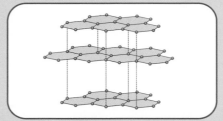

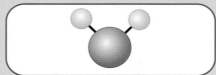

12 Match up the type of structure with the pictures below:

covalent molecules   ionic crystal
giant covalent structure

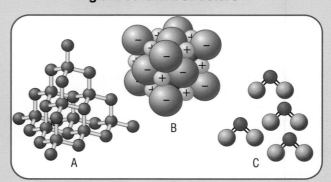

EXAM-STYLE QUESTIONS

1 Chemists want to know about the atom. There are three particles in the atom. We need to be able to describe the particles so that we can predict the behaviour of the atoms.

   a) What are the names of the three particles that make up an atom? (3)
   b) Which particle is positive? (1)
   c) Which particles are found in the nucleus? (2)
   d) What is the charge on the particle that orbits the nucleus? (1)

2 Scientists can show the atomic number and mass number of an atom like this:

$$^{235}_{92}\text{U}$$

The bottom number is the atomic number. The top number is the mass number.

   a) How many protons, neutrons and electrons does this atom of uranium contain? (3)
   b) Write a mathematical equation to show how you can use the atomic number and mass number to work out the number of neutrons in an atom. (3)

3 Fatima builds a circuit to test if something is a metal or a non-metal.

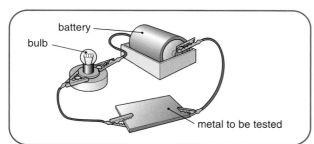

She tests various objects around her house.

   a) Draw a circuit diagram of her apparatus. (3)
   b) Explain what happens if there is a metal in the circuit. (1)
   c) Explain what happens if there is a non-metal in the circuit. (1)
   d) She finds that most of the objects in her house are covered in plastic. This doesn't conduct electricity. Explain why most objects in her home have no external metal parts. (1)

4 Chlorine is a gas. It dissolves in water.

   a) Why do we use chlorine in swimming pools? (2)
   b) What sort of chemical bond does chlorine have? (1)

5 Sodium chloride is a very useful compound.

   a) Write down two uses for sodium chloride. (2)
   b) Where do we get sodium chloride from? (2)
   c) What does the term 'compound' mean? (1)
   d) Explain why it takes a lot of energy to melt sodium chloride. (2)
   e) Brine is a solution of sodium chloride and water. What would happen if you put an electric current across the solution? (2)

6 Copper is often used in wiring and electrical fittings in the home. Copper is chosen, in particular, because it is a very good electrical conductor.

   a) Using a diagram, explain why the arrangement of atoms in metals makes them good electrical conductors. (4)
   b) Copper is also used to make water pipes. Describe which physical properties make it a good choice for this use. (4)

7 Copy and complete the following table, stating whether the elements are metals or non-metals and giving their chemical symbols.

Element	Metal/non-metal	Chemical symbol
sulfur		
oxygen		
potassium		
argon		
sodium		

(5)

9.1   Materials used in construction

LEARNING OBJECTIVES

1 How do we use limestone in the building industry?
2 What are the chemical formulas of limestone, quicklime and slaked lime?

Using limestone

The main substance in **limestone** rock is **calcium carbonate**. It is the most widely used substance in the building industry. Scientists play an important role in many stages of its use.

Made with limestone

Where does limestone come from?

A common type of limestone comes from the shells of ancient sea creatures. They died and sank to the bottom of the sea. The shells built up over hundreds of millions of years and eventually turned into sedimentary rock.

a) What type of rock is limestone?

A limestone quarry in Dorset

We extract more than 100 million tonnes of limestone from **quarries** in the UK every year. Explosives are used to blast faces of rock into smaller pieces.

What is limestone used for?

Limestone is mainly used in the construction industry. Builders can use it directly as solid blocks. They also use it after it has been turned into other building materials: **cement**, **concrete** and **mortar** are all made with limestone.

We can also produce lots of other substances using limestone. Here are some examples:

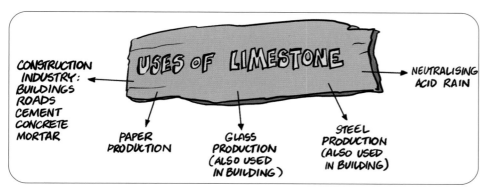

Limestone has many uses

Changing limestone

Chemists are responsible for changing the calcium carbonate in limestone into other substances. These have useful properties, which makes limestone an even more important substance.

Limestone has the chemical formula **CaCO₃**.

Limestone can be changed into a substance called **quicklime**. Quicklime has the chemical name **calcium oxide**. Its formula is **CaO**.

b) Which atoms have been taken away when limestone is changed into quicklime?

Quicklime can be changed into **slaked lime**. Slaked lime has the chemical name **calcium hydroxide**. Its formula is **Ca(OH)₂**. It is used in making mortar.

The details of how these changes take place are on the next two pages.

GET IT RIGHT!

In the exam, you will be expected to know the chemical names and formulas of limestone, quicklime and slaked lime.

TEST YOURSELF!

1   a) List six uses of limestone.
    b) Which of your answers to a) are from the construction industry?

2   Copy and complete the following table:

Substance	Chemical name	Chemical formula
Limestone		
Quicklime		
Slaked lime		

3   How was limestone formed?

KEY FACTS

- Limestone (containing calcium carbonate – CaCO₃) is used to make buildings, concrete, cement and mortar.
- Limestone can be chemically changed into quicklime (calcium oxide, CaO) and slaked lime (calcium hydroxide, Ca(OH)₂).

9.2 The chemistry of limestone

LEARNING OBJECTIVES

1 How is quicklime made from limestone?
2 How is slaked lime made from quicklime?
3 What are 'exothermic' and 'endothermic' reactions?

You have learned about the chemical names and formulas of limestone (calcium carbonate), quicklime and slaked lime. Now we will go into more detail about the chemical reactions involved in producing them.

Producing quicklime from limestone

First of all, limestone has to be extracted from a quarry with high explosives. Then, workers can crush it into smaller pieces. Most of the limestone goes to a cement works.

The crushed limestone is put into a **lime kiln**, where it is heated to over 1000°C. The high temperature breaks down the limestone into quicklime. This also produces carbon dioxide, which escapes through the top of the kiln.

a) What environmental problem could this release of CO_2 add to? (See page 143.)

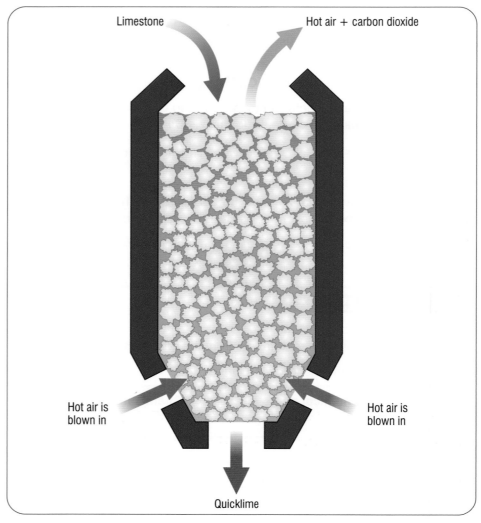

A simplified diagram of a lime kiln

Making quicklime in a lime kiln

Inside a lime kiln

The reaction is called **thermal decomposition**. That's because we use heat to break down the limestone. We can show the reaction with this equation:

$$\text{calcium carbonate} \xrightarrow{\text{heat}} \text{calcium oxide} + \text{carbon dioxide}$$
$$CaCO_3 \rightarrow CaO + CO_2$$

Another way to describe this reaction is **endothermic**. This means that energy is taken in from the surroundings when the reaction takes place.

Producing slaked lime from quicklime

Slaked lime is made by carefully adding water to quicklime. This is the equation for the reaction:

$$\text{calcium oxide} + \text{water} \rightarrow \text{calcium hydroxide}$$
$$CaO + H_2O \rightarrow Ca(OH)_2$$

In this reaction, a lot of heat is given out to the surroundings. We describe this as an **exothermic** reaction.

> ### KEY FACTS
> - Quicklime is made by heating limestone to high temperatures.
> - Slaked lime is made by adding water to quicklime.
> - Exothermic reactions give out (release) heat energy to the surroundings.
> - Endothermic reactions take in (absorb) heat energy from the surroundings.

TEST YOURSELF!

1 What waste gas is produced when we convert limestone into quicklime?

2 Describe the difference between exothermic and endothermic reactions.

3 How does the production of quicklime differ from the production of slaked lime?

4 How could you tell a sample of quicklime from a sample of limestone? Describe how you could use water and a thermometer to carry out the test.

9.3

Using limestone to make other construction materials

LEARNING OBJECTIVES

1 How do we manufacture cement and glass?
2 What are concrete and mortar, and how do we use them?

Making cement

Builders have used cement to bind buildings together for centuries. It was first used by the ancient Egyptians. They discovered that adding a little **gypsum** (**calcium sulfate**) to quicklime and water made a paste which was good at holding things together.

Cement has been around for a long time

Today, cement is made by heating powdered limestone with **clay** and gypsum in rotating kilns.

Cement binds things together because the quicklime reacts with the water. Crystals of calcium hydroxide slowly grow out of each grain of cement. This forms a network which holds the whole structure together. Over time, the calcium hydroxide reacts with carbon dioxide in the air to form calcium carbonate.

Using cement

You've probably seen cement mixers on building sites. Bricklayers use them to mix cement with sand and water to make a paste called **mortar**. The bricklayers spread the mortar onto bricks to hold them in place.

Working with mortar

Concrete is similar to mortar, but also contains small stones. Look around on your way home from school today – how many buildings can you see that use mortar or concrete?

a) What would happen to mortar if too much water was used?

Making glass

Look around your home for objects made with **glass**. It's not just for windows! Glass is a versatile material that can be specially made to have a number of useful properties.

Glass has many uses

Sand makes up over 60% of glass. Limestone and **sodium carbonate** are added in smaller quantities. This mixture is heated up to 1500°C and the raw materials react together to make glass. The molten glass becomes a solid as it cools down.

Glass is an unusual material. It looks like a solid, but shows some properties of a very thick liquid.

DID YOU KNOW?

A human thighbone is as strong as concrete.

KEY FACTS

- Limestone is heated with clay and gypsum to make cement.
- Sand or stones can be added to cement to make mortar or concrete.
- Sand, limestone and calcium carbonate are heated together to make glass.

TEST YOURSELF!

1 Copy and complete the following sentences using these words:

   calcium hydroxide   gypsum   limestone   clay   water

   Cement is made by heating _____, _____ and _____.

   When _____ is added, crystals of _____ _____ grow through

   the mixture and hold it together.

2 What is the difference between mortar and concrete?

3 An old shop with huge panes of glass in the windows was closed down. A scientist measured the thickness of the top and bottom of the glass. Why was the bottom slightly thicker than the top?

9.4 Using metals in construction

DID YOU KNOW?

Mercury is the only metal that is liquid at room temperature. If it gets into your body it can damage your nervous system, reduce your intelligence, and even kill you.

GET IT RIGHT!

You need to be able to explain which properties of metals make them useful for specific jobs.

Alloys

Name of alloy	Composition
Steel	Iron and carbon
Brass	Copper and zinc
Solder	Tin and lead

Metals can be mixed together or added to other materials to make alloys. **Alloys** are often stronger than pure metals. We say that they have a higher **tensile strength**.

Properties of metals

Most of the **elements** in the Periodic Table are metals. Scientists who work with metals are called **metallurgists**. Their role is to decide which metals are suitable for different jobs. They also combine metals with other metals (and some non-metals) to change their properties.

Working with metals

The properties of metals make them ideal for use in the building industry. This table lists some of the properties most metals share:

Property	Meaning
Hard	Metals are difficult to scratch
Strong	Metals don't break easily
Malleable	Metals can be beaten into different shapes
Ductile	Metals can be pulled out into wires
High melting point	Metals don't melt easily
Good conductors	Heat and electricity can travel through them easily
High density	They are heavy for their size because their atoms are packed closely together

a) Lightning rods are designed to channel lightning strikes harmlessly around a building. Which property makes copper a popular choice for lightning rods?

The structure of metals

If you could see the **atoms**, all metals would look fairly similar. They have a regular structure of tightly packed atoms. If you hit a metal hard enough, the atoms are able to slide over each other. This is why metals can be beaten into different shapes.

Metallic structures have another important feature. The metal atoms freely share their **electrons** with each other. The 'sea' of free electrons is able to move around – this is why metals can **conduct** heat and electricity.

Metals in construction

Builders use metals alongside other materials. Look at the reinforced concrete being made in the photo below. Metals add strength and a little flexibility to structures.

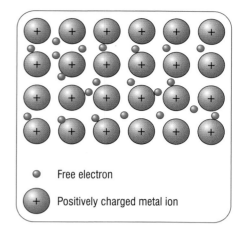

● Free electron

⊕ Positively charged metal ion

Metals conduct heat and electricity because the electrons in the sea of free electrons can flow through the structure

This builder is making reinforced concrete

b) Why aren't buildings made entirely of metal?
c) Make a list of places you would find metal objects in a newly built house. Explain why they are used for each object.

KEY FACTS

- Metals all share similar properties. They are malleable, ductile, strong, hard, have high melting points and are good conductors.
- The properties of metals make them useful for many jobs.
- The atoms in a metal are held in position by a 'sea' of free electrons.

TEST YOURSELF!

1 Copper is malleable, ductile, a good conductor and does not react with water.
   a) Which two of these properties make it good for making pipes?
   b) Which two of these properties make it good for making wires?

2 Describe how the structure of a metal could be compared to baked beans.

3 How does the structure of a metal make it good at conducting electricity?

4 Metal is more flexible than concrete. Suggest why metal is often used to reinforce concrete buildings.

9.5 Other materials used in construction

1 What are ceramics, polymers, and composites?
2 How do we use these materials in the building industry?

As well as metals and limestone-based materials, many other materials are used in the construction industry. A wide range of materials allows architects and engineers to be more creative and ambitious in their projects.

New materials allow architects to design more exciting buildings

DID YOU KNOW?

Ceramic tiles are also used to heat-proof the outside of space shuttles.

Ceramics

Ceramics are materials like clay or china. This is probably the oldest branch of materials science. People have been making pottery for thousands of years.

Ceramics are **strongly bonded** covalent compounds. (See pages 164–165.) Builders use ceramics in the bathroom or kitchen. Tiles, sinks, toilets, plates and mugs are all ceramics.

The properties of ceramics are:

● Electrical insulators.
● Strong.
● Very hard.
● Resistant to most chemicals.
● Very high melting point.
● Brittle (they can break easily).

a) Ceramics have **giant structures**. Why do these have such high melting points?

Ceramics in action

Polymers

Plastics are made of **polymers**, and are used in construction as well as in making other products. Polymer molecules are long chains of identical molecules. The small molecules that join together to make the polymers are called **monomers**).

Most polymers have these properties:

- Low density (light).
- Flexible.
- Soft.
- Low melting point.
- Insulators of heat and electricity.

Polymer scientists have developed different treatments to make plastics harder or more flexible. By linking the chains together, they can make a plastic harder. By adding chemicals called **plasticisers**, they make plastics more flexible.

b) What polymer do we use to make plastic bags?

c) What are the raw materials used to make plastics?

Plastic objects made of different polymers

Composites

Composites are one of the newest and most exciting developments in materials science. A composite is made when two or more other materials are put together to complement each others' properties. This is usually when a material has a really useful property but can't be used by itself.

They are interesting materials because they combine the best properties of different materials.

Fibreglass is a composite material. Painting a polymer coating onto sheets of glass fibres makes a strong, yet flexible material. Fibreglass is used to make the hulls of most modern boats.

d) What are the raw materials used to make glass?

Fibreglass production

TEST YOURSELF!

1 Which objects in your kitchen are made from ceramics?

2 Which properties of ceramics make them useful for bathroom tiling?

3 Why would a plastic window frame be more useful than a wooden one?

4 Suggest two advantages of using plastic bottles instead of glass.

5 There is an example of a composite material on page 177. Can you find it?

KEY FACTS

- Ceramics are hard but brittle insulators. They are resistant to chemicals and have a high melting point.
- Plastics made of polymers can be soft and flexible insulators. They can also have low melting points and low density.
- Composites are mixtures of more than one material.

9.6

Properties and uses of other construction materials

LEARNING OBJECTIVES

1 How do the properties of ceramics, polymers and composites make them good for particular jobs?
2 What are the advantages (and disadvantages) of building with these manufactured materials compared with natural materials?

Construction engineers and materials scientists need to choose the right material for any particular job. They use the properties of a material to help them make their decisions.

Why use ceramics?

The most common ceramic objects you will see in buildings are bricks. Bricks are made of clay. This is an ideal material because of its high melting point and its strength.

a) What are the advantages of building houses with bricks instead of wood?

You will also see a lot of ceramics in the bathroom. Ceramics are ideal materials for sinks, tiles and toilet bowls. This is because they are hard-wearing, easy to clean and resistant to cleaning products.

Tilers use the brittleness of ceramics to crack tiles in order to fit the area they need to cover.

A tiler at work

Why use polymers?

Polymers have been replacing more traditional materials since the 1900s.

Plastic is often used for garden furniture instead of wood. This is because it is easier to mould into different shapes and is resistant to weather. Plastic garden furniture is also lighter than wood.

Polymers often replace wood

Plastic carrier bags have replaced paper bags because they're stronger. They are also lightweight.

b) Can you think of one disadvantage of using plastic bags instead of paper ones?

Why use composites?

Because composites are made from a wide variety of materials, they have a wide range of properties. Their properties depend, not only on the materials used, but also on how much of each one is used. The possibilities are endless!

In the previous spread, we looked at fibreglass as a material for boats. Another reason it has replaced traditional materials (like wood) is that it is much lighter.

When concrete is reinforced with steel, is becomes a **composite**. Steel bars make buildings stronger because they add a bit of flexibility. They also stop cracks growing.

Steel-reinforced concrete

Steel reinforcement slows down cracking in concrete. This is because the crack needs to travel round the metal to continue.

Thin metal wires can be placed in glass so it doesn't shatter if broken. This composite is called **reinforced glass**.

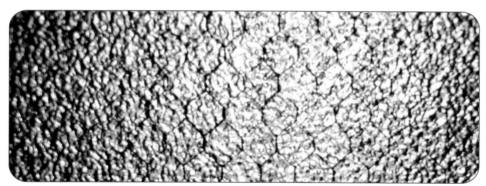

Reinforced glass is safer than regular glass

GET IT RIGHT!

You need to be able to explain why we use different materials for different jobs.

KEY FACTS

- The properties of composites depend on the properties of their components.
- Composites can be made with a wide range of properties for many uses.

TEST YOURSELF!

1 Why are ceramics used for bathroom surfaces?

2 a) Would you choose a ceramic or a polymer to make a saucepan?
   b) Why?

3 Explain why a plastic is a better coating for an electrical wire than a ceramic.

4 Why doesn't reinforced glass shatter if it's broken?

9.7 Construction materials: the ups and downs

Are quarries a good thing?

Imagine a beautiful countryside scene, and then put a quarry in it. A quarry is a great big hole where explosives are used to blow chunks out of it.

As well as looking unsightly, quarries damage the habitats of wildlife. Limestone that is washed away can affect the **pH** of rivers and lakes. And imagine the dust from the explosions (not to mention the noise)! The lorries used to take the limestone away will cause additional air pollution.

As you have read in this chapter, limestone is needed in order to produce many important materials. It is vital to society for the production of new buildings, roads, glass, paper and many other materials. The quarrying and construction industries also provide hundreds of thousands of jobs.

A scar on the landscape?

Quarry foreman

Activities

a) What would you write in a letter to your MP to try to stop the damage done by quarry workings? Work with a partner – swap your letters after writing them, and write a reply from an MP. Use information in Chapter 6 (pages 132–133) to help you structure your response.

b) Imagine you are the foreman of a quarry. How would you respond to the claims that your business damaged the environment?

Cement and the greenhouse effect

In order to make quicklime, limestone must be roasted in huge lime kilns. The waste gas from this process is carbon dioxide.

Scientists believe that increasing levels of carbon dioxide in the atmosphere are causing global warming.

Activities

a) What is the greenhouse effect?

b) What might be the effects of global warming?

c) Can we reduce carbon dioxide emissions from lime kilns?

The Earth is getting hot!

Polymers and recycling

Plastics are made from crude oil. Crude oil was formed millions of years ago. Scientists have estimated that, at the rate society is using oil, there is only enough left for about 30 or 40 years.

Most of today's plastics can be recycled. Recycling is important because it reduces the amount of crude oil used in the plastics industry.

World oil reserves running out!

End of oil supplies in sight?

Activities

a) Find out how plastics were invented.

b) What was the first plastic ever made?

c) What happens if we get rid of plastics by burning them?

Armour plating

All modern buildings contain glass somewhere. Materials scientists have come up with lots of ways to make it stronger. This means glass can be made to withstand bullet impacts and even small explosions.

However, making glass stronger traditionally means making it thicker. This can make it very, very heavy. Scientists have recently discovered a new transparent compound which is *much* stronger than glass. It's called **aluminium oxynitride** – some scientists have nicknamed it 'transparent aluminium'. Because it's stronger, transparent aluminium doesn't need to be as thick as reinforced glass.

Bullet holes in a sheet of glass

Activities

a) What uses are there for bullet-proof glass?

b) Research 'transparent aluminium' on the internet. Where was it discovered? How much does it cost?

c) How is it helpful for manufacturing armoured cars and tanks that transparent aluminium doesn't need to be as thick as reinforced glass?

SUMMARY QUESTIONS

1 You work for a large corporation which supplies materials to other companies. These are the companies you supply materials to, and what they do with them:

Company	What they produce
Alpha construction	Cement to sell to builders
Beta Bathrooms	Ornamental sinks
Gamma electrical	Electrical wires
Delta sports	Lightweight surfboards
Epsilon glass	Glass for windows

These are the materials you have in your warehouse:

limestone   copper   clay   gypsum fibreglass   china   quicklime   sodium carbonate

a) Which material(s) would you send to each company? (Hint: some companies will need more than one material.)

b) For Alpha Construction, and Epsilon Glass, explain **how** they use the materials you are sending them.

c) For Beta Bathrooms, Gamma Electrical and Delta Sports, explain **why** your choice of materials are best.

2 a) Describe two composites that use glass.

b) How are they different from each other?

3 Fill in the spaces in these equations showing the conversion of quicklime into slaked lime:

Word equation:

calcium oxide + _____ → calcium hydroxide

Symbol equation:

$CaO +$ _____ → _____

4 a) Is the reaction that changes limestone into quicklime exothermic or endothermic?

b) Explain your answer to part a).

5 Fibreglass is an example of a composite material. Explain why composites are more useful than traditional materials?

6 What is the difference between flexibility and malleability?

7 Look at the structure of copper below. Explain how the structure of a metal gives it its malleability?

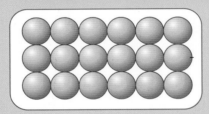

8 Identify the lables (A–E) on the diagram below:

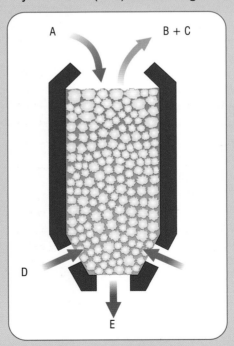

EXAM-STYLE QUESTIONS

1 Limestone is a very useful material. Limestone is mined from the ground. It is made from crushed shells of ancient sea creatures. It is made up of calcium carbonate.

a) Write down the word equation and the symbol equation for the breakdown of limestone by heat. (2)
b) Limestone is quarried in hilly regions of England like the peak district. What does this suggest about the geological history of England? (1)
c) Limestone is a very versatile building material. Suggest a reason why many more buildings and stonewalls are made from limestone in the peak district than in other parts of the UK. (1)
d) There is a lot of debate about whether or not new quarries should be opened. State two arguments for and two arguments against having a limestone quarry near your school. (4)

2 The chemical formula of the calcium carbonate in limestone is $CaCO_3$. How many elements and of which type make up calcium carbonate? (3)

3 a) What gas is released when limestone is heated? (1)
b) Lime is the chemical that remains. What is the chemical formula for lime? (1)
c) Water can be added to lime to make a new chemical that farmers put on their fields to neutralise acid rain. What is the name of this new chemical? (1)

4 Concrete can crack easily. Many buildings are made from concrete. They don't crack because there are steel rods inside the concrete that reinforces the concrete. This makes a composite material that is very strong.

a) What is a composite material? (1)
b) Explain what would happen if composite materials were not used on walkways. (2)

5 Limestone is used in the production of glass and cement, which are both important building materials. Cement is used to make mortar and concrete.

a) Name the other materials limestone is mixed with to make glass. (2)
b) Cement is made from clay, gypsum and which other material? (1)
c) What is mortar used for? (1)
d) Name 2 ingredients of concrete. (2)

6 There are many uses for limestone besides building with it as a raw material. Copy the table below and classify these industries as major users of limestone and minor users of limestone.

Types of industry	major user	minor user
Cement manufacturer		
Pharmaceutical industry		
Iron and steel industry		
Glass manufacturer		
Concrete manufacturer		
Blu-tack manufacturer		

(6)

7 Link up these materials to their properties.

Material	Properties
copper wire	lightweight
fibreglass surfboard	ornamental hard poor thermal conductor
rubber glove for washing up	ductile conducts electricity
ceramics for sink	malleable poor thermal conductor

(4)

10.1   Energy sources in the home

1 How can we compare different energy sources we use at home?

2 How can we be more energy efficient at home?

Does your house get too hot in the Summer and too cold in the Winter? Are your electricity and gas bills always *too high*? Do you get through lots of *expensive batteries*?

Maybe you should think about an *energy audit*!

Workman inspecting loft insulation

The amount of energy that you use at home is very important, for two main reasons:

● You can save money by using less energy.
● Using less energy means our planet's resources will last longer. (See page 142 for more about this.)

Part of the job of an Energy Consultant is to look around your house and work out how to make it more **energy efficient**. They will think about a wide range of issues, including these three:

1 Are you using the best energy source?

2 How much energy are you losing?

3 How efficiently are you using your energy?

Are you using the best energy source?
Some energy sources are naturally more **efficient** than others – but there are also big differences in prices. Have a look at this table, which compares several common energy sources used at home:

Energy source	Cost per kWh*	Advantage	Disadvantage
Mains electricity	8p	Easy to use	Devices left on cause waste
Natural gas	2p	Burns well	Wastes heat, non-renewable
Oil	1.5p	Can be used in remote places	Can run out, non-renewable
Normal batteries	£100	Portable/convenient	Need replacing, waste pollution
Rechargeable batteries	£5	Can be used many times	Recharging, waste pollution

*a kWh, or **kilowatt hour**, is a unit that energy companies use. You can read more about it on page 192, but for now you can think of it as the amount of energy used keeping a light bulb working for about 10 hours.

a) Why are batteries so much more expensive than mains electricity?
b) How do you think you could change the types of energy source you use?

You can read about the issues around energy source **renewability** in Chapter 7, but a couple of points are important here. Because gas, oil and most of our electricity come from **non-renewable** sources and cause **pollution**, we are looking for other sources of energy to use. A variety of 'alternative' and renewable energy systems could be used in your home, including:

Solar panels on a roof

Solar panels being installed

- Solar energy
- Biofuels
- Geothermal energy.

c) What are the advantages and disadvantages of using solar power in the UK?

How much energy are you losing?

One of the most expensive problems is the amount of heat that we lose from our houses. The diagram on the right shows five different ways this can happen.

On pages 194-195 we will look in more detail at how heat moves. Once you understand this, you can work out how to stop it being lost.

How efficiently are you using your energy?

No device that you use will ever turn all of its **input energy** into useful **output energy** – some is always wasted. Later on in this chapter (pages 196–197) we will look more closely at the idea of **efficiency**. More importantly, you will see how we can be more efficient.

d) How many of your electrical devices at home get hot when they shouldn't do? List as many as you can think of.

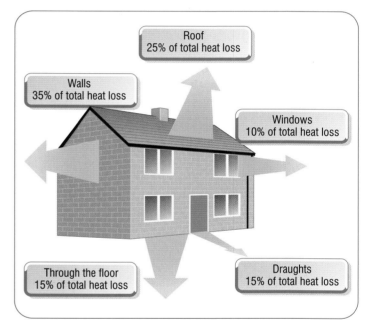

Roof
25% of total heat loss

Walls
35% of total heat loss

Windows
10% of total heat loss

Through the floor
15% of total heat loss

Draughts
15% of total heat loss

Heat is lost from a house in different ways

TEST YOURSELF!

1 a) List the five energy sources from the table on the opposite page, from cheapest to most expensive.

b) Draw a pie chart or bar graph to show how much heat is lost at home through all the different ways shown above.

c) How many home devices that use gas can you think of?

2 If batteries cost so much to use, why do we use them so much?

3 Carry out an energy audit of your own house. Look at:
a) which sources of energy you use
b) where you might be losing heat from your house
c) which electrical devices waste energy.

GET IT RIGHT!

When you are asked which type of energy is the best one to use ... there often is no right answer. Gas might be best for cooking, but electricity for running a fridge.

The important thing is to think about the advantages and disadvantages of each type carefully.

10.2   Electrical power

LEARNING OBJECTIVES

1 Why do different devices use energy at different rates?
2 How can we work out the power of electrical devices?

DID YOU KNOW?

In the UK, our home electricity used to be at 240 volts (V), but we changed to **230 V** so that we could use the same electrical devices that they use in Europe without expensive changes.

Power is a measure of how fast a device uses electrical **energy**. The faster a device uses electricity, the more it will cost.

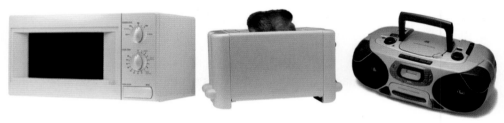

A microwave, a toaster and a CD player

a) Which of these three devices do you think is the most powerful? (Which one uses the most energy each second?)

There are two ways of finding out how powerful a device is:

1 Read the label that tells you.
2 You can work out the **power** if you know the **voltage** and the **current** that the device uses.

Read the label that tells you

On the back or bottom of every electrical device is a label with several numbers on it. It will look something like this:

Clear Boil Kettle
Model: CBK100

230V ~ 50Hz   2000W

This is the **voltage** – it is 230 V in the UK

This is the **frequency** of the voltage – it is 50 Hz AC in the UK

This is the **power rating** – in watts or kilowatts

Power is measured in **watts** (W). A power rating of 1 W means *1 joule (J) of energy is used every second*. A power of 1 kW means 1000 joules (or 1 kilojoule, kJ) of energy is used each second.

Read the label

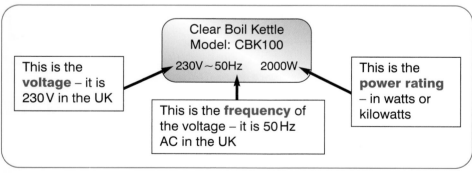

Microwave Oven	
2450 MHz 230V ~ 50Hz	
Input Power	1200W
Energy Output	800W
	Made in Korea

Toaster
230-240V
50-60Hz   1500W

CD player
Frequencies: 87.5-108 MHz
Power Supply: 230V ~ 50Hz
Max Power: 15W
This unit is double insulated

b) Now look at these labels for the devices shown above.
i) Which is the most powerful,
ii) Which uses the least energy every second?

More labels

Notice that the information is not always set out in the same way – but it is nearly always there. There is often other information about the device as well, like the working **frequencies** of the radio.

Sometimes, though, you can't find the **power rating** information...

You can work out the power if you know the voltage and the current that the device uses.

You can use this formula:

Power (watts) = **Voltage** (volts) x **Current** (amperes)

If the **voltage** is in **volts** and the **current** is in **amperes** (amps, A), then the power you work out will be in watts.

Worked example

A light bulb needs 230 V and 0.26 A to glow brightly. What is its power rating?

Power = Voltage x Current
       = 230 x 0.26
       = <u>60 W</u>

This formula can be rearranged – if you want to work out the voltage the device needs or the current that it draws when it is switched on:

$$\text{voltage} = \frac{\text{power}}{\text{current}} \quad \text{or} \quad \text{current} = \frac{\text{power}}{\text{voltage}}$$

If you can't find any of these numbers, you can always measure them with a **voltmeter** and an **ammeter**. The diagram on the right shows how to set up the **circuit**. Do not attempt this with mains (230 V) electricity!

c) A current of 2 A is measured through a small bulb when a 3 V battery is used. What is the power of the bulb?

GET IT RIGHT!

You can also use the equation for power with engines – to work out how much energy they use (or produce) each second.

In fact, you can use it with any device that transfers electrical energy.

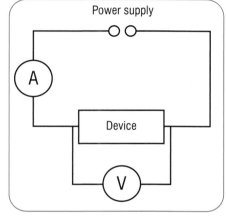

Measuring voltage and current

TEST YOURSELF!

1 Match each of these electrical quantities to its correct unit:

Quantities:	Units:
Current	joules
Voltage	amperes
Power	hertz
Energy	volts
Frequency	watts

2 a) A kettle draws a 4 A current when plugged into a 230 V socket. What is the power of the kettle?

b) A 100 W light bulb is switched on at 230 V. How much current does it draw?

3 Copy and complete this table, filling in any gaps:

Device	Current/A	Voltage/V	Power/W
Torch	0.25	6	
Pump	10		200
Electric fire		230	2000

10.3   Choosing and using fuses

1 Why do we use fuses and circuit breakers?
2 How do we work out what size of fuse to use in a device?

Sometimes electrical devices go wrong. They can develop faults that make too much **current** flow into them. This can make their wires overheat and even catch fire. It can even put you at risk of getting an **electrical shock**.

To make the devices safer, we use devices like **fuses** and **circuit breakers** in circuits. You can see how these safety devices work below.

Fuses

A fuse is usually just a thin piece of wire. It is designed to only allow a certain amount of electrical current to flow through it. When too much current flows, the piece of wire gets too hot and melts. We say that the fuse '**blows**'. This prevents any more current from flowing into the device.

> **DID YOU KNOW?**
>
> If a fuse is too small, it will blow when a normal amount of current is flowing. If a fuse is too large, it will allow too much current to flow before it blows.

Different types of fuse: a standard plug fuse and some car fuses

Because fuses are cheap, they can easily be replaced once the problem that caused the overload has been fixed. The alternative would be to buy a new device – much more expensive!

Choosing a fuse

Fuses are used in a variety of places, including plugs, house fuse boxes and cars. The size of fuse you need depends on the amount of current that the device normally uses. The fuse needs to let that much current flow, but must blow if it gets much bigger.

For this reason, you can get fuses in a range of sizes, including:

1A   3A   5A   7A   10A   13A   30A

These '**nominal values**' or 'fuse ratings' are in **amperes (A)** because they show the usual amount of **current** they will allow. Most fuses will blow before the current reaches twice their nominal value.

a) Which fuse size would you choose for ...
   i) A 20A electrical cooker?
   ii) An 8A kettle?

Working out which fuse to use

Imagine that you need to put a fuse in a device but aren't sure what size to use. You can use the information given on its label to work it out.

On page 189, you used the formula:

$$\text{power (watts)} = \text{voltage (volts)} \times \text{current (amperes)}$$

This can be rearranged so that you can work out the current:

$$\text{current (amperes)} = \frac{\text{power (watts)}}{\text{voltage (volts)}}$$

So the microwave oven described on the right uses ...

$$\text{current (amperes)} = \frac{\text{power (watts)}}{\text{voltage (volts)}} = \frac{1200}{230} = \underline{5.2 \text{ A}}$$

b) Use the list on the previous page to decide which fuse size is best for this microwave oven.

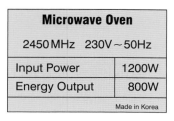

Microwave Oven	
2450 MHz 230V ~ 50Hz	
Input Power	1200W
Energy Output	800W
	Made in Korea

Label from microwave oven

Circuit breakers

A lot of devices have circuit breakers, as well as fuses. Your **fuse** box at home has probably got a row of 'trip switches' on its front. These have got two main uses:

1   So that a whole circuit in the house can be **switched off**. You might want to do this when you put in a new light fitting, for example.

2   When there is an **electrical fault**, the switch trips – turning off the circuit to make it safe. Then you can fix the problem before switching it back on – and you don't need to buy a new fuse!

Remember that mains electricity is dangerous and can kill! Any repairs carried out on main electrical circuits should only be done by an expert.

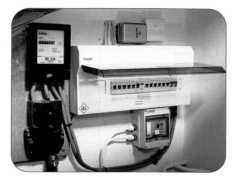

A fuse / circuit breaker box

TEST YOURSELF!

1   Here is a list of available fuse sizes:

    1 A   3 A   5 A   7 A   10 A   13 A   30 A

Pick the right fuse for each of these devices:

a) A kettle that draws a current of 4.2 A.
b) A lamp that draws a current of 0.3 A.
c) A cooker that draws a current of 16 A.
d) A pond pump that draws a current of 3 A

2   Work out what size fuse is needed for these two devices (remember to show your working out):

a) A radio rated at 230 V, 15 W.
b) A printer rated at 230 V, 1.2 kW.

3   Iain's 7 amp (A) toaster fuse blows, but he doesn't have any replacement fuses of the right size. What will happen if he uses:

a) a 5 A fuse?
b) a 10 A fuse?

10.4 The cost of using electricity

LEARNING OBJECTIVES

1 How can we work out how
   much electricity costs?
2 What is a kilowatt hour?
3 How do you read electricity
   meters and bills?

Electricity companies charge for the amount of electrical energy you use.

You can work out how much energy is used by a device from the equation:

$$\textbf{Energy (J)} = \textbf{Power (W)} \times \textbf{time (s)}$$

This gives the amount of energy in joules. For example:

A 100 W lamp on for 30 minutes uses ...

$$100 \times (30 \times 60) = 180\,000 \text{ J (or 180 kJ)}.$$

This is a large number, but one joule is a small amount of energy. You use a joule of energy just lifting an apple to your mouth!

The kilowatt hour – a big unit for electrical energy

When electricity companies charge for electricity, they use a bigger unit – the **kilowatt hour (kWh)**:

'If a 1 kW device is on for 1 hour, it uses 1 kWh of electrical energy.'

a) How many joules are there in 1 kWh? Copy out the workings below and then finish the calculation:

> Use Energy = Power x time
>
> $$= 1\text{ kW} \times 1\text{ hour}$$
> $$= 1000 \times (1 \times 60 \times 60) \text{ s}$$
> $$= \underline{} \text{ J} \qquad = \underline{} \text{ MJ}$$

b) A 2 kW electric fire is switched on for 3 hours. How many kilowatt hours (units) of electrical energy does it use in this time?

Charging for the electricity

A kilowatt hour is sometimes just called a '**unit**' of electricity. The companies typically charge about 8p for each unit – or 8p/kWh.

You can use this to work out how much a device costs to use, using the formula:

$$\textbf{cost (p)} = \textbf{energy used (kWh)} \times \textbf{unit cost (p/kWh)}$$

> **Worked example**
>
> How much does it cost to use a 1500 W hairdryer for half an hour?
>
> 1500 W = 1.5 kW   Half an hour = 0.5 hours
>
> energy used = power x time = 1.5 x 0.5 = 2.25 kWh
>
> so cost = energy used x unit cost = 2.25 x 8 = **18p**.

The cost for a whole house – your electricity bill

All the electricity that you use at home flows through an electricity meter. Your meter is usually in a cellar or cupboard.

There are two main styles of electricity meter. One type has wheels and an older style has dials; see the photos on the right for examples.

Whichever one you are reading, there are two points to remember:

- The number you use from each wheel or dial is the one it has just gone past.
- The red wheel or dial is tenths – so remember a decimal point.

c) What reading do the meter dials in the diagram below show?

Wheel-style electricity meter

Counting the cost

To work out how much electricity you have used – and how much it has cost – this is what you need to do:

1. Take two meter readings, say a week apart.
2. Subtract the first reading from the second to find out how many units (kWh) of electricity have been used.
3. Multiply this reading by the unit cost (e.g. 8 p/kWh).

(Remember to check that your answer is sensible at the end!)

Dial-style electricity meter

> **Worked example**
>
> Meter reading on Tuesday 12th = 2517.9
>
> Meter reading on Tuesday 19th = 2603.4
>
> **Units used** in the week = 2603.4 – 2517.9 = 85.5 kWh
>
> **Cost** = units used x unit cost = 85.5 x 8 = **684 p** (= £6.84)

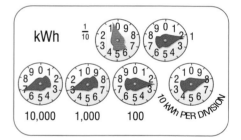

Close-up of the dials on a meter

TEST YOURSELF!

1. Copy and complete the following sentences using these words:

   3600   energy   kilowatt hour   1000   joules

   Electrical companies charge for each unit of electrical _____ used. A unit is also called a _____ ____. A kilowatt is a _____ watts and an hour is _____ seconds so 1 kWh is equal to 3 600 000 _____ of energy.

2. How much would it cost you to use:
   a) a 100 W lamp for 10 hours?
   b) a 20 W fridge for a week?

3. Pick one electrical device that you use most days at home.
   a) Record its power rating and how long you use it for each day for a week.
   b) Work out how much it has cost to use your device for the week (at 8p/kWh).

KEY FACTS

There are two conversions you often need to do:

1. **Time in hours**
   Remember – 60 seconds in 1 minute and 60 minutes in 1 hour – means 3600 seconds in 1 hour.

2. **Power in kW**
   There are 1000 watts in each kilowatt.
   (1 kW = 1000 W).

10.5   How heat is lost at home

LEARNING OBJECTIVES

1 How does heat travel?
2 How can we prevent heat being lost at home?

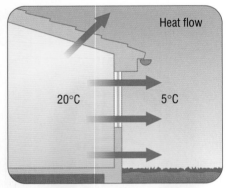

Heat flow

20°C 5°C

Heat flows from hotter places to colder places

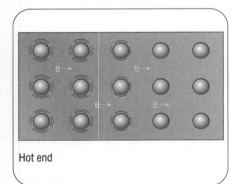

Hot end

Conduction of heat in a metal

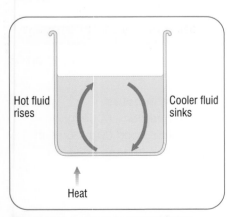

Hot fluid rises Cooler fluid sinks

Heat

Convection currents in heated fluids

Using energy efficiently

One of the ways that we can reduce energy costs is to stop our heat from being lost. We need to understand how heat is transferred before we can cut down on how much heat is lost from homes.

Heat energy can show itself in two ways:

- As **vibration** or movement of atoms. The hotter atoms get, the more they move.
- As **infra-red** rays (see page 242). Hotter objects give out higher energy waves.

How heat moves

The way heat moves, or transfers, depends on what the hot object is and what surrounds it. Because of these different factors, there are *three* ways that heat can travel:

1. Conduction	How to stop it
The diagram on the left shows how heat travels through **solids**. As the hot atoms **vibrate**, they give energy to the nearby atoms. These then vibrate more and pass the energy on. Materials with very regular arrangements of **atoms** (like metals) are better **conductors**. Metals also have free **electrons** to carry the energy along. **Graphite** is a **non-metal** (a form of carbon) but it also has electrons that are free to move along and a regular arrangement of atoms. This makes it a good **conductor** of heat. Other materials that have irregular (mixed-up) arrangements of atoms and no free electrons tend to be **insulators**.	Use an insulator Block the flow of heat with a material that heat can't flow through easily Good examples of insulators are non-metals and **foams**

2. Convection	How to stop it
The diagram on the left shows how heat travels through **fluids** (liquids or gases). As the atoms heat up, they move more. Because they are not fixed together, they push apart, so the hotter fluid becomes less **dense**. The less dense fluid floats up above the colder fluid, which then sinks, gets heated up and rises. In this way, a **convection current** is set up, with hot fluids rising and colder fluids sinking to take their place. Solids can't carry convection currents because the atoms are fixed in place and so are unable to flow upwards.	Block the fluid to stop it moving If the warm fluid can't flow upwards, it can't take the heat away with it An insulating material blocks the flow best

3. Radiation	How to stop it
When heat travels as **infra-red** radiation, it can travel through air or even empty space. Unlike conduction and convection, radiation doesn't need atoms to carry the heat energy; it travels on its own. Warm and hot objects **radiate** (give out) infra-red rays, depending on how hot they are and what colour they are. Light and shiny surfaces radiate much less than dark and matt (dull) surfaces. Another way that colours affect infra-red radiation is that it is reflected by light and shiny surfaces. Dark and matt surfaces absorb infra-red radiation the best.	Use a shiny surface This will reflect the infra-red rays back. So the heat won't be absorbed into any walls or other surfaces and won't be lost Silvered surfaces reflect radiation the best

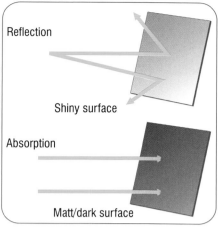

Shiny surfaces reflect radiation, whereas dark, matt surfaces absorb it

Controlling how heat moves at home

One of the best ways to keep heat in your house is to **insulate** the walls and loft. The photo opposite shows an insulation material that comes in sheets about 5 cm thick:

- Most of the material is foam. This is an excellent insulator because of the air trapped in it. So heat cannot **conduct** through it.
- The shiny side of the material reflects **radiant** heat back into the room.
- The material is solid and airtight, so warm air can't **convect** through it.

Roof insulation material

TEST YOURSELF!

1 **The table below is wrong.** Draw it out and rearrange the columns so that they show what heat travels through by each method and how the flow can be stopped.

Method	Through	To stop
Conduction	Air/space	Block it
Convection	Solids	Reflect back
Radiation	Fluids	Insulator

2 The three ways that heat travels are like getting a pen to the other side of the classroom. You could...

a) Throw it.
b) Carry it.
c) Pass it from person to person.

Which of these ways is like each of conduction, convection and radiation?

3 How many ways of keeping heat in can you find in your house?

DID YOU KNOW?

The best insulators stop two or three of the ways that heat can travel. For example, double glazing mainly stops conduction and convection.

10.6 Evaluating efficiency

LEARNING OBJECTIVES

1 What energy transfers take place in electrical devices?
2 How can we work out the efficiency of an electrical device?

Most electrical devices get hot after they have been switched on for a while. A lot of devices also make unwanted noise. Both of these are waste forms of **energy**. Most energy is usually wasted as unwanted heat.

Very efficient devices don't produce a lot of waste energy. Most of their **input energy** goes to producing useful **output energy**.

For example, a light bulb produces light as useful energy and heat as a waste. You can represent this with an **energy transfer diagram**:

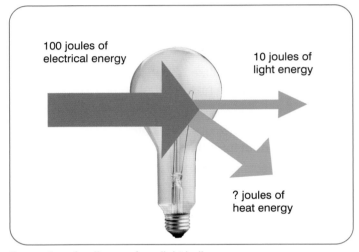

100 joules of electrical energy

10 joules of light energy

? joules of heat energy

Energy transfer diagram for a light bulb

GET IT RIGHT!

Energy transfer diagrams should always take this form:

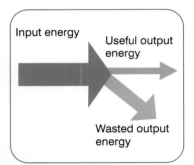

Input energy

Useful output energy

Wasted output energy

An example of an energy transfer diagram

a) Look at the diagram above. How much of the 100 J of electrical energy supplied is wasted as heat energy?

You can compare how much energy an **engine** device uses and how much it wastes. You can use this formula to work out efficiency:

$$\text{efficiency} = \frac{\text{useful energy output}}{\text{total energy input}}$$

(You can multiply by 100 to get a %)

You can use this formula to work out the efficiency of any device. All you need to know is:

● How much energy is supplied in a time – or its **input power**.
● The useful energy produced in that time – its **output power**.

b) What is the efficiency of the light bulb used in the example above? (Remember to show your working out.)

Because **power** (in watts) is a measure of how much energy is used each second, you can re-write the formula like this:

$$\text{efficiency} = \frac{\text{useful power output}}{\text{total power input}}$$

(You can multiply by 100 to get a %)

Exploring the efficiency of some devices

Here's the information label from the back of a **microwave oven** that we looked at on page 188:

Microwave Oven	
2450 MHz 230V ~ 50Hz	
Input Power	1200W
Energy Output	800W
	Made in Korea

Label from a microwave oven

Worked example

What is the efficiency of the microwave?

In this case, we have the power, instead of the energy, so we use:

$$\text{efficiency} = \frac{\text{useful energy output}}{\text{total energy input}}$$

$$= \frac{800 \text{ W}}{1200 \text{ W}} = \underline{0.67} \text{ (or 67\%)}$$

This means that about 33% of the energy is wasted – this is a lot less than many devices!)

Kettles are one of the most efficient electrical devices because most of the electrical energy supplied is turned into heat energy for the water. Not much heat is lost to the air, and the kettle also makes little noise.

c) An electric kettle takes about 3 minutes to boil. In that time it uses 360 kJ of electrical energy. The water in the kettle gains 324 kJ of heat energy.
   i)   Draw an energy transfer diagram for the kettle.
   ii) How much energy does the kettle waste?
   iii) Calculate the efficiency of the kettle.

An electric kettle

TEST YOURSELF!

1   Copy and complete these sentences about electrical efficiency. The first letter of each missing word is given:

   The efficiency of a device tells you how much of the i____ energy is

   turned into u_____ o_____ energy. Efficiency is always l___ than 100 %

   because some energy is always w_____, usually as h___ energy.

   Powerful devices use m___ energy and so they usually w_____ more,

   too.

2   If a 60 W light bulb is described as being 25% efficient ...
   a) How much energy does it use every second?
   b) How much light energy does it give out every second?
   c) How much heat does it produce every second?

3   Explain why a kettle is so much more efficient than a light bulb.

10.7   Improving energy efficiency

On pages 196–197, we looked at the idea of **efficiency** – as a way of telling how good a device is at not wasting energy. We want our devices to be as efficient as possible for three main reasons:

- If they waste less energy, we get better value for our money. We should then be able to spend less on our energy.
- If less energy is wasted, then less energy is needed to start with. This means that our existing **energy resources** can last longer.
- Less energy produced usually means less **pollution**.

Because of these reasons, electrical and mechanical engineers are always trying to improve the efficiency of devices they design. As well as this, the government are actively encouraging companies to make more efficient devices.

DID YOU KNOW?

If every household in the USA replaced one light bulb with a compact fluorescent light bulb, it would prevent enough pollution to equal removing 1 million cars from the road.

Energy-efficient light bulbs

The most common light bulbs waste about 90% of their input energy as heat – only 10% becomes light. This type of bulb is called an '**incandescent bulb**'.

There are other bulbs available that are more efficient; for example the '**compact fluorescent bulbs**'. These are more expensive than incandescent bulbs. However, a 15 W fluorescent bulb gives out the same amount of light as a 60 W filament bulb. Let's compare them:

60 W incandescent	15 W compact fluorescent
An incandescent light bulb	A compact fluorescent light bulb
10% efficient	35% efficient
Lasts 1000 hours – replace every year	Lasts 10 000 hours – replace every 10 years
Costs 50p to buy	Costs £3 to buy
Costs £3 a year to run	Costs 80p a year to run

a) How much would it cost to buy and run each type of light bulb for 10 years?

Energy-efficient domestic appliances

If a fridge or washing machine is energy efficient, it will use less electricity. So it will be less expensive to run and produce less **pollution**.

You might be surprised at the reasonable cost of energy-efficient appliances. They are often no more expensive to buy than similar appliances that are much less efficient.

Energy labelling

The European Union has introduced a compulsory energy labelling scheme for household appliances. It covers:

- refrigerators
- freezers and fridge-freezers
- washing machines
- tumble dryers
- washer-dryers
- dishwashers
- electric ovens
- lamps

Energy labels are displayed on these products in shops so that customers can compare how efficient they are.

The energy labels show how much energy the appliance is likely to consume in a year. They are also given an energy grading from A to G. (An A-rated appliance will use about half as much electricity as a G-rated appliance.)

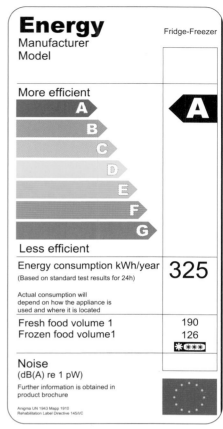

Energy efficiency label for a fridge-freezer

An open fridge door is bad for energy efficiency

Of course, how much electricity is used will depend upon how much you use the appliance, as well as where it is located. For example, a fridge that is next to a cooker will use more energy than one that is somewhere cooler. Kitchen layout is important to energy efficiency!

Some labels now also provide information on other aspects of the performance of the appliance. For example, they can tell you water usage for washing machines and even the amount of noise they make.

TEST YOURSELF!

1 Say if the following statements are **true** or **false**:
   a) Energy-efficient devices use more energy.
   b) Energy-efficient devices waste less energy.
   c) Energy-efficient devices are always more expensive.

2 Why do you think it is easier for a fridge to get an 'A' rating for efficiency than it is for a washing machine?

3 Design an advertisement for an energy-efficient device of your choice. Explain why a customer should buy your fridge over a slightly cheaper, but less efficient, one.

10.8   Energy at home

A cost-benefit analysis for energy-saving measures

The table lists several things that you could do to your home to make it more energy efficient. It shows how much each suggestion would save each year, how much it would cost and how long it would take to pay for itself.

Energy-saving measure	Saving per year	Installed cost	Payback/years
Cavity wall insulation	£115–145	£360–550	2–5
Solid wall insulation (internal)	£220–250	Approx. £2300	9–10
Solid wall insulation (external)	£220–250	£37 per m²	–
Roof insulation (new installation)	£100–120	£260–360	2–4
Roof insulation (top-up)	£25–35	£230–310	7–12
Floor insulation	£25–35	–	–
Replacement condensing boiler	£40–50	From £150	3–4
Full heating controls	£70–80	£125–250	2–4
Draught stripping	£10–15	£125–150	8–15

Activities

a) Which measure makes the greatest saving each year?

b) Which suggestion takes the longest to pay for itself? Why do you think this is?

c) If you were going to make one improvement to your house, which one would it be? Explain your answer.

How a circuit breaker works

This diagram shows a typical **electromagnet** design.

When the switch is flipped to the 'on' position, electricity can flow from the bottom terminal, through the electromagnet, up to the moving contact. Then it goes across to the stationary contact and out to the upper terminal.

The electricity magnetises the electromagnet. Increasing current boosts the electromagnet's magnetic force, and decreasing current lowers the magnetism.

When the current jumps to unsafe levels, the electromagnet is strong enough to pull down a metal lever connected to the switch linkage. The entire linkage shifts, tilting the moving contact away from the stationary contact to break the circuit. The electricity shuts off.

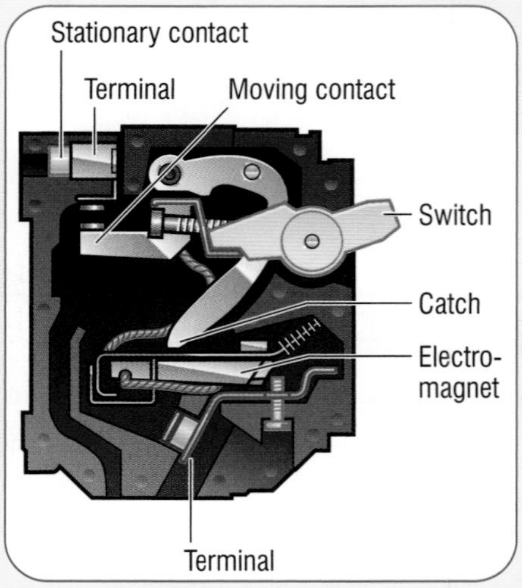

A typical electromagnetic circuit breaker

Activities

a) Draw a simple flow chart showing the main stages in how a circuit breaker works.

b) List four devices that should be plugged in through a circuit breaker.

How to build a low-energy home

Find the right people to work with

- Architects – who know about how to design for low-energy use – and have enthusiasm too.
- Builders – who understand what you want to do and will work with you.
- Tradespeople – plumbers and electricians with experience of low-energy construction.

Plan all the details

Cut down on heat losses
- Build in ventilation that can be completely controlled.
- Make your house compact.
- Fix draught strips around all openings.
- Insulate the walls and roof well.

Use the Sun's heat well
- Build your house to face south.
- Cut down the size of north-facing windows – put most windows on the south side.
- Locate main bedrooms and living rooms on the south side of the house.
- To reduce overheating in Summer, build in window shades.

Use efficient systems
- Install condensing boilers (oil or gas) if you can – with easy-to-use controls.
- Make sure your hot water system is the right size for your house.
- Use energy-efficient lighting and cooker.

Low-energy timber-frame house. Features include passive solar design, cellulose insulation and 'eco' paints.

Fit it right
- Don't install wet insulation – and keep it dry.
- Don't let heat escape where pipes and wires enter your home.
- Don't squash the insulation materials.
- Overlap insulation between your loft and walls.
- Keep air-spaces free of rubble and waste.

Do it right when you move in
- Let any wet plaster dry before painting.
- Buy low-energy fridges and freezers.
- Learn how to use your heating system – and then set it at the right level.
- Don't put up net curtains (they stop the sunlight coming in), but use thick curtains at night.

Activities

a) Pick 3 measures listed above and explain how they reduce **energy loss**.

b) Now choose 3 **different** measures not mentioned here – how else can they reduce heat loss?

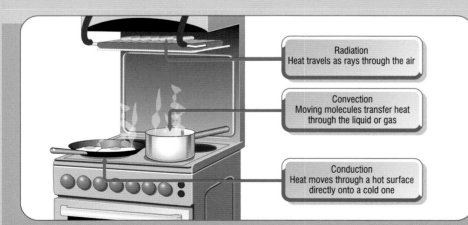

Radiation
Heat travels as rays through the air

Convection
Moving molecules transfer heat through the liquid or gas

Conduction
Heat moves through a hot surface directly onto a cold one

The processes of radiation, convection and conduction in cooking

Conduction, convection and radiation in cooking

Activity

Look at the diagram. Explain how heat cooks the ...

a) bacon under the grill.

b) peas in the pan.

c) eggs in the frying pan.

SUMMARY QUESTIONS

1 Choose 3 electrical devices that you use at home and draw energy transfer diagrams to show what they do.

2 Explain why putting a lid on a cup of coffee keeps it warm for longer.

3 A fridge uses 146 kWh of electricity a year. If electricity costs 8p/kWh, how much does this cost?

4 A 30 W stereo is plugged in to the 230 V mains electricity and used for 8 hours.
  a) How much current does it use?
  b) What size fuse does it need?
  c) How much energy does it use?

5 Which kettle is more efficient:

Kettle A – turns 80 J of every 110 J into useful heat energy.
Kettle B – turns 150 J of every 200 J into useful heat energy.

6 Here is part of a typical electricity bill. How much does Harry owe the company?

Kershaw Electricity

Mr Harry Haybridge
1 Brake Lane
Hagley

Please make sure that your payment is with us by 09/10/06

Your electricity statement
Bill date: 10th September 2006

		Reading Date:
Present reading:	11264	10/09/06
Previous reading:	10045	11/06/06
Electricity used:	_____ units	
	charged at 8p per kWh	
cost of electricity used:	£___.___	

Have you thought of using Kershaw electric as your gas, water and phone supplier?

7 Read your electricity meter at home every day for a week and record the readings in a table like this one:

Work out how much the week's electricity has cost (look back to pages 192–193 for help).

Day	Time	Reading	Change (kWh)	Cost (p)
Friday				
Saturday				
Sunday				
Monday				
Tuesday				
Wednesday				
Thursday				
Total change and cost for week:				

8 Use the following words to complete this paragraph about energy at home:

input, efficient, fuse, watts, watt, power, convection, output, kilowatt hours, flammable, joule, voltage, heat, electricity, energy, second, current, radiation, conduction, convenient, amperes, insulate

Different _____ sources are used at home for different reasons – batteries are expensive but _____, and gas is cheap but _____.

Power is a measure of how fast devices use energy. Power is measured in _____, where 1 ____ is equal to 1 _____ of energy each _____.

Electrical devices have labels on them so that you can find out their _____ rating and their _____. From these numbers you can work out how much _____ (measured in _____) flows into them, and so what size of ____ to use.

Electricity companies measure energy in larger units, called _____ _____, which cost about 8p each. You can read your _____ meter to see how much you use.

Heat energy moves by three methods, called _____, _____ and _____. If you _____ your house well, you can prevent a lot of your _____ loss.

Another way to avoid wasting energy is to use devices that are more _____ - this means that a larger amount of their _____ energy becomes useful _____ energy.

EXAM-STYLE QUESTIONS

1 Match these energy sources to their uses.

Energy source	Use
Lit match	To provide portable energy
Mobile phone battery	Growing crops
The sun	Light a fire
Hot spas	Warm water for health spas

(4)

2 A kettle is rated at 2kW.

a) What form of energy is transferred to the kettle from the national grid? (1)

b) What form of energy does the kettle mainly convert the energy to? (1)

c) How many joules of energy are transferred in 15 seconds? (3)

3 A plug connects an electrical device to the electricity supply.

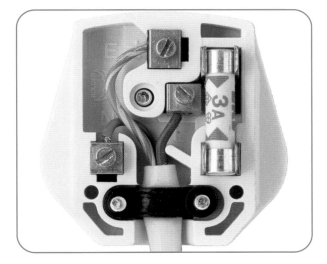

a) What does the fuse protect? (1)
b) How does the fuse work? (1)
c) The power rating of a device is 600 W. The voltage supplied to the device is 230 V. Calculate the current passing through the device when it is working normally. (3)
d) Charlie puts a 2 A fuse in the device. The device won't work. Explain why. (2)

4 Cassie uses a 900 W hairdryer for 30 minutes to dry her hair.

a) Calculate the cost of energy used if each unit is 8 p. (2)

b) She replaces her hairdryer with a more powerful 2 kW one. It only takes her 10 minutes to dry her hair now. Is it cheaper? (3)

5 In each of the three different situations below, movement of heat energy is important. State how heat is being transferred each time. (3)

A

B

C

11.1   Useful mixtures

1 Which useful mixtures do we use at home?
2 What are solutions, suspensions, gels, aerosols, foams and emulsions?

Mixtures are perhaps the most useful of all materials. Many of the substances in your home are really mixtures. Do you remember the definition of a mixture? (See page 125.)

A mixture is two or more substances that are combined, but not chemically bonded to each other. Seawater is an obvious example of a mixture. When you dissolve salt in water, no new substances are made. The salt and water just mix together. This means they are easy to separate.

a) How could you separate salt from seawater?
b) How would this process be different if you wanted to keep the water, and get rid of the salt?

There are different types of mixture, depending on which substances we mix together. The different types of mixture are:

- Solutions.
- Suspensions.
- Gels.
- Aerosols.
- Foams.
- Emulsions.

Why should we not really describe this as a pure substance?

What are the solvent, solute and solution here? Why is it easier to make coffee with hot water?

Solutions

A **solution** is the result of dissolving a substance in a liquid. We call the substance being dissolved a **solute**. The liquid it is dissolved in is called a **solvent**.

The solvent molecules get between the solute particles and free them from the particles next to them in the solid.

The movement of the liquid particles then spreads them evenly throughout the solution.

Suspensions

A **suspension** is what you get when you try to dissolve a powder of an insoluble solid in a liquid. It just sinks to the bottom, unless you stir or shake it up. If you do stir the mixture then the bits of solid spread throughout the liquid. If you add enough insoluble solid, you get a **paste**.

Gels

Have you ever used **gel** on your hair? A gel is really a liquid dissolved in a solid. The solid forms a framework with the liquid molecules spread out inside it.

Aerosols

An **aerosol** is a mixture of fine droplets of liquid or a powder spread out in a gas. We use spray cans to spread these mixtures where we want them.

c) Is a powder a solid, a liquid or a gas?

Foams

Foams are a good way of getting a liquid to take up a bigger space, by filling it with tiny bubbles of gas. An example of a liquid foam is shaving foam.

Foams are also useful as heat insulation, as it's difficult for heat to travel through the air-spaces. This is an example of a solid foam.

Emulsions

Emulsions are mixtures of liquids that don't dissolve in each other. The liquids are said to be **immiscible**, like oil and water.

You can usually tell a mixture is an emulsion if it separates into two layers of liquid when you let it stand for a while. Food scientists have to work out ways to keep the liquids mixed. Mayonnaise is an emulsion.

DID YOU KNOW?

Gelatin (the chemical used in jelly to make it a gel) comes from the bones, cartilage, connective tissue, and skin of cows and pigs.

You'd break your teeth if it wasn't a foam!

GET IT RIGHT!

Most of the exam questions you could get on this topic will be asking you to describe what type of mixture a particular material is.

TEST YOURSELF!

1 This table has been mixed up. Copy the headings and rearrange the information to summarise the key facts about mixtures.

Type of mixture	What's in the mixture?	Example
Aerosol	Immiscible liquids	Whipped cream
Emulsion	Gas with liquid suspended in it	Jelly
Foam	Solid with liquid dissolved inside it	Cola
Gel	Liquid with gas inside	Toothpaste
Solution	Liquid containing insoluble solid	Deodorant spray
Suspension	Liquid with solute dissolved in it	Correction fluid

2 What are the similarities and differences between a solution and a gel?

3 Orange squash bottles have 'shake before use' printed on them. What type of mixture does this form?

4 Using the information on this spread, try to sketch the structures of the six types of mixture, showing how the particles are arranged.

11.2   Mixtures in the home

LEARNING OBJECTIVES

1 Can you give examples of each type of mixture?
2 How does the composition of a mixture make it useful?

Some chemists have a very interesting job. They have to design mixtures to do a particular job. Then they test their new mixtures to see which works best.

Here, we will look at specific examples of mixtures and how they do their jobs.

Soluble aspirin

Soluble medicines are great for people who either can't or don't like taking tablets or capsules. By dissolving aspirin in water, you make it easier to swallow. Not only that, because it's already dissolved it's more easily absorbed by the body.

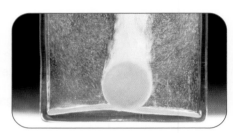
A solution for a headache

a) What other medicines come in soluble form?

Juicy bits

Orange squash or juice which claims to have 'juicy bits' is an example of a **suspension**. The solid part of the drink sinks to the bottom, and needs to be shaken up to spread it around the liquid.

Toothpaste

If toothpaste was a liquid, it would be hard to keep it on your brush. If it was a solid, it wouldn't be able to do its job as well. Because it is a suspension, it has some of the properties of a solid. For instance, it keeps its shape when you squeeze it out of the tube.

It also has some of the properties of liquids, though. For example, its particles are free to move around when you're brushing. Insoluble substances like cellulose (from plant cell walls) are used to thicken the product.

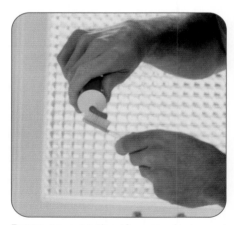
Pastes are examples of suspensions

Shaving foam

Like toothpaste, shaving foam wouldn't be as useful if it was just a liquid. It needs to have a thicker texture so it sticks to whatever's being shaved. Having bubbles helps to give it this texture.

b) What other bathroom products produce foams?

Wall cavity insulation

Foams are also used to stop heat loss, save money and reduce fuel use, because they are such good insulators. Liquid foam can be squirted into the gap between the inner and outer walls of a house. When it solidifies, the trapped air makes it more difficult for heat energy to escape through the wall.

Aerosols

Aerosols are very important for delivering substances. They are also good for getting a liquid to spread out evenly over a large area. A gas diffuses to fill the size of its container, so if it's carrying a liquid (or sometimes a powder), then that gets spread around as well.

Hair gel

The combination of liquid and solid in hair gel makes it easier to apply than just liquid. Also, when the liquid part of the gel dries up it leaves the solid framework behind. Then this supports the hairstyle.

Mayonnaise

Mayonnaise is an emulsion of vinegar (or lemon juice) and oil. Normally, these two substances don't mix. They separate into layers because they're immiscible. Mayonnaise recipes use egg yolk as an '**emulsifying agent**'; it allows the oil and vinegar to mix freely. The result – a thick cream, and lots of calories! Other foods containing a lot of fat or oil, such as chocolate, contain emulsifying agents. These keep the ingredients mixed up together. They stop them separating out into layers again.

GET IT RIGHT!

It's important to remember that the word aerosol doesn't just mean 'spray can'. It means any liquid or powder suspended in a gas.

Created by hair gel!

TEST YOURSELF!

1 Copy and complete this paragraph using the following words:

> **hair gel   deodorant   mixtures   emulsions   coffee**
> **evaporates   aerosols   toothpaste   foams**

_____ are an important class of everyday chemicals we see around

us. ____ ____ is a liquid trapped inside a solid; when the liquid

_____, the solid is left behind on the hair. Hair spray and _____

are examples of _____; these mixtures are used for delivering

chemicals to target areas. Other everyday mixtures are _____

(e.g. mayonnaise), _____ (e.g. whipped cream). Examples of solutions

and suspensions are _____ and _____.

2 How could you identify the following just by looking?
   a) A suspension.
   b) A foam.
   c) An aerosol.

3 Why are special foam tiles used in making the outside of the space shuttle?

11.3 Different solvents for different jobs

LEARNING OBJECTIVE

1 Can you give some examples of solvents and their use?

Scientists have to work hard to find the right solvent to dissolve a solid in. Otherwise, they end up with a suspension – and all the solid sinks to the bottom. Choosing solvents is also important for cleaning purposes, and solvents are important in paints and perfumes.

How do solvents work?

A solvent needs to be able to break down the structure of the solid being dissolved. So, the type of chemical being dissolved is the starting point for deciding which solvent to use.

Chemicals with an ionic structure (see page 163) often dissolve in water. This is because water has slight positive and negative charges at each end. The oxygen atom in each water molecule attracts the positive ions. The hydrogen atoms attract the negative ions. This pulls the solid apart.

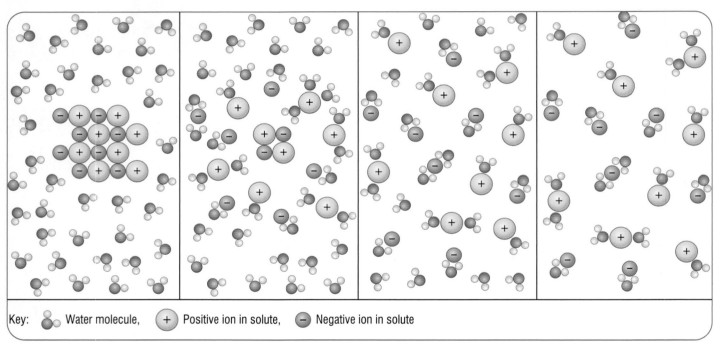

Key: Water molecule, (+) Positive ion in solute, (−) Negative ion in solute

Solvents at work

It's different for non-polar chemicals like oil. These substances have no positive and negative parts of their molecules. Water has little effect on their structure. For these chemicals, we need a solvent with different properties, like ethanol, or acetone.

Solvent chemistry is based on the idea that 'like dissolves like'. For a solvent to be useful, it needs to have characteristics similar to those of the chemical it is trying to dissolve.

a) Increasing temperature often makes solvents work faster. Can you explain why?

Organic solvents

Most of the time, scientists use the word solvent to describe **organic solvents**. Organic chemicals are chemicals containing carbon. Some of these chemicals are very harmful, causing chemical burns or even cancer.

Name of solvent	Uses
Ethanol (alcohol)	Perfume and aftershave
Acetone, propanone and ethyl ethanoate	Nail polish remover
Hexane	Stain remover
Tetrachloroethene	Dry cleaning

Solvents in paints

In paints, solvents are used to dissolve coloured chemicals called **pigments**. When the paint is applied, the solvent evaporates, leaving behind a film of dry pigment.

The same idea works for removing paint. A solvent similar to the original one is added, so the pigment dissolves again. This is how nail polish remover works, too.

Are solvents as interesting as watching paint dry?

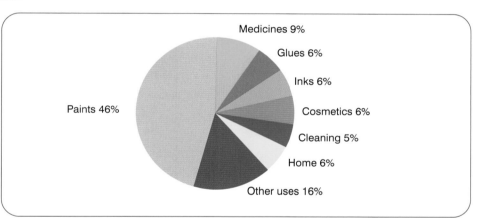

Medicines 9%
Glues 6%
Inks 6%
Cosmetics 6%
Cleaning 5%
Home 6%
Other uses 16%
Paints 46%

Uses of solvents

(Source: Solvent Industry Association: www.sia-uk.org.uk)

> **DID YOU KNOW?**
>
> The solvents industry employs more than 10 million people in Europe.

b) What is the advantage of making paints with solvents that evaporate easily?

> **KEY FACTS**
>
> * Solvents dissolve substances by breaking their solid structure apart.
> * The best solvent for the job has similar properties to the solute.
> * The main user of solvents is the paint industry.

> **TEST YOURSELF!**
>
> 1 How does water dissolve ionic compounds like salt?
> 2 Name three organic solvents.
> 3 Which solvent could you use to remove a grease stain from a shirt – ethanol or water?

11.4

When mixtures separate

Not all mixtures will stay the same if left alone for a long time. Some will start to separate a little; others will separate completely.

Shake well

Like orange squash, lots of products you find around your home have this label on them. This is because they are suspensions. You need to shake up the bottle so the solids in the drink are spread out evenly. Otherwise, the insoluble material would just sink to the bottom.

Some mixtures need re-mixing

a) If you didn't shake the orange squash, what would happen to its concentration as you got further down the bottle?
b) Some medicines are suspensions. Use your answer to (a) to explain why it's so important to shake them before use?

Replace cap after use

Fizzy drinks like cola and lemonade get their 'fizz' from dissolved carbon dioxide. If you leave the cap off a cola bottle, it goes 'flat'. This is because the dissolved carbon dioxide gas can escape from the solution.

c) Why can't the flavourings come out of the solution in the same way?

Pens, glues and toothpaste are other mixtures that last longer if kept sealed.

d) Which part of the mixture is able to escape from:
   i)   A marker pen?
   ii) A glue stick?
   iii) Toothpaste?

The lid keeps the solvent from evaporating

Separating mixtures

Scientists often need to separate mixtures on purpose. This is usually to purify substances.

We need information about the mixture when deciding which separation method to use. This includes: its state (solid, liquid or gas), the size of the particles, the boiling point and solubility.

Separation method	What can it separate?	Why does it work
Evaporation	Solutions, suspensions, gels (to collect the solid)	The solvent has a lower boiling point than the solute or solid
Distillation	Solutions (to collect the liquid)	The solvent has a lower boiling point than the solute
Filtration	Suspensions	Groups of insoluble suspended solid particles are bigger than liquid particles
Chromatography	Solutions with many solutes	Different solute particles have different solubilities. So they are carried different distances through a material that a solvent moves through
Sieving	Suspensions of solids	Clusters of solid particles are different sizes

GET IT RIGHT!

Exam questions on this topic will ask you to identify the type of mixture in a substance and explain how to separate it.

KEY FACTS

When some mixtures are left undisturbed or are left open to the atmosphere, we can get:

- Settling of suspensions.
- Escape of gas from solutions.
- Evaporation of solvents.
- Separation of emulsions, like salad dressing.

TEST YOURSELF!

1 Name two products that need to be shaken before you use them.
2 The following diagrams show how mixtures can be separated. Match the diagrams to the separation methods in the table above.

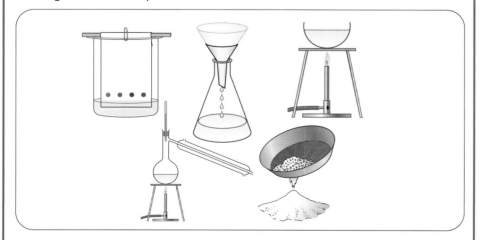

3 Plan an experiment to see if diet cola loses its fizz sooner than regular cola.

11.5   Dangerous mixtures

Organic solvents

Organic solvents

Organic solvents are great at dissolving fats – this includes the fats in your body!

Every cell in your body has a cell membrane containing fats, which means that organic solvents destroy cells. Coming into contact with an organic solvent is *very* dangerous, because your body can quickly absorb it.

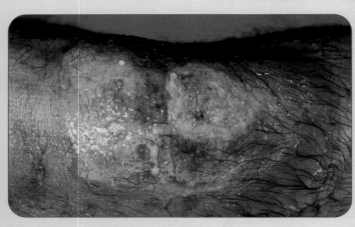

A chemical burn

Does your school's science department have special rules for disposing of organic solvents?

The Environment Agency has produced the 'Solvents Code' to reduce the environmental risk of industries using solvents. Their advice is to have:

- Sufficient space for moving and using solvents.
- Impermeable surfaces (surfaces that don't let liquids through) and secondary containment.
- Well positioned and maintained pipe-work.
- Good management of site traffic to avoid congestion.
- Good security to reduce the risk of vandalism.

Activities

a) Can you think of a reason for each of these pieces of advice?

b) Use the 'Solvents Code' to produce an information leaflet for solvents industries.

c) Explain the reasons behind each rule, and try to give suggestions to help companies follow them.

Aerosol cans

You saw on page 207 why aerosols are useful, but they can also be a problem.

Aerosol cans use chemicals called 'propellants'. Propellants pressurise the can so the aerosol mixture squirts out when you press the nozzle.

CFCs (chlorofluorocarbons) were once a common type of propellant, and have caused huge environmental problems for the planet because they destroy ozone.

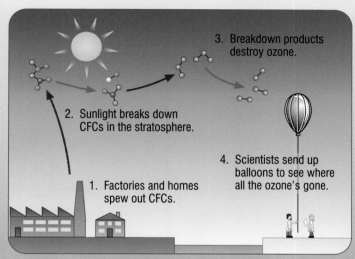

3. Breakdown products destroy ozone.

2. Sunlight breaks down CFCs in the stratosphere.

4. Scientists send up balloons to see where all the ozone's gone.

1. Factories and homes spew out CFCs.

How CFCs in aerosols can damage the ozone layer

Ozone is a gas in the Earth's atmosphere that absorbs harmful radiation from the Sun – without it, the Sun's radiation can cause sunburn and skin cancer.

One molecule of CFC gas is able to destroy more than 100 000 ozone molecules. Right now, there is a hole in the ozone layer the size of Australia!

Activities

a) What parts of the world have been most affected by the destruction of the ozone layer?

b) What chemicals are replacing CFCs in aerosol cans?

c) What other things do humans do that add CFCs to the atmosphere?

Fizzy mixtures

Cola is a great example of a mixture you might find in your home. It was invented in 1885, and was originally used as a medicine. Its name came from the kola nuts in the ingredients. Dozens of ingredients are used to flavour cola now, including: orange, lemon, nutmeg, vanilla, lime, lavender and coriander.

The major cola companies keep their exact recipes a strict secret. Some companies even store their secret formula in a locked vault!

What's the secret?

Activities

a) What type of mixture is cola?

b) Cola contains all three states of matter: solid, liquid and gas. Which gas is used in cola? How do the manufacturers get it in?

c) Research the creation of cola – find out why early cola was said to have cocaine in it.

SUMMARY QUESTIONS

1 What is the difference between a compound and a mixture?

2 The label below is from a bottle of cold remedy.

Mellman's non-drowsy decongestant

Dose: 2 x 5ml spoons every 4 hours
Do not exceed 4 doses in one day
Active ingredient: Pseudoephedrine
Also contains caffeine

For ages 12 and up

Shake well before use

a) Which type of mixture is the medicine?

b) Which piece of information on the label helped you answer part a)?

3 Instant coffee is made by adding coffee granules to hot water. In a cup of coffee:

a) What is the solvent?

b) What is the solute?

c) Why do the coffee granules dissolve?

4 a) Name two household products that are foams.

b) Which two states of matter are mixed in a foam?

5 Which of these diagrams shows:

a) How to find out which coloured dyes are in a marker pen?

b) How to remove solid particles from orange squash?

c) How to get a pure sample of salt from salty water?

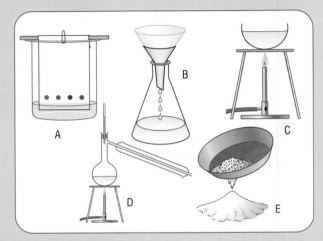

Some separation methods

6 Explain how you could find out how much solid is present in a 10 g sample of toothpaste.

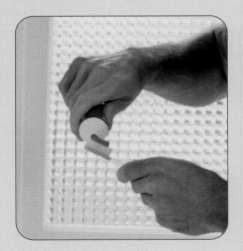

EXAM-STYLE QUESTIONS

1 A designer was asked to design a wrist rest for people working at a keyboard. He made some from gel and some from foam. The gel wrist rests were the most popular.

   a) i) What is the correct definition of a gel? Choose A, B or C. (1)
      A Two liquids mixed together but not dissolved.
      B Liquid filled with gas.
      C A liquid trapped inside a solid structure.
   ii) Why do you think gel wrist rests were more popular than foam? (1)
   iii) Some gels are also used in the manufacture of a baby's nappy. Suggest a property that these gels have. (1)

   b) i) Foams can either be in a solid or liquid form. Give an example of a liquid foam used in the home. (1)
   ii) What is the advantage of the mixture being in the liquid form? (1)

2 The information on a product label can often tell you what type of mixture it is.

   Read the following labels:

A
| Carbonated water |
| Glucose |
| Lemon juice |
| Citric acid |
| Flavourings |
| Preservative |

B
| Vinegar |
| Tarragon |
| SHAKE WELL BEFORE USE |

   a) i) A is a solution. What is a solution? (1)
   ii) Name a solid dissolved in A used to sweeten the liquid. (1)
   iii) Name a gas found in A used to make it fizzy. (1)
   iv) Suggest what type of mixture B is. (1)
   v) Give a reason for your choice. (1)

3 Paint has many uses around the home and in industry.

   a) Suggest why metal surfaces are often painted. (2)

   b) i) Some paints are called emulsions. What is an emulsion? (1)
   ii) How could you tell if a mixture was an emulsion? (1)

   c) Paint can be applied to a surface using an aerosol or brush.
   i) What is an aerosol? (2)
   ii) Which would be the best method for painting a car. Explain your anwer. (2)

   d) Aerosol cans should never be put into a fire. What does this suggest about the gas used as a propellant in a spray can? (1)

4 Solvents are used in many industries.

   a) i) What is known as the universal solvent? (1)
   ii) Organic solvents are used in paints. What element do these solvents all contain? (1)
   iii) Name another product that contains an organic solvent. (1)

   b) People who work in the solvent industry are given safety guidelines. The following information appeared in a leaflet given to workers in the dry cleaning industry.

   'Make full use of the ventilation equipment provided.
   Do not smoke or use any naked lights.
   Use the minimum amount of solvent for the job and keep lids on containers.
   Avoid skin contact.'

   What three properties of solvents are indicated by these guidelines? (3)

5 a) Explain the changes that can occur to

   A – lemonade
   B – perfume
   when they are left open to the atmosphere. (4)

   b) Explain the changes that occur to

   A – paint
   B – orange squash
   when they are left undisturbed. (4)

6 Inks can be made by dissolving a pigment (coloured chemical) in a suitable solvent.

   a) Describe what happens to the particles in a solid pigment as it dissolves in a solvent. (2)

   b) Some ink has been spilled on a tabletop. You have tried to clean it off using water but it didn't work. Name two other solvents you could use to clean the ink off. (2)

   c) Organic solvents can be very harmful. Why? (1)

4 | Transport and Communications

In this section you will learn about:

Moving

- Velocity.
- Acceleration.
- Stopping distances.
- Safe driving.

Fuels for transport

- Types of fuel.
- Combustion – when fuels burn.
- Efficiency of engines.
- Transport pollution.
- Alternative fuels.

Communications

- Infra-red and ultra-violet light.
- Using waves to communicate.
- Gamma rays and X-rays.
- Fibre-optics.
- Radio waves and microwaves.
- Astronomical observations.
- How the Universe began.

This section is tested by examination

Vehicle designer

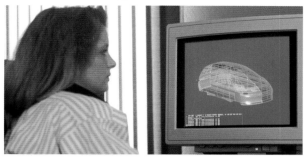

"Vehicles don't just happen – they are the products of inspired imaginations."

Medical physicist

"There's huge variety in what I do – from Radiotherapy and Radioprotection to Nuclear Medicine and Radiology. And Physics is being used in more and more areas in medicine – like blood flow measurements and bone strength analysis."

Telecommunications engineer

"The customer just needs a phone that works. It's my job to understand the technology behind it – the microwaves and the optical fibres, as well as the wires!"

Career opportunities

Alternative fuels researcher

"We have been developing a small inexpensive aircraft powered on renewable fuels, designed to investigate air pollution with a miniaturised instrument package."

Traffic police

"It's not about catching people – it's about making it safe for people to travel. To do that, we need to measure people's speed – and control it."

Astronomer

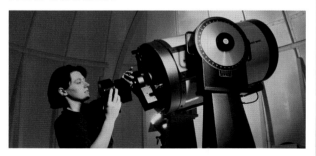

"It has to be the best job on the planet ... discovering new stars and planets – and trying to work out the origins and fate of the universe! Big Stuff!"

12.1   Vehicle velocity

In the UK, we have **speed** limits on all of our roads. You have probably seen signs like these, that tell us how fast we are allowed to drive in an area:

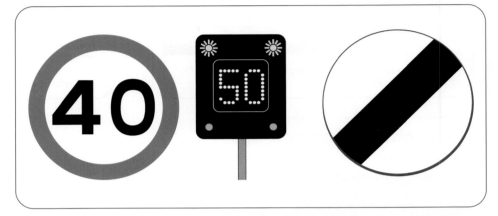

Three road signs

GET IT RIGHT!

The two words **velocity** and **speed** mean almost the same thing. The only difference is that **velocity** describes the **direction** you are going in, as well as your speed.

a) What do these three signs tell you? Where would you normally see each one?

Speedy units

All three signs above tell you the speed limits in **miles per hour** (mph). This is the **unit** we use to measure road speed in the UK.

Most other European countries describe their road distances in **kilometres** – and so they measure their speeds in **kilometres per hour (km/h)**. If you look on the speedometer of a car, you can compare mph with kph:

A speedometer

b) What speed does the speedometer above show, i) in mph and ii) in km/h?

When scientists want to know the **velocity** (or speed) of a vehicle, they need to make **two** measurements first. They need to know how far the vehicle has travelled (the **distance**) and how long it took to travel that distance (the **time**).

To work out the velocity, you can use the **formula**:

$$\textbf{velocity (m/s)} = \frac{\textbf{distance travelled (m)}}{\textbf{time (s)}}$$

Notice that, because distance is measured in **metres** and time is in **seconds**, velocity is measured in **metres per second (m/s)**.

Comparing units

Have a look at this table, so you can see how speeds measured in the three different units compare:

Description	Miles per hour (mph)	Kilometres per hour (km/h)	Metres per second (m/s)
Walking	4.5	7	2
Sprinting	22	i)	10
Driving in town	30	48	13.5
Motorway driving	70	110	30
Train	ii)	145	40
Fastest cyclist	125	200	iii)
Formula I race	iv)	320	90
Jet plane	550	885	245

Land-speed record attempt vehicle

c) What are the missing speeds in this table (use the speedometer on the previous page to help you).

Distance and time

If you know how fast a vehicle is going, you can work out how far it will go in a certain time:

$$\text{distance travelled (m)} = \text{velocity (m/s)} \times \text{time (s)}$$

...or how long it will take to go a certain distance:

$$\text{time (s)} = \frac{\text{distance travelled (m)}}{\text{velocity (m/s)}}$$

For example, a sprinter running at 10 m/s for 5 seconds will run:

$$
\begin{aligned}
\text{distance travelled} &= \text{velocity} \times \text{time} \\
&= 10 \text{ m/s} \times 5 \text{ s} \\
&= \underline{50 \text{ m}}
\end{aligned}
$$

GET IT RIGHT!

1 kilometre is 1000 metres.

1 minute is 60 seconds.

1 hour is 60 minutes.

Remember to read questions carefully – you often need to change kilometres into metres and hours into minutes or seconds.

TEST YOURSELF!

1 Say whether each of these statements is **true** or **false**:
a) Trains travel faster than cars.
b) 120 km/h is faster than 80 mph.
c) The fastest cyclist could break the motorway speed limit.

2 What is the average speed of a cyclist who cycles 800 metres in 40 seconds?

3 A car travels at 15 m/s.
a) How far will it travel in 30 s?
b) How far will it travel in 5 minutes?
c) How long will it take to travel 90 m?

4 A train covers 400 metres in 10 seconds.
a) What is its velocity?
b) How far will it travel in 1 minute?
c) How long will it take to travel 2 km?

12.2   Automobile acceleration

LEARNING OBJECTIVES

1 What is 'acceleration' and 'deceleration'?
2 How can we work out acceleration?

A racing car

GET IT RIGHT!

To work out the change in velocity, you take the old speed away from the new one (see worked example).

If a vehicle is slowing down (decelerating), the change in speed is **negative**.

When you are speeding up you are **accelerating** and when you are slowing down, you are **decelerating**. Both are changes in velocity and can be worked out using this formula:

$$\text{acceleration (m/s}^2) = \frac{\text{change in velocity (m/s)}}{\text{time taken for change (s)}}$$

Notice that acceleration is measured in **m/s²** – said as "metres per second squared". Watch out …! This equation only works for vehicles travelling in a straight line and accelerating constantly.

Acceleration tells you how quickly speed changes. That is why you work it out using how much the speed has changed and how long it took to change.

Worked example

A runner in a long distance race breaks into a sprint for the last 100 metres. She takes 2 seconds to speed up from 6 m/s to 10 m/s. What is her acceleration?

Change in velocity = 10 – 6 = 4 m/s   Time for change = 2 s

So her acceleration = $\frac{4}{2}$ = $\underline{2 \text{ m/s}^2}$

(Notice how all workings are shown here – if you do this, you will be more likely to get all the marks for a question.)

---

a) A car accelerates from 10 m/s to 30 m/s in 5 s. What was its acceleration?
b) A car is driving at 30 m/s. It needs to stop in 3 seconds. What will its deceleration have to be?

Car performance statistics

Car manufacturers spend a lot of money advertising cars. One piece of information they like to use is how quickly the car can go from 0 to 60 mph (0–100 km/h) – in other words, its acceleration.

A Vauxhall Astra

This table shows some important statistics for four cars:

Car make	0–60 mph (0–100 km/h) /seconds	Top speed/km/h	Fuel consumption mpg
Vauxhall *Astra*	13.50 s	172 km/h	61.41 mpg
Ford *Focus*	12.50 s	183 km/h	51.36 mpg
Nissan *Almera*	18.80 s	185 km/h	37.55 mpg
Ford *Puma*	8.80 s	203 km/h	38.17 mpg

c) Which of these four cars has the best acceleration? (Think!)

d) Is the car with the highest acceleration the best one to buy? What does the other information in the table tell you?

Designing for high acceleration

When car designers are trying to make a car with a rapid acceleration, they have to consider a range of factors that include:

- Mass of the car.

- Engine power.

- Streamlining (aerodynamics).

Think about how these factors affect each of the cars in the table above.

e) Use these ideas to explain why motorcycles have higher accelerations than lorries.

GET IT RIGHT!

When an exam question asks you to work out acceleration, it will usually be in m/s^2.

However, you can use the basic ideas with any of the units – the highest acceleration means the biggest change in speed in the smallest time.

TEST YOURSELF!

1 Copy and complete the following sentences using these words:

acceleration   deceleration   time   velocity

Speeding up is called _____ and slowing down is called _____. Both of these involve a change in _____ (or speed) in a certain ____.

2 Which of the following units are right for a) speed, b) acceleration and c) distance?

m   m/s   m/s²

3 Which has the greatest acceleration – a motorcycle going from 10 m/s to 40 m/s in 3 s or a car going from 20 m/s to 40 m/s in 2.5 s? (Show your working out.)

12.3   Stopping distances

LEARNING OBJECTIVE

1 What affects the stopping distances of cars?

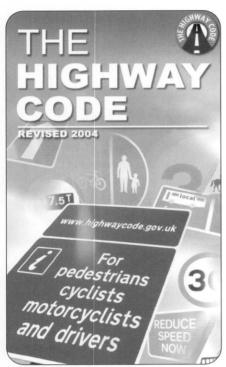

The Highway Code

It is important for drivers to accelerate and drive quickly at times. It is even more important to be able to stop when you want to.

The **Highway Code** is a booklet written to help people use the roads safely. Its rules apply to all road users: drivers, motorcyclists, cyclists, pedestrians, as well as horse riders.

This is what the Highway Code has to say about stopping distances:

Stopping distances

105: Drive at a speed that will allow you to stop well within the distance you can see to be clear. You should:

- leave enough space between you and the vehicle in front so that you can pull up safely if it suddenly slows down or stops. The safe rule is never to get closer than the overall stopping distance (see Typical Stopping Distances diagram on next page)
- allow at least a two-second gap between you and the vehicle in front on roads carrying fast traffic. The gap should be at least doubled on wet roads and increased still further on icy roads
- remember, large vehicles and motorcycles need a greater distance to stop.

Use a fixed point to help measure a two second gap.

---

a) The diagram below (from the Highway Code) demonstrates the two-second rule. Explain the important points shown in the diagram.

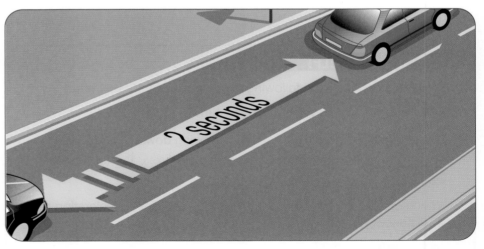

The two-second rule   (Source: The Highway Code)

b) Why should the gap you leave be longer when the weather is bad or for other types of vehicle?

What affects stopping distance?

When you are driving along and need to stop suddenly, there are two sets of factors that affect how far you travel before you stop:

- **Human factors** – these affect your reaction time, which affects how far you travel before you even put the brakes on. This is called the **thinking distance**.
- **Mechanical factors** – these affect how well the brakes work to stop you, or how far you travel after the brakes are put on. This is called the **braking distance**.

The figure below is from the Highway Code. It shows how **thinking distance** and **braking distance** combine to form a **total stopping distance** at different speeds:

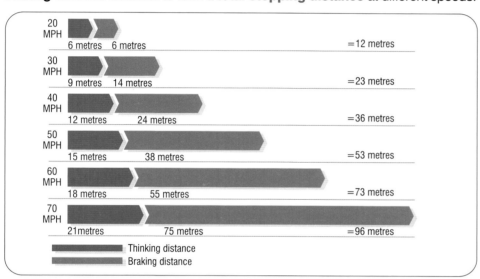

Table from the Highway Code showing stopping distances   (Source: The Highway Code)

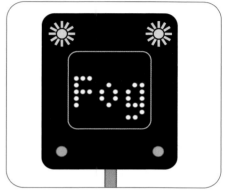
c) Here is a list of some factors that affect stopping distance. Explain why each one has an effect – and whether it affects thinking distance, stopping distance or both:

- using a mobile phone
- type of road surface
- a tired driver
- the speed of the vehicle
- how heavily loaded the vehicle is
- condition of the brakes and tyres
- weather conditions (e.g. wet/icy roads)
- drinking alcohol or taking drugs

TEST YOURSELF!

1 **True** or **false**? (Explain your answers.)
  a) Drinking alcohol improves your stopping distance.
  b) Wet roads increase your braking distance.
  c) Heavy vehicles take longer to stop.
  d) Faster cars have shorter stopping distances.
  e) Friction affects your braking distance.

2 A few years ago, a road safety advert used the phrase 'only a fool breaks the two-second rule'. What were they trying to say?

3 Why is it important for drivers to understand what the Highway Code has to say about stopping distances? Include examples in your answer.

12.4   Safe driving

LEARNING OBJECTIVES

1 What affects a driver's reaction time?
2 How can we try to improve transport safety?

Vehicle testing station logo

Accidents on the roads cause many deaths each year. Some of the ways we try to improve transport safety include:

- A qualification test for drivers.
- Road safety signs.
- The breathalyser test.
- MOT tests on older vehicles.

a) Explain how each of the four points listed above helps to improve road safety.

It is fairly obvious that if you are tired, or have been using drugs or alcohol, your reaction times will be slower. The Highway Code also says that ...

> **126: Safe driving needs concentration.**
>
> Avoid distractions when driving such as:
>
> - loud music (this may mask other sounds)
> - trying to read maps
> - inserting a cassette or CD or tuning a radio
> - arguing with your passengers or other road users
> - eating and drinking.

b) Why do you think the Highway Code needs to mention all of these other factors?
c) How might tiredness also affect concentration and therefore safe driving?

One problem that has increased a lot over the last few years is the use of mobile phones by drivers. This is what the Highway Code says about this issue (it also refers to the laws about it):

Highway code logo

> **Mobile phones and in-car technology**
>
> **127:** You MUST exercise proper control of your vehicle at all times. You MUST NOT use a hand-held mobile phone, or similar device, when driving or when supervising a learner driver, except to call 999 or 112 in a genuine emergency when it is unsafe or impractical to stop. Never use a hand-held microphone when driving. Using hands free equipment is also likely to distract your attention from the road. It is far safer not to use any telephone while you are driving – find a safe place to stop first.
>
> *Laws RTA 1988 sects 2 & 3 & CUR regs 104 & 110*

 Is it safe to use a 'hands-free' phone when driving? Discuss.

Alcohol and drugs

There are a large number of accidents every year that are caused by drivers who have been using alcohol or drugs. So there are very strict laws and penalties for anyone caught.

Look at the table shown on the right:

 Do you think the penalties shown in this table are fair? Do you think they should be more or less severe? Discuss.

Why is alcohol a problem?

Alcohol can affect different people in different ways, but there are certain effects that it almost always has.

Alcohol will...

- Give a false sense of confidence.
- Reduce coordination and slow down reactions.
- Affect judgement of speed, distance and risk.
- Reduce your driving ability, even if you are below the legal limit.
- Take time to leave your body; you may be unfit to drive in the evening after drinking at lunchtime, or in the morning after drinking the previous evening.

The effects of other drugs and medicine are unpredictable. However, they can be even more severe than alcohol and also result in many serious road accidents.

d) What are sedatives? How will they affect your driving?

Drink driving and the law

If you are convicted of:	The maximum penalty is:
Causing death by careless driving when under the influence of drink or drugs.	14 years imprisonment, banned from driving for at least 2 years and required to take an extended driving test.
Driving or attempting to drive whilst above the legal limit or unfit through drink.	6 months imprisonment, plus a fine of £5,000 and banned from driving for at least 12 months (3 years if you're convicted twice in 10 years).
In charge of a vehicle whilst over the legal limit or unfit through drink.	3 months imprisonment, plus a fine of £2,500 and a ban from driving.
Refusing to provide a specimen of breath, blood or urine for analysis.	6 months imprisonment, plus a fine of £5,000 and banned from driving for at least 12 months.

Drink driving and the law

GET IT RIGHT!

When you answer an exam question, remember …

'Alcohol' doesn't affect your driving... 'drinking alcohol' does!

TEST YOURSELF!

1 Which of these shouldn't you do when you are driving? Explain your answers.
   a) Drink wine.
   b) Eat a sandwich.
   c) Answer a phone call.
   d) Use a hands-free kit.
   e) Read a map.
   f) Take a sleeping pill.

2 Why do you think the introduction of the MOT test for older cars has led to a reduction in the number of road accidents that happen each year?

3 Road traffic accidents are often described as having both 'actual costs' and 'human costs'. Use examples to explain what this means.

12.5　Speeding up and slowing down

When someone steps out in front of you,
30 mph suddenly doesn't feel that slow...

At 30 mph, you can stop...
...here

What about at 35 mph?

Just this five mph faster would add an extra
six metres onto your stopping distance.

Not just that... you would hit the pedestrian - and still
be travelling fast enough to hit the child at 17 mph.

It's 30 for a reason!

Remember – even the best driver in the world can't stop any sooner.
The faster you go, the longer it takes to stop – and just that extra
5 mph increases that stopping distance from 23 m to 29 m.

'Think! Slow down' poster

A road safety campaign

The poster on the left was produced as part of a campaign to make people drive more slowly in built-up areas.

Activities

a) Look back to the stopping distance table on page 223. What are the total stopping distances for a car at i) 30 mph and ii) 40 mph?

b) The stopping distances given assume that all conditions are good. What conditions might make the car take even longer to stop?

c) What are the two most important parts of a car to check in order to stop in as short a distance as possible?

Driving in adverse weather

202: In wet weather, stopping distances will be at least double those required for stopping on dry roads. This is because your tyres have less grip on the road. In wet weather:

- you should keep well back from the vehicle in front. This will increase your ability to see and plan ahead
- if the steering becomes unresponsive, it probably means that water is preventing the tyres from gripping the road. Ease off the accelerator and slow down gradually
- the rain and spray from vehicles may make it difficult to see and be seen.

205: When driving in icy or snowy weather:

- drive with care, even if the roads have been gritted
- keep well back from the vehicle in front as stopping distances can be ten times greater than on dry roads
- take care when overtaking gritting vehicles, particularly if you are riding a motorcycle
- watch out for snowploughs which may throw out snow on either side. Do not overtake them unless the lane you intend to use has been cleared
- be prepared for the road conditions changing over relatively short distances.

Read Highway Code sections 202 and 205 on the left.

Activity

Bad weather doesn't just affect stopping distances. Think about what other problems are caused by:

a) Wet weather?
b) Icy weather?

How fast should I drive?

The Highway Code includes the following table showing maximum speeds for vehicles:

Activities

a) Give two reasons why the speed limits are lower in built-up areas than on motorways.

b) Why do you think larger vehicles have lower speed limits than smaller ones do?

Speed limits	Built-up Areas	Single carriage-ways	Dual carriage-ways	Motorways
Type of vehicle	MPH	MPH	MPH	MPH
Cars and motorcycles	30	60	70	70
Cars towing caravans or trailers	30	50	60	60
Buses and coaches	30	50	60	70
Goods vehicles (not exceeding 7.5 tonnes)	30	50	60	70
Goods vehicles (exceeding 7.5 tonnes)	30	40	50	60

Table showing speed limits on different roads

How speed cameras work (even when they don't!)

If you drive a car, there's a good chance that you worry about getting caught by a speed camera. As you see the warning signs, you make sure you are within the speed limit and wonder if there is really a camera there – but do you ever wonder about how the speed cameras work? There are several different kinds of speed camera:

- Some can detect the speed you are travelling at by using radar. If they detect that you are travelling above the speed limit, they take a photograph and save the information about your speed. These radar cameras are often set up at accident 'black spots' to make people slow down.
- Time-and-distance cameras measure how long you take to travel between two checkpoints and then calculate your speed over that distance. In many places, like Northamptonshire, Nottingham and the M6, these are permanent, but the police sometimes set up temporary cameras in different places.
- The large yellow box cameras are either connected to a radar detector or to induction loops buried in the road. These take two pictures that show how far you travel between the flashes, so that your speed can be worked out.

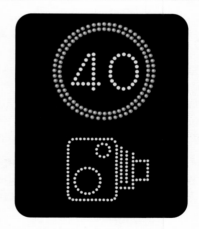

40 mph speed limit and speed camera signs

Most speed cameras are set to take a photo only if you are travelling more than 10% above the speed limit – but as technology improves, there's no reason why you can't be fined for driving only slightly too fast.

Funnily enough, speed cameras can have a calming effect even when they are not there. Drivers know that there are often speed camera signs, but no cameras – we all slow down, just in case. When a set of cameras were recently installed on the A6, just south of Bedford, drivers started slowing down before the bin bag covers were even taken off the cameras!

Activities

a) Use diagrams to describe how speed cameras work out how fast you are driving.

b) What speed will usually trigger a speed camera in a 30 mph area?

SUMMARY QUESTIONS

1 a) Write down the formula used to calculate velocity.

   b) How fast is a car travelling if it covers 160 metres in 4 seconds?

   c) Which is faster, a car that travels 90 metres in 3 seconds or a bicycle that travels 50 metres in 2 seconds?

2 A sprinter runs at a speed of 9 m/s.

   a) How far would he run in 1 minute?

   b) How long would it take him to run 1 kilometre?

   c) If he slowed down and only covered 300 metres in the next minute, how fast would he be running then?

3 a) Write down the formula used to calculate acceleration.

   b) What is the proper name for a 'negative acceleration' – a slowing down?

   c) If a motorcycle accelerates from 10 m/s to a velocity of 30 m/s in 5 seconds, what is its acceleration.

   d) When you drop an object, it accelerates at 10 m/s². How fast will it be falling after 3 seconds?

4 A car can accelerate at 3 m/s².

   a) What will its velocity be after 5 seconds?

   b) How long will it take to reach a speed of 30 m/s?

5 At 30 m/s, a car can decelerate at 4 m/s². At 60 m/s it can only decelerate at an average of 1 m/s².

   a) Calculate how long it takes to stop from these two speeds.

   b) Why is the effective braking force less at higher speeds?

6 Explain the difference between 'thinking distance' and 'braking distance'. How are these two distances linked?

7 Explain how each of these three tests helps to improve road safety:

   a) MOT test.

   b) Breathalyser test.

   c) Driver's eye-sight test.

8 The Highway Code advises against using any mobile phones while driving. Why are hands-free kits not safe to use?

9 Copy and complete the following sentences using these words:

metres per second squared, time, accelerating, change, thinking, time taken, distance, miles per hour, metres per second, kilometres per hour, speed, decelerating, velocity, safety, braking, MOT, Highway, road, reaction

Velocity is another word for _____. It can be measured in ____ ___ ____ (mph), in _____ ___ ____ (km/h) – or _____ ___ _____ (m/s). To work out the velocity of a vehicle, you need to divide the _____ it travels by the ____ it takes.

Speeding up is called _____. Slowing down is called _____. Acceleration is measured in _____ ___ _____ _____ (m/s²) and can be worked out by dividing the _____ in _____ by the ____ _____ for that change.

The total distance a car travels when it stops is made up of two parts. The _____ distance is how far it travels during the driver's _____ time. The further distance travelled after the brakes are put on is called the _____ distance.

Much is done to make driving safer, including: ___ tests for cars, road _____ signs, and the _____ Code is published to give advice on ____ safety.

EXAM-STYLE QUESTIONS

1 An athlete runs a 100 m race in 10.08 s.

   a) Calculate his speed. (2)
   b) How far would the athlete go if he ran for 3 minutes? (2)
   c) Why would this not be possible? (2)

2 The highway code provides minimum stopping distances as a guide for drivers. You will need to learn these for your driving test.

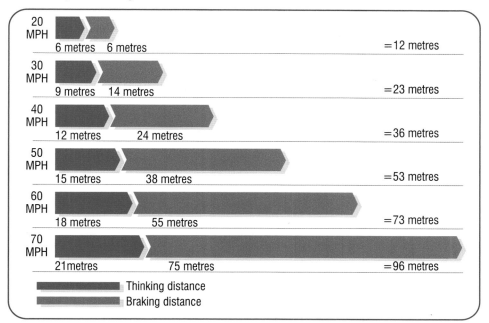

20 MPH — 6 metres 6 metres = 12 metres
30 MPH — 9 metres 14 metres = 23 metres
40 MPH — 12 metres 24 metres = 36 metres
50 MPH — 15 metres 38 metres = 53 metres
60 MPH — 18 metres 55 metres = 73 metres
70 MPH — 21 metres 75 metres = 96 metres

▬ Thinking distance
▬ Braking distance

   a) What are the two components of stopping distance? (2)
   b) What is the stopping distance of a car travelling at 30 mph? (1)
   c) Explain why the stopping distance for a lorry is longer than the stopping distance of a car. (2)
   d) Plot a graph showing the increase in thinking distance against speed. (3)
   e) How might the stopping distance be affected if a driver has been drinking alcohol? (1)

3 A motorcycle accelerates from traffic lights at 4m/s²

   a) How much does the speed increase by every second? (3)
   b) The motorcycle accelerates for 8 seconds. What is the final speed of the motorcycle? (2)

4 A car travels 600m in 20 seconds.

   a) What is its average speed? (2)
   b) How far would the car travel in 4 minutes? (2)
   c) How fast is the car travelling in km/h? (2) (Show your working.)

5 A driver slows down at a speed camera. The speed camera is set to photograph cars travelling over 20 m/s. The car was travelling at 34 m/s. The brakes decelerate the car by 2.5 m/s².

   If the brakes are applied for 4 seconds will the speeding car get caught? Show your working out. (4)

6 Speed cameras are often fixed outside school gates.

   a) Explain why. (2)
   b) In Northern Ireland speed cameras recorded 5.2 million vehicles passing 50 speed survey sites. 2.5 million vehicles were travelling faster than the speed limit. 163,000 vehicles were travelling 15 mph or more over the speed limit. How might speed cameras help to solve this problem? (source: police service Northern Ireland website) (2)
   c) Why are some people opposed to speed cameras? (2)

13.1　Burning fuels

LEARNING OBJECTIVES

1　What is a hydrocarbon?
2　What fuels do we get from crude oil?
3　What happens when fuels burn?

On pages 142–143, you saw the wide range of substances that we make from **crude oil**. We can burn many of these substances as fuels. Our transport system relies on fuels from crude oil. Here are the fuels we can get from crude oil:

- Fuel gas, LPGs (liquid petroleum gases – propane and butane).
- Petrol, gasoline – car fuel.
- Naphtha – not a fuel, but can be broken down to make fuels.
- Paraffin, kerosene – used as domestic heater fuel, jet fuel.
- Diesel oil, gas oil – used by some cars and larger vehicles.
- Fuel oils and waxes – central heating oil, candles.

These different parts (or **fractions**) of crude oil are separated out from each other in tall steel fractionating columns. Look at the one shown in the photo.

The lighter fractions (the gases) come out at the top and the heavier ones, like bitumen (tar), come out at the bottom. (See page 127.)

An oil refinery

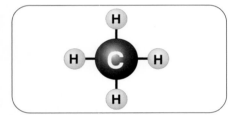
A methane molecule

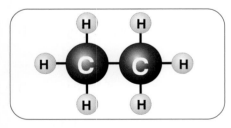
An ethane molecule

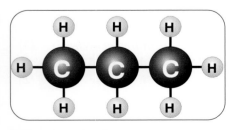
A propane molecule

Fuel molecules

Most of the different substances we find in oil are compounds called **hydrocarbons**. This means that they are molecules made up of only hydrogen and carbon.

On the left is a diagram showing a molecule of methane – the simplest of all hydrocarbons. The black atom in the centre of the molecule is carbon. The four smaller white atoms are hydrogen. The **chemical formula** for methane is CH_4.

a)　Look at the other two molecules on the left. What are the chemical formulas of ethane and propane?

These three compounds are all called **alkanes**. They are the start of a family of hydrocarbon molecules found in crude oil. They all release energy when they burn (or **combust**) by reacting with oxygen.

Combustion of hydrocarbons

When we burn hydrocarbons in air, carbon dioxide and water form. Look at this general word equation for the **combustion** of a hydrocarbon:

hydrocarbon + oxygen → carbon dioxide + water

What the equation doesn't show is that heat energy is released by this reaction – it is **exothermic**.

The word equation does show that oxygen is needed for combustion. This oxygen reacts with both the carbon and the hydrogen in a fuel:

carbon + oxygen → carbon dioxide (CO_2)

and

hydrogen + oxygen → water (H_2O)

We can write symbol equations to show the combustion of a hydrocarbon. For example, here is the symbol equation for ethane:

$$2\,C_2H_6 + 7\,O_2 → 4\,CO_2 + 6\,H_2O$$

b) How many oxygen atoms are in the seven oxygen molecules used in this equation? Explain why this many are needed.

Longer molecules release more energy but ...

Heat energy is needed to start combustion – to break the **bonds** between the carbon and hydrogen atoms.

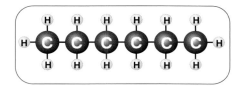

A hexane molecule

However, even more energy is given back out when the carbon and hydrogen atoms join with the oxygen atoms to make CO_2 and H_2O.

So, the longer the hydrocarbon chain, the more energy given out when the fuel burns;

but, the longer the hydrocarbon chain:
- The more difficult it becomes to ignite the fuel, and
- The more black smoke is given off as it burns.

TEST YOURSELF!

1 Copy and complete the missing words in these sentences – the first letters are given:

C_____ oil contains a mixture of long chain m_____ – called

h_____ because they are made of h_____ and c_____. When

they burn, they produce w_____ and c_____ d_____.

2 Butane has four carbon atoms in it and pentane has five. Draw diagrams showing these two hydrocarbon molecules.

3 Write symbol equations for:
   a) carbon joining with oxygen to make carbon dioxide.
   b) hydrogen joining with oxygen to make water.

13.2 Engine energy and efficiency

When car engines burn fuel, the **combustion** reaction releases a lot of heat. This energy is used to make the motor turn, which makes the wheels turn. A simplified energy transfer diagram for an engine looks like this:

chemical → heat energy of → kinetic energy
energy gases in engine of wheels/car

One big problem is that not all of the **chemical energy** from the petrol goes to heat the gases in the engine. Also, not all of the heat energy goes to make the car move. In other words, a lot of the energy is wasted – usually about 70% of it, in fact.

Because of these large losses, we say that motor vehicle engines have a very low **efficiency**. Only a small amount of the chemical energy from the fuel actually goes to making the vehicle move.

A car engine

Energy transfers in an engine

The energy transfer diagram below shows a more detailed description of what happens to the energy from the petrol (or diesel).

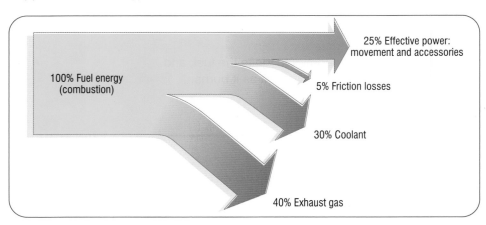

Energy transfer diagram for a typical petrol engine

Of the 100% energy available from the fuel combustion:

- Only about 25% actually gets applied to moving the car or running the accessories (e.g. lights and heating).
- About 5% is lost because of friction in the engine.
- Coolant systems take away 30% to stop the engine overheating.
- The last 40% is lost in hot gases through the exhaust pipe.

a) Draw a pie chart showing where energy goes in a car engine.

Energy conservation

It is important to realise that, although an engine wastes most of its energy, that energy doesn't just disappear. The engine gets hot, the exhaust and coolant systems get hot and the car makes noise, too.

> b) Add the wasted energies (orange) to the useful energy (green) – what do you get as your answer?

So the total amount of energy coming out of the engine is equal to the amount of energy supplied. In other words, the amount of energy is **conserved**. This is always true.

Whenever energy changes from one type to another, it tends to spread out and become less useful. There is as much energy left afterwards as there was beforehand, but a large proportion of it has been wasted.

Engine efficiency

The idea of **efficiency** is a good way of saying how much of an engine's fuel energy gets turned into useful energy. You can work out the efficiency of any device using the formula:

$$\text{efficiency} = \frac{\text{useful energy output}}{\text{total energy input}}$$ (You can multiply by 100 to get a %)

So the efficiency you work out is always between 0 and 1 or between 0 and 100%.

Worked example:

For every 1000 J of fuel energy supplied, a motorbike turns 340 J into movement energy (kinetic). How efficient is the motorbike?

$$\text{efficiency} = \frac{340\,J}{1000\,J}$$

$$= \underline{0.34} \text{ (or } \mathbf{34\%}) \text{ efficient}$$

GET IT RIGHT!

Unfortunately, you can never reach 100% efficiency because some energy is always wasted in energy transfers. Be suspicious if your answer even gets near 100%.

Engineers always work to reduce waste so that they can get the highest possible efficiency.

TEST YOURSELF!

1 Say if the following are **true** or **false**:

   a) Most of the chemical energy from fuel is wasted in an engine.
   b) Sometimes energy just disappears.
   c) Most engines are only about 30% efficient.
   d) Sometimes a really good engine can be 110% efficient.

2 Which is more efficient: a motorcycle that turns 64 J out of every 200 J of chemical energy in its fuel into movement energy or a diesel car that can turn 100 J out of every 300 J into movement?

3 Explain why engineers are always trying to increase efficiency – but why they can never reach 100%.

13.3 Transport pollution

LEARNING OBJECTIVES

1 How is pollution caused by engines?
2 How can we try to reduce this pollution?

Almost all the pollution caused by vehicles comes out through the exhaust pipe. The main exhaust emissions are:

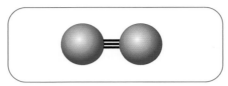

A nitrogen molecule

Nitrogen gas (N_2) – The air taken into the engine is 78% nitrogen gas, and most of this passes through the car engine unaffected.

The next two gases are products of **combustion**. (See pages 230–231.)

Carbon dioxide (CO_2) – The carbon in the fuel bonds with the oxygen in the air.

Water vapour (H_2O) – The hydrogen in the fuel bonds with the oxygen in the air.

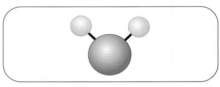

A water molecule

A carbon dioxide molecule

a) There are four different chemical elements shown in the molecules above. Make a key to identify each of them.

Most of these gases are harmless – although CO_2 emissions contribute to global warming. (See page 143.)

Incomplete combustion

There are two main reasons why fuel combustion is never perfect:

- The fuel is never completely pure.
- There isn't always enough oxygen to react completely with the carbon atoms. We call this **incomplete combustion**.

Because of this, small amounts of more harmful gases are also made in car engines. The most common of these are:

GET IT RIGHT!

Pollution can cause two main types of effect:

1 Human effects, such as asthma.
2 Environmental effects, including acid rain and smog.

Gas	Source and effects
Carbon monoxide (CO)	Produced by incomplete combustion. A colourless, odourless and toxic gas.
Hydrocarbons or **voltatile organic compounds** (VOCs)	Produced mostly from unburned fuel. These can then break down, forming ozone (O_3), a major component of smog.
Nitrogen oxides ('NOx') NO and NO_2	These add to smog and acid rain, and can also cause breathing problems.

Soot (carbon) is also produced as a result of incomplete combustion.

b) Draw diagrams showing the molecules of carbon monoxide, nitrogen monoxide, nitrogen dioxide and ozone.

Cleaning up exhausts

Carbon monoxide, VOCs and NOx are 'regulated emissions' – they are checked and have to be kept low. Cars over 3 years old have to pass an MOT (Ministry of Transport) test each year. Part of the test is a check that exhaust gases are within legal limits. Mechanics carry out the test with an electronic 'sniffer' attached to a detector.

This mechanic is testing exhaust emissions for pollutant gases

If an old car is making a lot of carbon monoxide, it is belching out toxic gas on to the streets. Not only that, the owner is wasting money. That's because incomplete combustion of petrol gives out less energy than complete combustion.

These days most vehicles have **catalytic converters**, connected into their exhausts. These are designed to reduce the emission of the pollutant gases.

In catalytic converters, there are different **catalysts** that make the pollution gases react to form less harmful gases. The two main stages in a catalytic converter are:

- Toxic carbon monoxide gas is changed to carbon dioxide.
- Nitrogen oxides are changed to harmless nitrogen gas.

A catalytic converter

TEST YOURSELF!

1 Which of these gases produced by car exhausts are dangerous and which are harmless?
   a) Carbon dioxide.
   b) Carbon monoxide.
   c) Water vapour.
   d) Nitrogen oxides.
   e) Hydrocarbons.
   f) Nitrogen.

2 How do you think incomplete combustion affects the efficiency of an engine?

3 Longer hydrocarbon molecules release more energy during combustion – but this also means they need more oxygen. How do you think this will affect the products of combustion?

13.4 Alternative fuels

LEARNING OBJECTIVES

1 Why do we need to find other fuels to use?
2 What different types of fuel can we develop?

A petrol station

LPG gas canisters

A hydrogen fuelled car, showing large hydrogen tanks

Most vehicles are fuelled by **petrol** or **diesel**, but we need to find other fuels to use. This is not just because the fuels that come from crude oil cause pollution when we burn them.

By the year 2020, the world is expected to reach its 'peak oil' point. After this, because crude oil is **non-renewable**, we will be able to find less and less oil each year.

Even now, geologists working for oil companies have to search the most remote places on Earth for new oil fields.

We need alternative fuels for our vehicles that cause less **pollution** and noise, as well as coming from **renewable** resources. The petrol station, as we know it, will have to change.

Alternative combustion fuels

Another fuel fraction from crude oil is called **LPG** (liquid petroleum gases – propane and butane). Cars can be made to run on LPG with high **efficiency**. They also produce much less in the way of pollution emissions – especially **VOCs** and **NOx**. (See pages 234–235.)

Using LPG to fuel cars will make the oil supplies that we have last longer. However, they are still from a non-renewable resource and so will run out as the oil does.

Alcohol

You might be surprised to learn that most cars can be converted to run on alcohol, instead of petrol. In the 1970s, Brazilian engineers built engines that could burn alcohol or a mixture of alcohol and petrol. They call the mixture **gasohol**. The alcohol is produced from the fermentation of sugar cane – a renewable energy source.

The pure alcohol they used, called **ethanol**, not only provides a renewable source of energy – it is also very clean, releasing only water and carbon dioxide when burnt.

a) Explain why alcohol is a renewable source of energy.

Hydrogen

We can also burn hydrogen gas as a fuel. It could possibly be a long-term alternative to **fossil fuels**. When it burns, it produces none of the polluting gases that fossil fuels do – it only makes water:

$$\text{hydrogen} + \text{water} \rightarrow \text{water}$$
$$2\,H_2 + O_2 \rightarrow 2\,H_2O$$

Hydrogen could be an ideal energy source if we could manufacture it by the **electrolysis** of water, e.g. using solar cells. One problem is that the gas tanks needed to carry the hydrogen are bulky and heavy.

Alternatives to combustion – electric cars

We have had cars that use **rechargeable** batteries as their energy source for many years. Because they don't burn a fuel, they don't produce any pollution. You usually have to plug the car into a socket to charge up its batteries.

However, some types recharge by using **solar power**. This is better than using electricity from oil-, coal- or gas-fuelled power stations, which produce pollution and use up fossil fuels.

Unfortunately, the batteries take much longer to charge up than they do to run down. They are also heavy, as well as not providing enough energy for fast travel.

Because of the limitations of electric cars, a half-way compromise called the **hybrid car** has been invented. It runs on a battery when it first starts up and when it is going slowly. When you want to go fast, it starts up its petrol engine and recharges its battery from the petrol motor at the same time.

An electric car

Hydrogen fuel cells

These are a different way of using hydrogen. Fuel cells produce electricity to run an **electric motor**, instead of burning the hydrogen.

Hydrogen and oxygen are separated from water by electrolysis – which can be solar-powered. The gases are stored in tanks.

A **catalyst** is then used to make the hydrogen and oxygen recombine, producing electricity.

The fuel cell doesn't release as much energy as petrol. However, it doesn't produce carbon dioxide or carbon monoxide either.

Problems with fuel cells include:

- Getting a good source of electricity to split the water in the first place
- Having large storage cylinders for the hydrogen and oxygen needed.

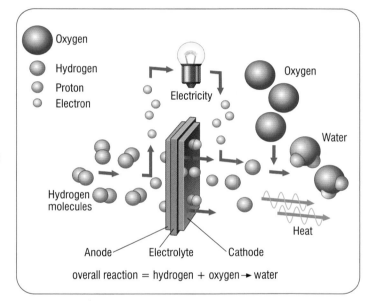

overall reaction = hydrogen + oxygen → water

Key processes in a hydrogen fuel cell

TEST YOURSELF!

1 Say whether the following are **true** or **false**:
   a) You could make your own alcohol at home to power your own car.
   b) Solar power can be used to turn water into a fuel for cars.
   c) All cars have a battery to start them – but some can run on only a battery.

2 a) Why do we need to find other car fuels to use instead of petrol?
   b) Why won't diesel make a good alternative to petrol?

3 Make a list of advantages and disadvantages of each type of engine fuel described on these two pages. Compare each one with petrol.

KEY FACTS

When you compare different fuels, there are several key factors to consider:

- Cost (of the engine, as well as the fuel).
- Efficiency.
- Pollution effects on people and the environment.
- Availability of fuel.

13.5   Fuel matters

Problems with alcohol cars in Brazil

After the 1970s' oil crisis, Brazil announced the world's first alcohol-powered car, making use of its plentiful supplies of sugar cane. The sugar could be purified and distilled to produce ethanol, an alcohol that burned with little pollution. By the middle of the 1980s, demand for the cars had become huge, with 90% of new cars being alcohol-fuelled.

Unfortunately, the sugar cane workers were prone to striking and the distribution network for the alcohol was unreliable. In 1989, alcohol supplies dried up, causing prices to rise out of control. A running feud between the sugar growers and the automobile manufacturers meant that, by 1997, fewer than 1% of new cars used ethanol.

Alcohol is a renewable fuel, as well as causing much less pollution than petrol and diesel do. Although the Brazilian car producers are now keen to manufacture a whole new generation of alcohol-fuelled cars, they won't be in a position to go ahead until the ethanol companies reduce their prices.

Ethanol prices are unpredictable, though. When the cost of the alcohol fell to a third of the price of petrol, the car companies began to move forward with their eco-friendly plans, but then prices started to rise again and the developments stalled. No one will buy an alcohol-fuelled car if they can't rely on the price of alcohol staying low. Meanwhile, the sugar cane industry is drowning in its own alcohol output, as there just aren't enough alcohol-fuelled cars being bought to use it all up.

Isn't it a shame! An effective, pollution-busting alternative to petrol has been lost amongst all the politics. How many other chances will we get?

Activities

a) Why are the alcohol-fuelled cars described as 'pollution-busting' and 'eco-friendly'?
b) Why do you think that cars fuelled by alcohol are not as popular as they used to be?

Hydrogen power for your car

Read this publicity information about a new car powered by hydrogen.

Activities

a) How many hydrogen fuel cells are needed to provide enough power for the car?
b) How does the car get the power to accelerate rapidly when it needs to?

Fuel cell stack – up to 200 fuel cells are stacked together to generate enough electricity to power the car. In each fuel cell, the hydrogen mixes with oxygen from the air – a chemical reaction that produces electricity.

Fuel tank – where the liquid hydrogen is stored. When it is needed, it is pumped to the fuel cell stack.

Hydrocar

Electric motors – usually powered by electricity from the fuel cell stack and from the battery pack when larger bursts of energy are needed.

Battery pack – this provides the energy necessary for sudden and rapid acceleration. In quiet moments, the spare electricity from the fuel cell recharges the battery pack.

Section of Hydrogen car

ABB's *e=motion* vehicle

ELECTRIC CAR ATTEMPTS SPEED RECORD

British design engineers Colin Fallows and Mark Newby have been putting their new high speed electrical car, the *ABB e=motion*, to the test in the Nevada desert.

This 10 metre-long bright orange torpedo-shaped vehicle has two 37-kW motors, powered by four packs of 52 lead-acid batteries. AC (alternating current) power for the two motors is generated from the 600 Volts (V) DC (direct current) provided by the batteries through a variable-speed driver technology. To make sure the two motors do not overheat during the record attempt, a ventilation system uses a series of fans to keep the motors below their maximum operating temperature of 180°C.

Electric cars have obvious environmental benefits

ABB claims that the technology used in e=motion cuts carbon dioxide emissions by 68 million tonnes annually. It is employed in a range of settings world-wide, from water pumps to steel mills. "One day all cars will be electric", claim Mr Newby and Mr Fallows.

To break the record, the car has to complete two runs over a distance of 1 kilometre at more than 394 km/h, within an hour. After the first attempt, the batteries will be replaced before the car makes its second run.

The engineers say that its performance in test runs has looked promising, reaching 237 km/h over a kilometre stretch. "In its first ever test run, e=motion easily reached 146 mph. In fact, the only reason we had to stop the car was because we ran out of road!"

An 'electrical gremlin' foiled the team's second attempt at the record

The team's first attempt at the record in Nevada had to be aborted because of battery problems and gusty winds. "It's an electrical gremlin. It could be related to cold, damp temperatures in the Nevada desert" said the British design engineers, Fallows and Newby.

"Record breaking is the only business that, when you achieve your goal, you're redundant. You wait for the next guy to break it. Then you can start over" said Colin Fallows, a retired Royal Air Force engineer from Northamptonshire.

ABB's *e=motion* vehicle

Activities

a) 52 batteries are needed to provide the 600 V that the engines need. How much voltage does each battery supply?

b) If the car reaches its target speed of 394 km/h, how long will it take to travel 1 km?

c) The car's motors generate a lot of heat. What does this tell you about its efficiency?

d) Do you think that we should replace petrol-powered cars with battery power? Why?

SUMMARY QUESTIONS

1 a) Name five substances that we can separate from crude oil.

   b) Write an 'F' next to the substances in your list that can be used as fuels.

2 a) What is a hydrocarbon?

   b) Write the word equation for the complete combustion of a hydrocarbon.

   c) Complete this symbol equation for the complete combustion of methane:

   $CH_4 + \_O_2 \rightarrow CO_2 + \_H_2O$

   d) Then try this more difficult one for propane:

   $C_3H_8 + \_O_2 \rightarrow \_CO_2 + \_H_2O$

3 Complete this table about the alkanes:

Name of Alkane	Chemical Formula	Number of Carbon atoms	Number of C-H bonds
Methane	CH_4	1	4
Ethane			6
Propane	C_3H_8		
Butane			
Pentane		5	

4 a) Draw an energy flow diagram for a car engine.

   b) How efficient is a motorcycle that wastes 1300 J of each 2 kJ of fuel energy that it uses?

   c) If a car engine is 30% efficient, how much of 2 kJ of fuel energy is wasted?

5 Car engines often produce carbon monoxide, due to incomplete combustion.

   a) Complete this chemical equation for the incomplete combustion of ethane:

   $2 C_2H_6 + \_O_2 \rightarrow \_CO + \_H_2O$

   b) Now complete this equation to show how catalytic converters turn the carbon monoxide into carbon dioxide:

   $\_CO + \_O_2 \rightarrow \_CO_2$

6 Ethanol (C_2H_5OH) and hydrogen (H_2) can both be used as engine fuels. Write word equations for their complete combustion.

7 Draw a simple flow chart to show how hydrogen fuel cells work.

8 Complete the following sentences about engines and fuels using these words:

catalytic, movement, wasted, nitrogen oxide, hydrogen, exothermic, water, petrol, ethane, combustion, chemical, heat, oxygen, fuel, hydrocarbon, carbon dioxide, alcohol, efficiency, methane, renewable, complete, energy, polluting

Crude oil is a non-_____ fossil ___ that is made up from a number of different fractions, including fuel gas, _____, paraffin, diesel and other fuel oils. Many of these fractions are long-chain _____ molecules, called alkanes. Two common alkanes are _____ (CH_4) and _____ (C_2H_6).

When hydrocarbons burn in air, they react with the _____ in a chemical reaction called _____. If there is enough oxygen, the products of the _____ combustion are _____ _____ and _____. Because it gives out lots of ____ energy, it is called an _____ reaction. The longer the hydrocarbon molecule, the more _____ it releases. When an engine burns fuel, the _____ energy stored in it is converted into useful kinetic (_____) energy. But engines have a low _____ – so about 70% of the energy is _____ as heat.

Burning fuels can produce _____ gases like carbon monoxide, _____ _____ (NOx) and VOCs. One way in which car engineers reduce these emissions is by using _____ converters. We are also looking for different ways to power cars. These include LPG, _____, electricity and fuel cells.

EXAM-STYLE QUESTIONS

1 Name the missing fuels, A and B, as well as the missing uses, C and D in the table. (4)

Fuel	Uses
Natural gas	Camping stoves, gas cookers, Bunsen burners
Petrol	C
A	Aeroplane
B	Truck and TDi car
Fuel oil	D

2 Fossil fuels are non-renewable.

a) What are the three fossil fuels? (3)

b) What do we mean by non-renewable? (2)

c) Some people propose we generate more energy using wind turbines. State and explain the benefits of wind turbines. (4)

d) What are the drawbacks of wind power? (2)

e) How else could we generate energy for the future? (3)

3 Not all of the energy in petrol is used to make a car move. Much of it is wasted. This is inefficient. A car needs 156 kJ of petrol in order to produce 39 kJ of kinetic energy.

a) Calculate the efficiency of the engine. (2)

b) Where has the rest of the energy gone? (2)

c) A new electric car is 43% efficient. It has poorer acceleration than a petrol car. Why are more people starting to invest in electric cars? (2)

4 The simplest hydrocarbon fuel is called methane. It is used in Bunsen burners.

a) What state of matter is methane? (1)

b) What is the chemical formula for methane? (1)

c) Methane is a hydrocarbon.

   i) What elements does it contain? (2)

   ii) Which gas does methane react with when it burns? (1)

d) Copy and complete the word equation for this reaction: (3)

Methane + ... ➤ .... + ...

5 Propane is used in camping gas stoves because it is highly combustible.

a) What does combustible mean? (1)

b) The chemical equation for propane is C_3H_8. How many carbon and hydrogen atoms are bonded together in propane? (2)

c) Write a balanced chemical formula for the combustion of propane. (3)

6 State and explain the problems associated with burning fossil fuels. (6)

7 Holly performs an experiment on fuels. Here are her results:

Fuel	Estimated energy per litre (MJ)
Unleaded petrol	35.5
Coal	25
Diesel	37.7
Kerosene	36.5

a) Which fuel is the most flammable? (1)

b) Which fuels are used in motor vehicles? (2)

c) Which fuel is used in aircraft? (1)

d) The first trains used coal to power them. Why do modern trains use diesel instead? (3)

8 When there is not enough oxygen, hydrocarbons produce carbon or carbon monoxide instead of carbon dioxide when they combust. Explain why this is a problem inside a boiler. (3)

14.1

Introduction to electromagnetic waves

Waves carry energy from one place to another, as **vibrations**. Sound waves carry energy as vibrations we can hear. Light is a type of wave that our eyes can see.

Light travels much faster than sound – at about 300 000 000 m/s (or 186 000 mph). It vibrates at a **frequency** of around 600 000 000 000 000 Hz – that's 600 million million vibrations every second. These vibrations aren't moving air particles, like sound is, they are **electromagnetic**. This means that light doesn't need air to carry it along. So it can travel across empty space.

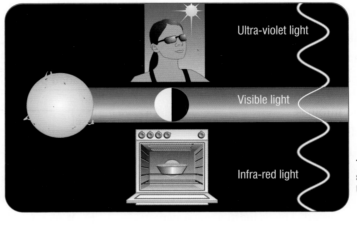

Ultra-violet light

Visible light

Infra-red light

The visible light spectrum between UV and IR

The colours of light that we can see (from red to violet) are called the **visible spectrum**.

a) Name the **seven** colours of the visible spectrum, in order.

Beyond visible

Just like there are sounds too high for us to hear, there are colours too high (and low) for us to see.

For example, the Sun also gives out electromagnetic waves of lower frequency than visible light, called **infra-red** (IR), and higher frequency, called **ultra-violet** (UV).

The spectrum of visible light

IR image of a person holding a cigarette

Infra-red radiation

Infra-red radiation waves are lower energy than visible light and have two main areas of use:

● Hot objects give off infra-red – so it is used for heat therapy and thermal imaging (and making toast!).
● Infra-red is also good for short-range communications – like remote controls and computer interfacing.

Ultra-violet radiation

Ultra-violet radiation waves are **higher energy**, which means they can behave in interesting ways:

- They can make materials fluoresce – or glow in the dark.
- They tan your skin – although too much ultra-violet can cause skin cancers.

These waves are invisible to your eyes, but some insects, like bumble bees, can see them. The photos on the right show how a flower would look different to an insect that can see in ultra-violet.

What lies beyond?

It turns out that there are even more different types of electromagnetic wave than visible light, infra-red and ultra-violet:

- At **lower frequenc**y (and energy) there are **microwaves** and **radio waves**.
- At **higher frequency** (and energy) are **X-rays** and **gamma rays**.

So there is a whole **electromagnetic spectrum** of waves, as shown below:

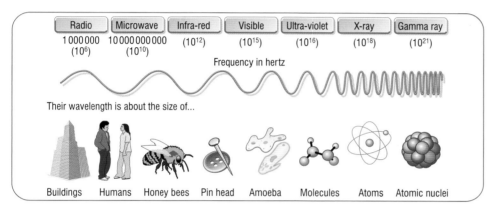

The electromagnetic spectrum

Remember, these are all waves of electromagnetic radiation – and they can all travel at 300 000 000 m/s. You can read more about them in the next few pages.

A club scene showing fluorescent items

A flower photographed in normal and UV light

TEST YOURSELF!

1 Which type of electromagnetic wave…
  a) Has a wavelength about the size of buildings?
  b) Causes skin tanning?
  c) Has the highest frequency?
  d) Is also called 'heat rays'?
  e) Can we see?
  f) Is the size of atoms?
  g) Travels the fastest?

2 a) Give 2 uses of infra-red radiation.
  b) Explain how both infra-red and ultra-violet waves could be harmful to your skin.

3 a) What do we mean by the 'frequency' of a wave?
  b) What is the unit of frequency?
  c) List all the parts of the electromagnetic spectrum in frequency order, starting with the highest.

DID YOU KNOW?

The energy given out by the Sun is made up of:

- 40% visible light.
- 50% IR.
- 9% UV.
- 1% X-ray, radio, etc.

14.2 Communicating with waves

LEARNING OBJECTIVES

1 How do we use waves for communication?
2 Which types of electromagnetic waves do we use in communications?

Waves carry energy from one place to another. This makes them very useful for communication.

We use **sound waves** to talk to each other – but they can't travel very far. There are other kinds of waves that are better for different uses.

The first kind of fast, long-distance communications used light. Chains of bonfires on beacon hills across England quickly sent warnings of invasions to London. Later, this idea was improved and used between boats with a system called **semaphore**.

a) Send a message (one word) across the room to a friend using the **semaphore** alphabet on the left. Did they decode your mystery word?

Using visible light to communicate in this way had its drawbacks. You could only communicate with people you could see. It also depended a lot on the weather conditions.

Communications engineers have developed a wide range of ways to communicate. They make use of how different types of **electromagnetic radiation** move as waves, carrying energy over huge distances. A few of these are described on these pages.

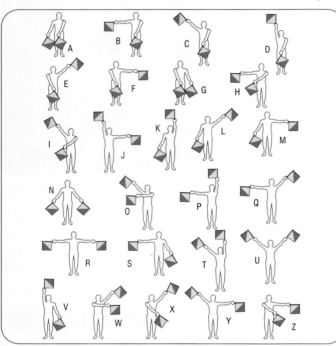

The semaphore alphabet

Radio waves – TV and radio

Radio and television signals are transmitted using **radio waves**.

There are different types of radio waves, called short-wave, medium-wave and long-wave.

Radio waves have the lowest **frequency** of all electromagnetic waves – and the lowest energy, too. Because of their long **wavelength** though, they don't get stopped easily. Astronomers have detected radio waves that have travelled most of the way across the universe!

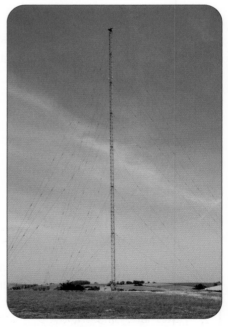

A radio transmitter

b) Write down as many different uses of radio communication as you can think of.

Microwaves – mobile phones and satellites

Microwaves are like radio waves, but with a higher frequency (and shorter wavelength). Because of this, they can contain more information than radio waves. However, they can't travel as far.

Mobile phones and **satellites** use microwaves to communicate because of the amount of information they can carry.

Infra-red – computer links and remote controls

Because of their high frequency and short wavelength, infra-red (IR) waves are often used in electronic communications over short distances. Examples include infra-red wireless computer keyboards and mice.

Infra-red is right next to red light in the **electromagnetic spectrum** (see page 242) and so behaves in some of the same ways. Most importantly, the waves travel in straight lines. This is why you can't use your television remote control from around corners.

A mobile phone mast

c) What sort of information do you think could be sent to your computer using an infra-red link?

You can send information from your mobile phone to your PC using infra-red

Visible light – fibre optic cables

Visible light has a higher frequency still, but needs a clear path to travel. To use light in long distance communication, engineers have developed **fibre-optic cables**. These keep the light inside by a process called '**total internal reflection**'. The light reflects along the inside of the glass cable for long distances.

Fibre-optic cables are used to carry signals for computer and phone communications, as well as for cable television.

The end of a fibre optic bundle with light shining out of the end

TEST YOURSELF!

1 Say whether the statements are **true** or **false**:
   a) Radio waves are the longest wavelength of electromagnetic waves.
   b) Microwaves are only used in cooking.
   c) Infra-red waves can travel around corners.
   d) Light can travel along curved fibre-optic cables.
   e) People can see infra-red light.

2 How many different kinds of communications technology do you make use of at home?

3 If you were a communications engineer, how would you decide which kind of waves to use in a new communication system?

DID YOU KNOW?

Optical fibres are only about a tenth of a millimetre wide – but they can carry light for over a hundred kilometres!

14.3 Properties of electromagnetic waves

1 How do higher energy electromagnetic waves behave?

2 What are they used for?

Electromagnetic waves aren't just used for communication. There is a wide range of uses for them. What these other uses all have in common is that the waves carry energy from one place to another.

In this section and the next, we will look at the **electromagnetic spectrum** in order. We will work from the highest **energy** (and **frequency**) waves to the lowest.

High energy waves

In this section, we will look at the electromagnetic waves that have higher energy and frequency – **gamma rays**, **X-rays**, **ultra-violet** and **visible light**. As you read about these waves, you will see that, as well as being useful, higher energy waves can be hazardous too.

Gamma rays

These very high energy rays are dangerous, for example when they are produced by **radioactive decay**. They can damage and even destroy living cells. However, we can make use of this to kill bacteria. It is possible to use gamma rays to **sterilise** surgical equipment – and even food.

Gamma rays can also be used in **medical imaging**. **Radioisotopes** are put into a person and the gamma rays given out can be detected. This helps to identify medical problems like blood clots.

We can also use gamma rays to treat certain cancers (**radiotherapy**). You can read about more medical uses on pages 90 and 91.

X-rays

These are used for **medical imaging** and treatment. (See pages 86–87.) Sometimes a doctor or dentist says that "you need an X-ray". They (or a radiographer) use X-rays to take a picture of your bones or teeth.

X-rays have got enough energy to pass through your skin and muscles, but not enough to pass through your bones and teeth. This means that breaks and other damage can be seen in these 'shadow' pictures.

Radiotherapy is a process where doctors use high energy X-rays to kill cancer cells. The rays are focused very accurately onto a tumour so that only the cancerous cells are destroyed.

a) Look at the two pictures on the left showing how X-rays and gamma rays are used in medical imaging. Describe the main differences shown in these pictures.

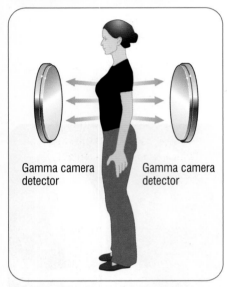

Gamma rays can be used for medical imaging

Gamma camera detector   Gamma camera detector

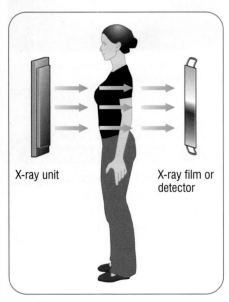

X-ray unit   X-ray film or detector

X-rays can be used for medical imaging and treatment

Ultra-violet (UV)

When ultra-violet is shone on some **fluorescent** materials, they give visible light back out. It looks as if they are glowing in the dark. This is not just a pretty display – it can also be used to security-mark property. This means that you can write your name and post code on your property so that it can be identified if it has been stolen.

A UV security marking pen

UV sun bed

Ultra-violet lamps are also used for tanning, because they produce the same rays as the Sun. You need to be careful though, as too much high energy ultra-violet can cause skin cancer – that's why your skin darkens to protect you.

b) Why do you think the woman on the tanning bed is wearing dark goggles?

Visible light

Most of our uses of visible light are for seeing things – light bulbs, projectors and so on. There are also other uses of **fibre-optic cables** that aren't for communication.

Endoscopes are devices that make use of two sets of optical fibres to look inside objects, and even people. The first set of fibres shines light inside and the second set carries the reflected light back to a camera.

Surgeons use endoscopes in 'keyhole surgery' and aircraft engineers use them to look inside engines and turbines.

GET IT RIGHT!

Waves and **rays** are pretty much the same thing.

Rays show the direction that waves are travelling-like light out of a torch.

Surgeons use endoscopes in keyhole surgery

TEST YOURSELF!

1 Match each wave type with its use:

Wave type:	Use:
Gamma ray	Endoscopes
X-ray	Security marking
Ultra-violet	Imaging broken bones
Visible light	Sterilising equipment

2 Explain how X-rays are used to take pictures of broken bones.

3 Find out how your body could be harmed if you are exposed to too much:
   a) Ultra-violet.
   b) Visible light.
   c) Gamma rays.

14.4

Properties of electromagnetic waves – 2

1 What are the waves at the lower end of the electromagnetic spectrum?
2 What effects do these waves have?
3 What are these lower energy electromagnetic waves used for?

Electromagnetic waves have a wide range of uses, including communication. In the previous spread, you read about the use and hazards of the higher energy end of the electromagnetic spectrum.

Low energy waves

Now we will look at the electromagnetic waves that have **lower energy** and **frequency** than visible light – **infra-red**, **microwaves** and **radio waves**. These lower energy waves tend to be less hazardous than the higher energy ones. However, there can still be some dangers linked with their uses.

Infra-red (IR)

Anything warm or hot gives off infra-red waves. So these are the heat given out when cooking grills and radiators are used.

Physiotherapists use infra-red lamps to provide heat therapy. This can provide relief for strained and tired muscles.

a) Why do you think patio heaters have large curved metal pieces at the top?

Patio heaters work by giving off IR waves

Microwaves

Microwave ovens use microwave radiation for cooking. These heat up any water, oil or fats in the food.

Water molecules are made of two hydrogen atoms joined to a larger oxygen atom. Microwaves of exactly the right frequency make the bonds between these atoms vibrate. This makes the water heat up.

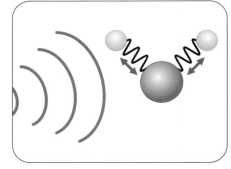

Microwaves exciting a water molecule

The **frequencies** of microwaves used in mobile phones are different to those used in microwave ovens. This means that they shouldn't be dangerous, but not everyone agrees that mobile phones are completely safe to use. (See page 255 for more details.)

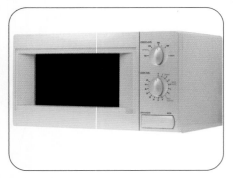

A microwave oven

GET IT RIGHT!

1 GHz is a 'GigaHertz' – that means a frequency of a billion hertz – or a thousand million waves each second.

Microwave frequencies range from 1 GHz to 300 GHz. Water, sugar and fats absorb energy best at 2.4 GHz. Mobile phones work between 1 and 2 GHz. Discuss whether you think that's different enough to be safe?

Radio waves

Radio waves have been in use in communication since the late 1880s. They are still the most common type of wave used in communication.

You have probably heard that **digital radios** are becoming more popular now. So it looks like radio waves will be with us for a long time to come.

Using this idea, **radar** systems are used by planes to work out how far they are from other planes, mountains and the ground.

Like all other electromagnetic waves, there is a range of wavelengths of radio waves, with a range of properties. There is one particular wavelength, 5.6 cm long, that reflects back off rain and snow. This wavelength of radio wave is used by **weather satellites** to locate clouds for weather forecasts.

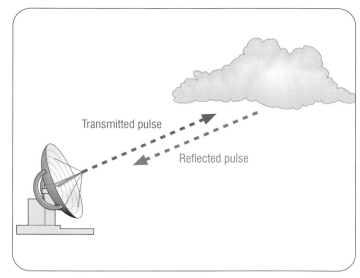

Transmitted radio waves being reflected off clouds

Electromagnetic waves in space

All types of electromagnetic waves are used by **astronomers** to look out into the universe. We will talk more about this on the next two pages.

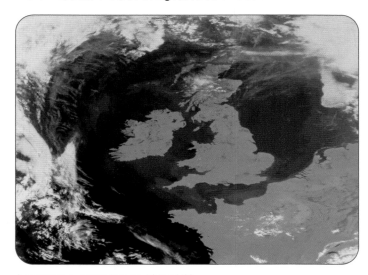

A weather satellite image of the UK

TEST YOURSELF!

1 Copy and correct these sentences by crossing out the **wrong word**, where there is a **choice**:
   a) Anything **hot / cold** gives off infra-red rays.
   b) They are used in **heat lamps / fridges**.
   c) Microwave ovens make water molecules **vibrate / stop moving** to **heat up / cool down**.
   d) Radio waves are used in **radar / sonar** to detect objects that **can / can't** be seen.

2 Draw a short series of cartoons to explain how radar works.

3 Explain how infra-red and microwaves are used in cooking.

4 How are the following pairs linked in waves:
   a) Energy and frequency?
   b) Frequency and wavelength?
   c) Energy and wavelength?

14.5

Looking out into the Universe

LEARNING OBJECTIVES

1 Which electromagnetic waves come from space?
2 How do astronomers look at these waves to find out about the universe?

People have never travelled further than the Moon – and we aren't ever likely to leave the **Solar System**.

So how do we find out about the rest of the **universe**? How do we know about the **planets** of our Solar System, the billions of other stars in our **galaxy** and even the billions of other galaxies? The simple answer is that we look at them.

Astronomers can use all the waves in the **electromagnetic spectrum** to look at objects in space. There are **telescopes** that are made to detect much more than visible light. They can 'see' every other type of electromagnetic wave, from **radio waves** to **gamma rays**. We can use these to produce amazing images.

This is what the Earth looks like, viewed in visible light

Ultra-violet imaging

Our Sun emits light at all the different wavelengths in the electromagnetic spectrum. But it is ultra-violet waves that are responsible for causing sunburn. To the right is an image of the Sun taken in ultra-violet by a satellite named SOHO.

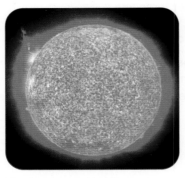

The Sun imaged in UV

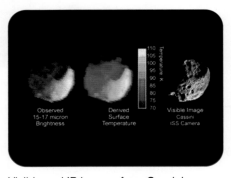

Visible and IR images from Cassini

Infra-red imaging

Because warm objects give off infra-red, astronomers use it to measure temperatures. This image of Phoebe (one of Saturn's moons) was taken by the Cassini probe in 2004. The brighter colours are warmer.

Microwave telescopes

Because microwaves can penetrate clouds and smoke, these waves are good for viewing Venus. This NASA image of volcanoes on Venus is from microwave radar images through the clouds.

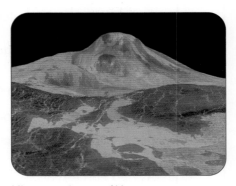

Microwave image of Venus

Radio telescopes

Radio telescopes

Radio telescopes point toward the skies at planets, **comets**, **nebulae**, stars and galaxies. Astronomers can learn what these objects are made from, as well as how they are moving, from radio waves.

Radio astronomy also has the advantage that sunlight, clouds, and rain do not affect observations.

X-ray observations

Many things in deep space give off X-rays. When a star is near a **black hole**, gas is pulled off the normal star. This gas spirals into the black hole and heats up to very high temperatures. When something is heated to over a million degrees, it gives off X-rays!

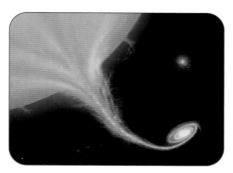

Gas from a star spiralling into a black hole

Gamma ray imaging

Gamma-rays are also produced by violent events like **supernova** explosions, and by **neutron stars**, **pulsars** and black holes.

(They are also produced by **radioactive decay**.)

A supernova

TEST YOURSELF!

1 Copy and complete these sentences (the first letter of each word is given for you):

A_____ use different types of t_____ to look out into the Universe. They can get images in all parts of the e_____ spectrum, from r_____ waves to g_____ rays. H_____ objects give out higher e_____ waves.

2 Which types of electromagnetic waves *could* you use to get images of:
   a) Mars?
   b) The Moon?
   c) The Sun?
   d) Distant neutron stars?

3 Why do you think we can only ever look at other stars, instead of visiting them?

14.6   The universe is getting bigger!

LEARNING OBJECTIVES

1 How do we think the universe started?
2 What is the evidence to support the theory?

An explosion

You have probably heard of the 'Big Bang' theory. It says that the universe started with a large explosion. The theory also says that this explosion happened about 15 billion years ago. That is a long time before even our Sun was born. So how do we know?

You can now find out about the two main pieces of evidence for the Big Bang theory. All of this evidence comes from observations made with different types of telescopes.

Explosions

Before we look at the Big Bang evidence, it is important to think about explosions. After any explosion, there are always two main pieces of evidence that it has just happened:

● Things flying outwards.
● Heat.

---

a) Imagine you have just turned on your television half a second after a car has exploded. What can you see on screen that tells you that you've just missed an explosion?

So astronomers looked for evidence of an explosion and found ...

Cosmic background microwave radiation

In the 1960s, two scientists at Bell Laboratories were using their radio telescope. They detected low-level microwave radiation coming from space. It was coming from every direction – even the emptiest patches of space appeared to contain this energy. The scientists named it the 'cosmic microwave background radiation'.

DID YOU KNOW?

Microwave energy isn't very hot – it shows that empty space is only about 3 degrees above absolute zero. (That's a temperature of about –270°C.) The important thing is that the left over energy is there!

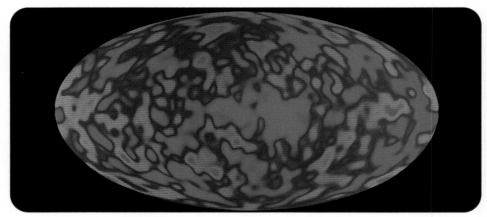

Cosmic microwave background, from COBE

This picture produced by the Cosmic Background Explorer (COBE) shows the slightly uneven microwave radiation at all angles. This is now thought to be the energy left over from the Big Bang.

Moving away – Doppler shift

Before we look at the second piece of evidence for the Big Bang, you need to think about how the **pitch** of a vehicle changes as it drives past you. Think of the sound you hear as a Formula 1 racing car or an ambulance zooms past. As it moves:

- Towards you – the pitch is higher.
- Away from you – the pitch is lower.

This change in the pitch, or **frequency**, of the sound wave you hear is called the **Doppler shift**. It happens with all waves where movement is involved. With light waves, it is called a blue- shift or **red-shift**.

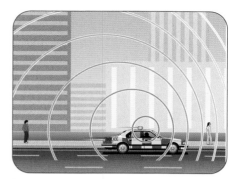

The Doppler shift. Sound waves are squashed together at the front and spread out behind a moving police car.

Galactic red-shift

The light from our sun can be split up using a prism. Look at the **spectrum** produced on the right:

You can see dark lines. These are caused by the **elements** that make up the Sun (mainly hydrogen and helium). When astronomers look at the spectra from nearby stars, they see that they are made of similar elements because the patterns of lines are similar.

However, looking at the spectra of distant **galaxies**, they notice something strange. The patterns of dark lines are the same, but they are moved towards the red end of the spectrum. This is known as a **red-shift**. It gives us evidence that these distant galaxies are all moving away from us.

Not only that but, the further the galaxies are from us, the more red-shifted their spectra are. In other words – they are moving away faster.

b) Does a red-shift mean an object is moving towards you or away from you?

Spectrum of our sun

Spectrum of a distant galaxy

KEY FACTS

- Background microwave radiation is left-over heat that is everywhere.
- The red-shift is evidence of galaxies all flying outwards.
- Together, they provide evidence for a very **Big Bang** indeed!

TEST YOURSELF!

1 Copy and correct these sentences by crossing out the **wrong** word, where there is a **choice**:
   a) The Universe has been **expanding** / **contracting** since the Big Bang.
   b) We know this because the **red** / **blue** shift of distant galaxies tells us they are all moving **towards** / **away** from us.
   c) The **gamma ray** / **microwave** background radiation is the heat left over from the Big Bang.

2 Imagine you had your eyes closed and an ambulance raced passed. How would you know, just from the pitch of its siren, the exact moment when it passed you?

3 Draw a short cartoon strip to explain to younger students how we know that the Universe started with a Big Bang. (Make sure you include a picture of a huge explosion!)

14.7   Waves and communications

SUNLIGHT IS BAD FOR YOU

The main cause of skin cancer is ultra-violet radiation from the sun. This condition affects about 50 000 Britons each year. More than 2% of them are killed by its most dangerous form, 'malignant melanoma'.

Babies' skin can't produce enough melanin to protect them from ultra-violet light, so they are at greater risk than most and need to be covered up.

Even in countries like Britain, with our cloudy weather, you could sunburn in only half an hour.

Skin damage

Every time your skin becomes sunburned or tanned, your individual skin cells and DNA are damaged. Cells may eventually become defective and cancerous if they cannot repair themselves.

Skin problems

Some people have more sensitive skin than others, and too much sunlight can cause allergic rashes.

Light can blind

High exposure to sunlight has also been linked to an increased likelihood of developing cataracts.

SUNLIGHT IS GOOD FOR YOU

Scientists have found that sunlight can have many benefits – it can even help to protect you from some types of cancer.

Sunshine can make you less SAD

Most of us are more cheerful on a sunny day, but we know that the Sun can affect your mood chemically and even prevent a kind of depression called SAD or '**seasonal affective disorder**'. Many people who don't get enough sunlight during the darker winter months don't produce enough serotonin, which can lead to depression.

Vitamin D

This vitamin strengthens our bones and muscles as well as boosting our immune system. We produce our own vitamin D when our skin is exposed to sunlight.

Scientists claim that just 10 minutes of sunlight a day will help us produce enough vitamin D. The main job of this vitamin is to help calcium to move across cell membranes, including its absorption in the intestines. This keeps your nervous system healthy and your bones strong.

Does UV light cause cataracts?

ACTIVITIES

a) Is sunlight good for you? Pick one side of the argument and produce a poster or leaflet to argue your case.

b) About half of all Australians develop skin cancer. What advice would you give them?

c) Research the differences between UVA, UVB and UVC.

Tropical beach

DERBY RESIDENTS MARCH AGAINST MASTS

One new mobile phone mast was more than enough for a Derby community – so they took to the streets to protest against a second.

Protesters complained that the Vodafone masts, close to the junior school and the war memorial were going to be positioned in inappropriate places.

The residents were joined on their march by the South Derbyshire MP, Mark Todd, as they walked to the Red Lion pub in Chellaston from the war memorial on Shelton Lock Green.

The council had already granted the company planning permission to erect a mast on the junction of the Parkway and Derby Road. Residents are now waiting for the decision to be taken on the second site, on the green.

ACTIVITES

Research on the Internet why people like those in Derby object to having mobile phone transmission masts put up near them? What are the dangers that worry them?

Chandra X-Ray Observatory Satellite Looks at a Black Hole

This Chandra X-ray Observatory image is a spectrum of a black hole, which is similar to the colourful spectrum of sunlight produced by a prism. The X-rays of interest are shown here recorded in the bright stripe that runs rightward and leftward from the centre of the image.

These X-rays are sorted precisely according to their energy, with the highest-energy X-rays near the centre of the image and the lower-energy X-rays further out.

A team of scientists led by Jeffrey McClintock (Harvard-Smithsonian Center for Astrophysics) observed the black hole binary system known as XTE J1118+480 on 18 April 2000. This 'X-ray nova' gives out occasional eruptions, followed by long periods of nothing. It contains a Sun-like star orbiting a black hole.

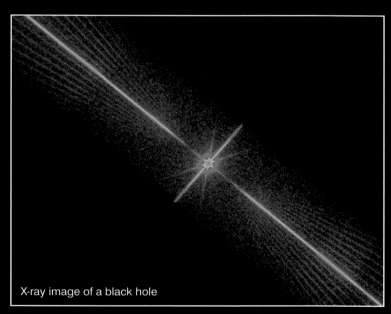

X-ray image of a black hole

ACTIVITES

Research on the Internet:

a) Why was the Chandra Observatory built to detect only X-rays?

b) Why is the Chandra Observatory in space and not positioned on the ground?

c) Find out about 3 other satellites that astronomers use to look out into space.

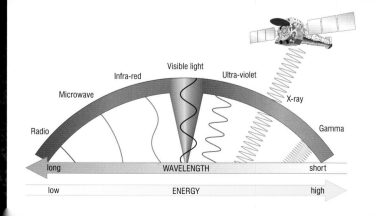

UNIT 2 SECTION 4 CHAPTER 14: COMMUNICATIONS

SUMMARY QUESTIONS

1 Copy and complete the following table showing all the parts of the electromagnetic spectrum. Include what they are used for and what hazards they have.

Wave Name	Uses	Hazards
Radio Waves		
Microwaves		
Infra-Red		
Visible Light		
Ultra-Violet		
X-Rays		
Gamma Rays		

2 Draw a mind map (or 'spider-diagram') to show all the different ways that electromagnetic waves are used in communication.

3 Why do you think doctors or dentists leave the room while taking an X-ray picture of you?

4 Draw a poster advertising all the ways that electromagnetic waves are useful in medicine.

5 Find out how a radio telescope is different from one that uses visible light. Draw labelled diagrams to show the main differences between them.

6 The Big Bang theory suggests that the universe started 15 billion years ago. Find out how long ago ...

a) The Earth formed.

b) The first life appeared on Earth.

c) The first humans evolved.

7 Binary star systems are made up of two stars orbiting each other. When we observe them, we see that one star is red-shifted and the other is blue-shifted. Which one is coming towards us and which is going away? Explain your answer using the Doppler Effect theory.

8 Copy and complete the following sentences about waves using these words:

shift, universe, imaging, violet, controls, frequency, satellite, black, cosmic, treatment, optical, heat, waves, phone, cancer, Bang, electromagnetic, Gamma, seven, electromagnetic, communication, outwards, rays, sterilise, spectrum, wavelength, Infra, security

The _____ spectrum is a family of types of _____. Each different type of wave has its own _____ (and energy) and so has its own properties and uses.

- Radio waves have the longest _____ and are used mainly for _____.
- Microwaves are used for _____ and mobile _____ communication – not just cooking!
- _____-red rays are _____ rays, but are also used in remote _____.
- Visible light is split up into its own _____ of _____ colours and is used in communication when it is sent down _____ fibres.
- Ultra-_____ rays can cause skin _____ and are used for _____ markings.
- X-rays are used in medical _____ and _____.
- _____ rays can be used to _____ medical equipment – and even food!

Astronomers can detect every type of _____ wave to get information about the _____. For example, infra-red gives us information about temperatures in space and gamma _____ prove that _____ holes exist.

Galactic red-_____ and the microwave _____ background radiation give us strong evidence that the universe started with a Big ____ and is still spreading _____.

EXAM-STYLE QUESTIONS

1 What are the two missing waves in this electromagnetic spectrum: (2)

Radio waves		Infra-red	Visible light		X-rays	Gamma rays

2 Choose the correct statement that completes the sentence.

All electromagnetic waves are

a) transverse and travel at different speeds in a vacuum.

b) longitudinal and travel at different speeds in a vacuum.

c) transverse and travel at the same speed in a vacuum.

d) longitudinal and travel at the same speed in a vacuum. (1)

3 a) Which part of the electromagnetic spectrum is the most energetic? (1)

b) Which part of the electromagnetic spectrum has the longest wavelength? (1)

c) Which part of the electromagnetic spectrum has the second highest frequency? (1)

4 A night club owner decides to install new ultra-violet lights in his club.

He wants to make it possible to read invisible ink that can be written across the walls. Why would this present a danger to clubbers? (2)

5 Airports have special machines to "see" inside people's bags.

a) Which part of the electromagnetic spectrum is used? (1)

b) How can this help security? (2)

6 Link these pictures to parts of the electromagnetic spectrum.

Remote control for TV

Camera

CB radio

X-ray photograph

Strawberry

Sun cream

Mobile phone

(7)

7 Scientists believe that the universe is expanding.

a) Explain the evidence for this. (3)

b) Why does an expanding universe suggest there was a Big Bang? (2)

c) What may happen to the size of the universe in the future? (3)

EXAMINATION STYLE QUESTIONS

1 Genetic counsellors advise families on their chances of having a child with a genetic disorder.

Cystic fibrosis is a recessive genetic disease affecting 1 in every 2500 children.

a) What is meant by the word recessive? (1)

b) A family went to a genetic counsellor. The diagram shows the cases of cystic fibrosis in their family. Study their family tree and answer the following questions.

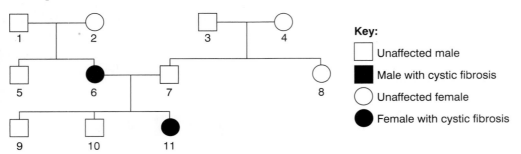

Key:
☐ Unaffected male
■ Male with cystic fibrosis
○ Unaffected female
● Female with cystic fibrosis

See page 74

i) Give the numbers of three people in their family who must be a carrier for cystic fibrosis. (2)

ii) Couple 6 and 7 are having another baby. Using the symbols C= unaffected gene c = affected gene, show using a suitable genetic diagram, how they could have another child with cystic fibrosis. (4)

iii) What is the probability of their having a child with cystic fibrosis? (1)

iv) Cystic fibrosis can cause infections that can be treated using antibiotics. Give an example of an antibiotic that could be used. (1)

GET IT RIGHT!

Remember to start with the genotypes of the parents before you do your punnet square. Make sure your C's can be identified as big and small.

2 a) A student carried out an experiment to investigate photosynthesis in a Geranium plant. The table shows how the experiment was set up.

Leaf	Leaf A	Leaf B	Leaf C
Condition grown in	Full sunlight	Dark cupboard	Full sunlight

See pages 98–99

The glucose made during photosynthesis is stored as starch. The student carried out a starch test on the leaves using iodine. Iodine turns black if starch is present. The results of her experiment are shown in the picture below.

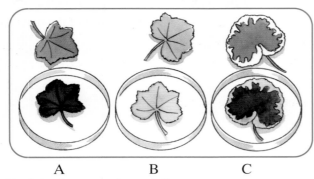

A   B   C

GET IT RIGHT!

Remember to describe each leaf A, B and C.

i) Explain these results as fully as you can. (6)

ii) What is the glucose made during photosynthesis used for? (3)

3 Dairy farmers keep cows which give us milk.

   a) What two other useful products are obtained from cows? (2)

   b) Milk can be used to make cheese. The diagram shows this process.

See page 114–115

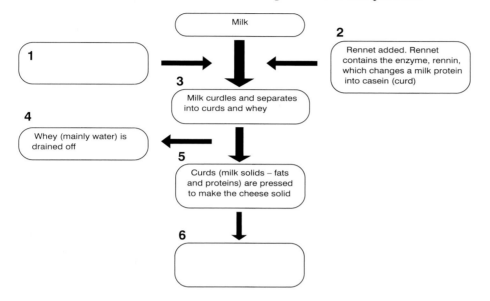

GET IT RIGHT!

The process of anaerobic respiration is involved here. Try to think what may be produced that would curdle milk.

   i) A microorganism is added at stage 1. What type of microorganism is it? (1)

   ii) What product is formed when the microorganism acts on lactose (milk sugar) found in milk? (1)

   c) Suggest how the cheese maker could improve the flavour of the cheese at stage 6. (3)

See page 147

4 Solar panels can be used to heat up water in a house.

   a) Give **three** advantages of heating water in this way. (3)

   b) Solar power can also be used to generate electricity. A solar tower built in Manchester has 7000 photovoltaic panels and produces 182,000 units of electricity.
      i) How many units of electricity are produced by each panel? (1)
      ii) How many panels would be needed to generate enough electricity to power a 3 bedroom house which uses 1560 units of electricity? (1)
      iii) Give two disadvantages of generating electricity in this way. (2)

   c) Give two reasons why wind power would not be suitable for generating electricity in a city. (2)

GET IT RIGHT!

When performing calculations, check that your answer makes sense. Calculations are always easier and more accurate with a calculator, so make sure you use one.

END OF QUESTIONS

1.1   Developing scientific skills

1 What is involved in these Unit 3 practical coursework tasks?
2 How is the coursework assessed?
3 How do we follow standard procedures?

In this unit you will complete practical tasks:

1 Investigating living organisms, like a microbiologist.
2 Applying chemical analysis techniques, like an analytical chemist.
3 Investigating properties of materials, like a materials scientist.

So you will get an insight into how scientists work.

The 'assessment evidence grid' or mark scheme for Developing Scientific Skills is shown on the opposite page.

It will make up 27.5% of your total GCSE marks.

Each skill will be assessed **at least three times**.

The final mark comes from the **best mark obtained for each skill**.

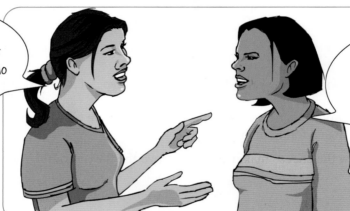

I like the idea that it is the best mark that counts, as I may not do so well in one task.

Yes and by the time we get to the third task we should improve matching our write-up to the mark scheme.

The best mark counts

Scientists use certain practical skills every day. Practising them will help to improve your accuracy and build your confidence.

A **standard procedure** describes exactly how to carry out an experiment. The procedure may describe how to:

● Carry out measurements.
● Prepare or purify a compound.
● Monitor a change.

A standard procedure ensures that whoever carries out the experiment does it in exactly the same way.

When following a standard procedure:

● Read it and check if there is anything you do not understand.
● Collect the equipment and materials you need.
● Carry out a **risk assessment** for the activity.
● Follow the instructions one step at a time to make accurate observations or measurements.
● Identify possible sources of error and repeat, if need be, to improve reliability.

Stage 1	Stage 2	Stage 3
Planning and following instructions		
• Carry out a risk assessment, given clear guidelines • Follow instructions, with guidance, in simple standard procedures, one step at a time	• Carry out a risk assessment, given some guidelines • Follow instructions in standard procedures, with little guidance for the more complex tasks • Select and prepare appropriate laboratory equipment and use it correctly and safely	• Independently carry out a risk assessment • Independently follow instructions in standard procedures • Select and prepare laboratory equipment of appropriate precision and use it correctly and safely
1A 1–4 marks	**2A** 5–8 marks	**3A** 9–12 marks
Obtaining evidence by experimenting		
• Make simple observations and measurements • Record them in tables and in charts or graphs with guidance	• Make careful and accurate measurements and observations • Recognise with little guidance when it is necessary to repeat measurements and observations • Record results accurately in tables and graphs where appropriate, using lines of best fit where appropriate	• Make careful and accurate measurements and observations consistently • Independently repeat measurements and observations when necessary • Independently record and present data in an appropriate form
1B 1–4 marks	**2B** 5-8 marks	**3B** 9–12 marks
Analysing and considering evidence		
• Offer simple explanations for your findings • Carry out simple calculations with guidance	• Identify and explain patterns within data • Carry out simple calculations when needed • Make conclusions which are consistent with the evidence	• Identify relationships where appropriate • Manipulate data using a variety of sophisticated techniques • Make and present well structured and accurate conclusions from the data which illustrate an in-depth understanding
1C 1–4 marks	**2C** 5–8 marks	**3C** 9–12 marks
Evaluating evidence		
• Give a simple evaluation of your practical activity	• Give an evaluation of your practical activity • Suggest an improvement to the method that would allow the collection of more reliable data	• Review your practical activity by presenting a well structured, logical evaluation of its strengths and weaknesses • Describe improvements to the method that would allow the collection of more reliable data
1D 1–2 marks	**2D** 3–4 marks	**3D** 5–7 marks
Workplace application		
• Give a use for this practical activity in a workplace that uses science	• Describe how the practical activity is used in a workplace that uses science	• Explain why the practical activity is useful in a workplace that uses science • Give examples of the types of organisation that use this type of activity
1E 1–2 marks	**2E** 3–4 marks	**3E** 5–7 marks

GET IT RIGHT!

It is important that you think about the results you obtain and how to interpret them. You will need to be able to:

• Present data in appropriate tables and graphs.

• Carry out calculations, analyse and interpret your results.

• Evaluate your investigation and suggest improvements.

GET IT RIGHT!

When writing a report ask yourself if there is:

• A risk assessment of the standard procedure.

• An in-depth conclusion (after obtaining, recording and analysing the data).

• An evaluation (referring to accuracy, reliability and improvements).

• An explanation of the how the practical work can be used in the workplace.

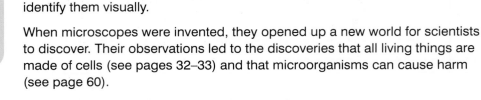

1.2   Using microscopes

LEARNING OBJECTIVES

1 How do we use microscopes?
2 How does focusing help when viewing microscope slides?

Scientists use microscopes to look at things that are too small to see with just your eyes. There are millions of different viruses, fungi and bacteria that are too small to see. It is important that we are able to view them so that we can identify them visually.

When microscopes were invented, they opened up a new world for scientists to discover. Their observations led to the discoveries that all living things are made of cells (see pages 32–33) and that microorganisms can cause harm (see page 60).

Scientists need to make slides to use under a microscope.

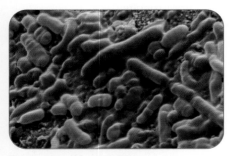

There are millions of different viruses, fungi and bacteria that are too small to see with the naked eye

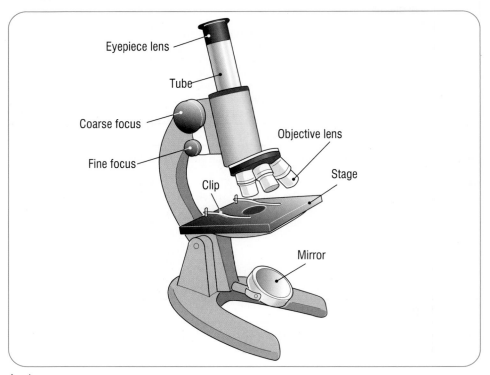

Eyepiece lens
Tube
Coarse focus
Fine focus
Clip
Objective lens
Stage
Mirror

A microscope

STANDARD PROCEDURE

Preparing a slide

1 Carefully cut a piece of onion.

2 Using tweezers, pull off a thin piece of onion skin from inside the onion.

3 Place this onion skin on a microscope slide.

4 Using a pipette, put a drop of iodine onto the onion skin.

5 Put a cover slip over the onion.

You have now prepared a slide for viewing under a microscope.

STANDARD PROCEDURE

Using a microscope

1 Always carry the microscope using both hands: one on the arm of the microscope and one on its base.

2 Place your slide on the stage and clip it securely.

3 Select the lowest power objective lens.

4 Before looking down the microscope, wind the stage up as far as it can go without touching the slide.

5 Then look down the eyepiece lens and use the focus knobs to move the stage slowly downwards until you see a clear image.

6 Carefully draw a diagram of the image and label it.

7 Repeat steps 4 to 6 with more high-powered lenses.

GET IT RIGHT!

To work out how much the image has been magnified, you multiply the magnification of the eyepiece lens by the magnification of the objective lens.

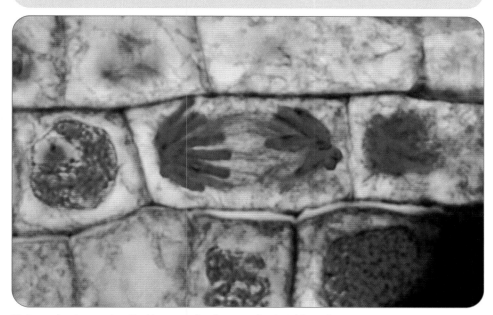

Picture of onion root cells. You can clearly see mitosis taking place.

TEST YOURSELF!

1 How can you safely carry a microscope?

2 Geraldine uses a microscope which has an eyepiece lens with a magnification of 10x and an objective lens with a magnification of 24x. What is the total magnification?

3 Explain what your diagrams of the onion show. Label each part of your diagram and explain its function.

4 Try the experiment without staining your onion slide. What difference does it make?

1.3   Haemocytometers

LEARNING OBJECTIVES

1 How can we use a microscope to make measurements?
2 How can doctors use a microscope to find out if you are anaemic?

It is important to know the condition of a person's blood. It is a very good measure of how healthy a person is.

Blood is made up of four main components:

- Red blood cells.
- White blood cells.
- Plasma.
- Platelets.

Red blood cells transport oxygen around our body so that our cells can carry out respiration. If someone has too few red blood cells, then we say that they are anaemic.

a) What are the four components of blood? (see page 41)
b) What do we mean by anaemia?

Doctors count red blood cells using a microscope and a haemocytometer. The haemocytometer is a special (and very expensive) type of microscope slide that has a very, very fine grid of lines on it.

This grid is a bit like graph paper. Each small square is very small, with an area of $1/400 \, mm^2$. If we count how many red blood cells are in one square, we can multiply up to find out how many red blood cells are in our blood.

Doctors can then work out if we are anaemic or not.

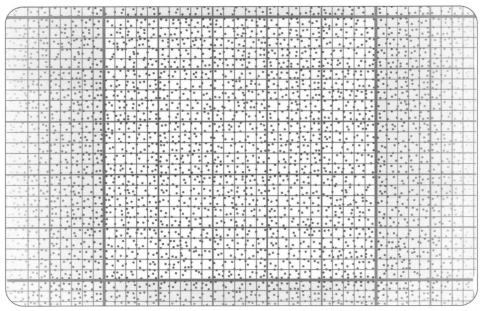

Diagram of what can be observed in a haemocytometer   Not to scale

STANDARD PROCEDURE

1 Wash the haemocytometer slide with distilled water and dab it dry using a paper towel.

2 Find the grid lines on the haemocytometer under the microscope at 100× power.

3 Carefully remove the haemocytometer slide.

4 Place the tube into your test liquid (either blood or yeast solution).

5 Lift out the tube and there should be some liquid inside.

6 Place the capillary tube over the top of the haemocytometer slide (take care not to touch it!) Then take your thumb off. Liquid will pour out onto the slide.

7 Put a cover slip over the slide.

8 View under the microscope and count number of cells in a random square.

9 Repeat until you have 4 readings.

10 Repeat experiment.

Calculations

If each square is $1/400\,mm^2$, then 4 of them is $4/400\,mm^2 = 1/100\,mm^2$.

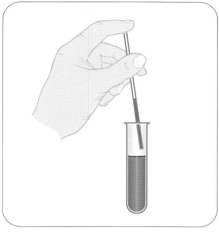

Using a capillary tube

c) How many cells are there in $1\,mm^2$?
d) How could we calculate the number of red blood cells in $1\,mm^3$ of blood?

TEST YOURSELF!

1 Why would someone want to count numbers of cells?

2 The experiment has lots of repeats in it. Why do scientists repeat experiments?

3 Write a risk assessment for this activity. Be careful to include hazards and risks to do with all the materials, apparatus and the procedure used.

1.4   Microorganisms – use and safe disposal

1 How do you culture microorganisms and dispose of them safely?
2 What are aseptic techniques?

Bacteria are not always a bad thing. They don't just cause sickness, they can also help cure it. For example, the antibiotics prescribed for bad earache were probably made by microbes themselves.

Microorganisms can harm our pets and plants too.

 Discuss how you can be harmed by a fungus, bacterium or virus. (See pages 60–61.)

Inoculating agar plates

Imagine you are a microbiologist. You have been asked to investigate bacteria that grow in environments like the soil, water and your skin. The aim is to inoculate or deliberately infect some agar with bacteria. Nutrient agar is food on which a single bacterium can grow into a colony that you can see.

Biohazard warning sign

Safety first

Since some of the microorganisms could be pathogenic and cause disease, it is essential you always follow proper **aseptic technique**. Aseptic techniques are precautionary measures, taken to prevent contamination of yourself, your experiment or your environment.

● You will be given sterile agar plates. To keep them sterile and free from microorganisms in the air, the plates should be kept covered at all times except when streaking them.
● Treat all microorganisms as potential pathogens:

   1 Use antibacterial hand-wash to clean your hands.
   2 Spray the bench with disinfectant and dry with a towel.
   3 Do not put bags, books, etc. on the bench.
   4 Avoid putting your hand or pen-top to your mouth.

Select a known bacterial culture provided by your teacher. Before inoculating this sample of bacteria, write the details on the bottom of the Petri dish, near the rim.

Streaking

● Put the sample on the side of the agar with a swab or inoculating loop. (We always flame inoculating loops until red hot before and after use.)
● Gently spread the bacteria out with a sterile loop.
● Repeat 2-3 times, moving around the agar plate.
● Dispose of swabs and loops in a safe bin and disinfectant.

Streaking the agar plate

What should happen is that single bacterial cells get isolated by the streaking. Then, when the plate is incubated, the resulting colonies will each have started from just one bacterium.

Incubating

Put one piece of tape across the top of the Petri dish but do not seal all the way round. Invert your Petri dish so that the lid is on the bench-top and the agar is bottom up. We incubate plates upside-down so that drops of condensation do not fall on the agar surface. In a few days, look for colonies of bacteria on the plates.

Colonies of *E. coli* growing on agar plate

Safety last

Finally, disinfect the bench once again and use antibacterial hand-wash.

Safe disposal of agar plates

Plates, once finished with **must** be made safe before throwing away.

We put the agar plates inside an autoclave bag which is sterilised by autoclaving at over 120°C for 15 minutes. An **autoclave** is like a pressure cooker. The autoclave uses steam to sterilise equipment and kill all the bacteria, viruses and fungi in the bag. After the bag has cooled down it can safely be thrown away.

An autoclave

When scientists culture (or grow) a colony of a single type of microorganism, they make sure that there is no contamination from other microorganisms. They also avoid handling the organisms directly, as this may be dangerous. Using aseptic techniques ensures both these things happen.

a) When experimenting, why must we avoid:
   i) Bacteria from our **experiment** getting out into the **environment**?
   ii) Bacteria from our **environment** getting into our **experiment**?

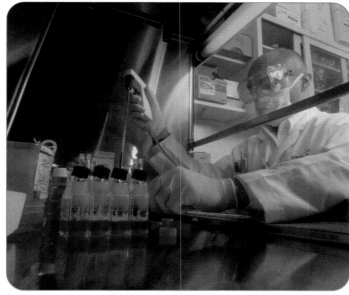

Andrew works in a microbiology laboratory. His safety cabinet draws air in from the laboratory. This filters out microorganisms in the air so they do not return to the laboratory environment where he is working.

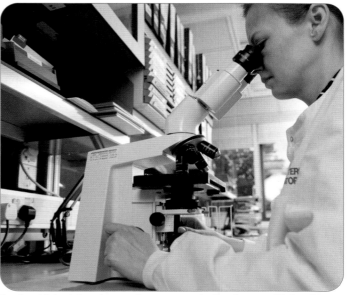

A microbiologist, using a microscope, studies the sensitivity of bacteria to antibiotics. Her task is to find out which antibiotics will be effective in combating an infection. You can find more details of the disc diffusion test on the next page.

TEST YOURSELF!

1 Explain the disease triangle:

'Disease development requires a virulent pathogen + a susceptible host + a favourable environment'.

Susceptible host

Virulent pathogen

Favourable environment

The disease triangle

1.5

Is your microbe resistant to antibiotics?

1 How do we apply aseptic techniques?
2 Can different antimicrobial agents affect microorganisms differently?

Mastitis is a bacterial infection of the mammary (udder) tissue. The udder becomes red, warm and hard.

Microorganisms like bacteria can harm us too. (See pages 60–61.) You have probably heard of salmonella food poisoning and pneumonia. Yet most bacteria are useful, as in live yoghurt.

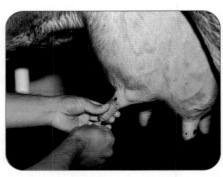

This cow has got mastitis!

Vets use antibiotics to kill the bacteria that cause mastitis in cows – bacteria like *Staphylococcus aureus (S. aureus)* and *Escherichia coli (E. coli)*. The vet prescribes the most effective antibiotic to treat a bacterial infection. Hopefully, one that the bacteria are unable to resist.

Measuring antibiotic sensitivity using the disc diffusion test

Aim: To see how sensitive some strains of bacteria are to various antibiotics and antiseptics. Remember that some bacteria are resistant to antibiotics.

a) What happens to the concentration of antibiotic as you get further from the disc?

We swab bacteria onto nutrient agar and put antibiotic discs on top. Antibiotic diffuses into the agar. If bacteria are susceptible to the antibiotic, there is NO growth round the disc.

The disc diffusion test

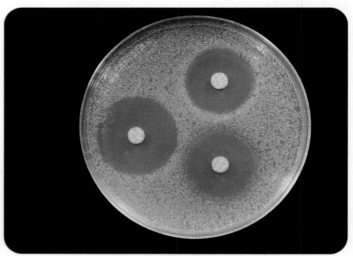

The ring around the disc is called the **zone of inhibition**

Write a **risk assessment** for the investigation before you start.

'Antibiotic sensitivity testing kits' contain discs of antibiotic like **penicillin** and **streptomycin**. You can make your own antiseptic disc with a hole punch and filter paper.

Dip your disc into a solution like dilute bleach or antiseptic hand-wash.

STANDARD PROCEDURE

Here is an example: *(Light your Bunsen burner. Put on gloves.)*

1 Label the *bottom* of a sterile agar plate with your name, the date, the strain of bacteria, the type of antibiotic being used (or the name of your own antiseptic disc being used).
2 Soak a sterilised cotton swab into the liquid bacteria culture.

Open the plate and *gently streak* the swab evenly across the agar so that the surface is covered.

Repeat twice more, turning the plate each time so you implant the bacteria (**inoculate**) evenly. Replace the lid for 5 minutes.

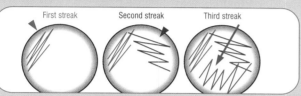

First streak   Second streak   Third streak

Spreading the swab across the agar

3 Use sterile tweezers to place an antibiotic disc 25 mm from the side of the plate. Gently push the disc down on the agar.

On the opposite side, place your own antiseptic disc, the one you made yourself.

Maintain a sterile environment and do not contaminate the culture. Keep your plate closed unless you are streaking your culture or putting discs in place. When your plate is open you are:

- exposing the plate to bacteria that are in the air, and
- exposing yourself to bacteria that are on the agar.

4 Put one piece of tape across the top of the Petri dish and leave it upside-down. Disinfect your desk and wash your hands.
5 After incubating the bacteria for about 48 hours, measure the diameter (in mm) of the zone of inhibition around each disc.

This gives an indication of the effect of the antibiotic on the particular bacteria.

6 Prepare a table with headings for class results showing bacteria, antibiotics, diameters of zones of inhibition (mm), averages and conclusion (*resistant, intermediate or susceptible*).

(You could pool class results to obtain averages, before writing your conclusion and evaluation for this investigation.)

SAFETY MATTERS

Scientists always use aseptic techniques to avoid contamination.

Use caution. We do not want to contaminate the lab or ourselves with bacteria.

- Wear gloves throughout.
- After opening the bacteria bottle, '**flame**' the top of it. Don't put the lid down.
- Use a safe disposal container for used swabs and tweezers.
- Clear up any spills with disinfectant.
- Afterwards, disinfect your desk and wash your hands.
- Do not open taped-up dishes.

Placing an antibiotic disc on the agar. The discs come in a little tube.

TEST YOURSELF!

1 Why do doctors have a problem treating patients with MRSA? (See page 29.)

2 Explain how an agar plate inoculated with sterile water would act as a control.

3 a) What do we call the clear area around an antimicrobial (antibiotic) disc?
   b) Why do bacteria grow right up to some discs?
   c) Why don't we see bacteria grow round some discs?
   d) The larger the zone, the more s_____ the bacteria are to the antimicrobial agent.

DEVELOPING SCIENTIFIC SKILLS

1.6 Flame tests – qualitative analysis part 1

LEARNING OBJECTIVES

1 How do we carry out flame tests?
2 How do we use flame tests?
3 What is forensic science?

Forensic scientists want to work out what has happened or what is present in samples to solve crimes. They use scientific tests to find the answers.

In one of the tests, they can find out which metal ions are present in soil samples. Scientists can easily see which ions are present by doing a flame test. Different metal ions produce different colours. By matching up colours we can see which metal ions are in the test sample.

STANDARD PROCEDURE

The flame test is a very easy test to perform; the standard procedure is:

1 Clean the loop in hydrochloric acid.

2 Place the loop in the hot Bunsen flame.

3 Dip the loop in hydrochloric acid again.

4 Dip the loop into the sample.

5 Place in the hot Bunsen flame.

6 Record the colour of the flame in a table.

(see diagram below)

Flame tests are an example of **qualitative analysis**. They tell you what is present in a sample, but not how much of it there is.

a) Do a risk assessment for the flame tests. Be careful to include all hazards and risks. (See page 21 for help.)
b) Draw up a table of results to show the metal ions present and the different colours seen when they are heated.
c) How do chemists make firework displays so colourful?

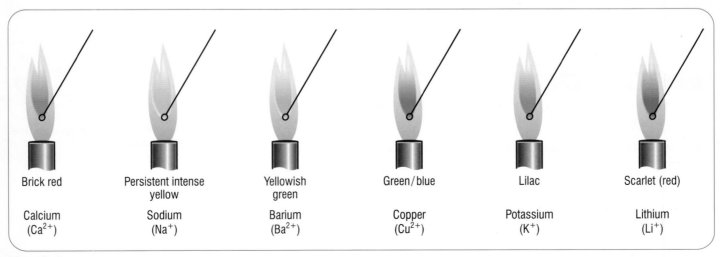

| Brick red | Persistent intense yellow | Yellowish green | Green/blue | Lilac | Scarlet (red) |
| Calcium (Ca^{2+}) | Sodium (Na^+) | Barium (Ba^{2+}) | Copper (Cu^{2+}) | Potassium (K^+) | Lithium (Li^+) |

Flame tests

Gardeners want to know what ions are in the soil to help their plants grow. Plants get nutrient ions from the soil and that helps them grow and flower. Gardeners put fertiliser on the ground to provide extra nutrients.

Chemistry is important to gardeners

The plant above has a unique talent. The flowers are different colours in different soils. When the soil is slightly acidic, it produces blue-coloured flowers. When the soil is slightly alkaline, it produces red flowers. The gardener has put lime on the soil to neutralise acid and increase the soil's pH so that the plant produces two different-coloured flowers.

d) How is this plant different from universal indicator?
e) What experiments could we do to find out?

Police can often find themselves in a situation that requires them to test soils in the tread of people's shoes in order to find out where they have been. It is an important part of the police forensic scientists' work.

TEST YOURSELF!

1 Copy and complete the following sentences using these words:

ions   colours   metal

We can use flame tests to find out which _____ ions are in a sample.

The different metal _____ produce different _____ of flame. Carbon produces the orange/yellow flame of fire we are used to.

2 How do you do a flame test?

3 How do police use flame tests in their investigations?

4 How can gardeners use flame tests to help them produce better conditions for their plants?

5 What does 'qualitative analysis' mean?

1.7

Chemical tests – qualitative analysis part 2

Always protect your eyes

Forensic scientists want to work out what has happened or what is present in samples to solve problems. They use scientific tests to find the answers. In this second test they can find out which ions are present in a sample.

Sodium hydroxide test for positive ions

Sodium hydroxide is a strong alkali. We can use it to test for many different ions. The sodium hydroxide reacts with different metal ions to give different coloured **precipitates**. (A precipitate is an insoluble solid formed in a solution.)

The colour of the precipitate tells us which ion is present.

Sodium hydroxide requires the use of different types of goggles at different concentrations. If the concentration is $0.5\,mol/dm^3$ or higher, you should wear safety goggles that completely cover the eye. Read the hazcard very carefully when writing your risk assessment before carrying out your experiment.

1 Place your sample in a test tube.

2 Add a few drops of sodium hydroxide.

3 Record the result in a table.

4 Add more drops of sodium hydroxide and see if the precipitate dissolves.

5 Record the result in a table.

6 Use the table below to identify the ion.

Name of ion	Effect of a few drops of sodium hydroxide	Effect of excess sodium hydroxide
Aluminium, Al^{3+} (or lead, Pb^{2+})	White precipitate	Precipitate redissolves
Calcium, Ca^{2+}	White precipitate	Precipitate insoluble
Ammonium, NH_4^+	Ammonia gas released (when warmed)	Ammonia gas released (which turns damp red litmus paper blue)
Copper, Cu^{2+}	Blue precipitate	Precipitate insoluble
Iron(II), Fe^{2+}	Green/grey precipitate which turns orange/brown if left	Precipitate insoluble
Iron(III), Fe^{3+}	Orange/brown precipitate	Precipitate insoluble

a) Write a risk assessment for this experiment.
b) Draw up a table of results to show which ions were present in your sample.
c) Draw conclusions and write an evaluation for the experiment.

Testing negative ions

These chemical tests are more complex. You should remember that acid plus carbonate produces carbon dioxide from Key Stage 3. Try these tests, but make sure your risk assessment is completed beforehand.

Ion	Test	Positive result
Carbonate, CO_3^{2-}	Add hydrochloric acid	Carbon dioxide gas released (which turns lime water milky)
Chloride, Cl^-	Add dilute nitric acid and then silver nitrate solution	White precipitate
Bromide, Br^-		Cream precipitate
Iodide, I^-		Pale yellow precipitate
Sulfate, SO_4^{2-}	Add dilute hydrochloric acid and then barium chloride solution	White precipitate

d) When performing the carbonate ion test (CO_3^{2-}), how could we tell if the gas was carbon dioxide or not?

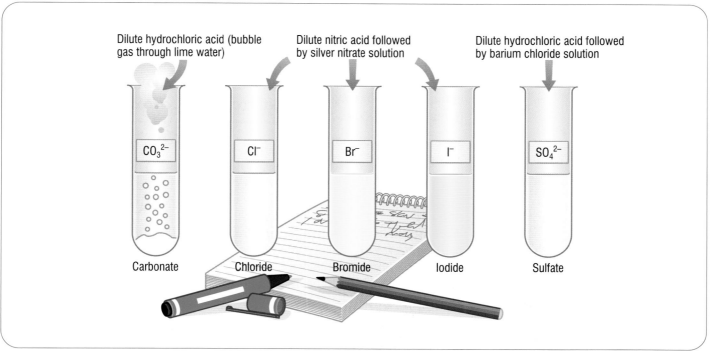

Chemical tests

TEST YOURSELF!

1 Write down a list of all of the ions that you have tested.

2 Which ion have you tested in two different ways?

3 Draw a poster showing all the different tests and the ions tested.

Try to make the poster into a flow chart or key for someone to follow when doing chemical tests themselves.

1.8

Understanding equations – chemical quantitative analysis

1 How does an equation help to explain a chemical reaction?
2 What is a 'mole'?
3 How do you calculate relative formula mass?

GET IT RIGHT!

The relative formula mass describes how heavy one molecule is compared with another.

On page 124, we saw that an **element** is a substance made up of only one type of **atom**.

When atoms **bond** together chemically, we can get molecules formed, e.g. oxygen (O_2); water (H_2O); methane (CH_4); ethanol (C_2H_5OH).

The formula of an oxygen molecule is O_2.

The **relative atomic mass** of oxygen is 16. We can think of an oxygen atom as 16 times heavier than the lightest of all atoms, the hydrogen atom. Hydrogen has a relative atomic mass of 1.

Therefore the **relative formula mass** of O_2 is 32 ($16 + 16 = 32$).

Similarly, the **relative formula mass** of H_2O is 18 ($1 + 1 + 16 = 18$).

a) What is the relative formula mass of methane (CH_4)?
b) What is the relative formula mass of ethanol (C_2H_5OH)?
(The relative atomic mass of C = 12)

32 g of O_2 (oxygen) and 18 g of H_2O (water) both contain exactly the same number of molecules.

That number is called a '**mole**'.

If you work out the **relative formula mass** of a substance and weigh out that mass in grams, you know it contains 602 000 000 000 000 000 000 000 atoms, molecules or ions!

The mole is just a number!
1 mole = 6.02×10^{23}, that is
602 000 000 000 000 000 000 000

The mole

Chemical equations

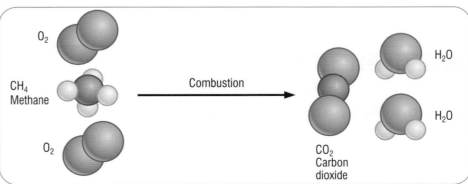

O_2

CH_4
Methane

O_2

Combustion

H_2O

H_2O

CO_2
Carbon dioxide

This diagram shows the reactants and products when methane burns in oxygen

Burning methane (CH_4)

The 'word equation' for the reaction is:

methane + oxygen → carbon dioxide + water

The next equation is a 'symbol equation', but it is not 'balanced':

$$CH_4 + O_2 \rightarrow CO_2 + H_2O$$

There must be the same number of atoms on both sides.
You balance an equation by putting numbers in front of the formulas:

$$CH_4 + 2O_2 \rightarrow CO_2 + 2H_2O$$

c) Copy and complete the table below showing the number of atoms in the balanced equation:

Elements		Reactants (on left)	Products (on right)
carbon	C	1	1
hydrogen	H	4	
oxygen	O		

Calculating the relative formula mass (in grams) for each symbol gives:

CH_4	+	$2O_2$	→	CO_2	+	$2H_2O$
$(12+1+1+1+1)$		$2(16+16)$		$12+16+16$		$2(1+1+16)$
$= 16$ g		$= 64$ g		$= 44$ g		$= 36$ g

1 mole of CH_4 + 2 moles of O_2 gives 1 mole of CO_2 + 2 moles of H_2O.

Burning 16 g of methane produces 44 g of carbon dioxide.

● Notice that the total mass doesn't change before and after the reaction.

TEST YOURSELF!

1 Calculate the relative formula mass for:
  a) nitric acid – HNO_3
  b) calcium carbonate – $CaCO_3$
  c) calcium nitrate – $Ca(NO_3)_2$
  (The relative atomic mass of H = 1, C = 12, N = 14, O = 16, Ca = 40)

2 a) Copy and balance this equation for the neutralisation reaction between nitric acid and calcium carbonate:

  $$HNO_3 + CaCO_3 \rightarrow Ca(NO_3)_2 + H_2O + CO_2$$

  b) When balanced, how many atoms of nitrogen are on each side?
  c) When balanced, how many atoms of oxygen are on each side?
  d) If 100 g of calcium carbonate react, how many grams of carbon dioxide are produced?
  e) i) How many grams of nitric acid do we need to react with 100 g of calcium carbonate?
     ii) How many moles is that?

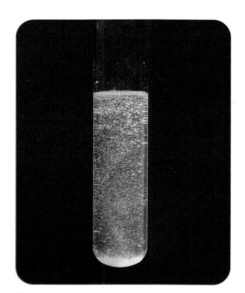

Bubbles of carbon dioxide produced when calcium carbonate reacts with acid

1.9

Drain cleaner titration – chemical quantitative analysis

LEARNING OBJECTIVES

1 How do you carry out a titration?
2 How do you calculate the concentration in units of mol/dm³ and g/dm³?

Blockbuster drain cleaner

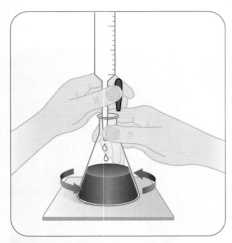

Swirl and add acid drop by drop near the end point

Mr Jones is surprised that his bottle of 'Blockbuster' drain cleaner is not strong enough to clear his drain. In his frustration, when adding more 'Blockbuster', he accidentally splashes some into his eye. After washing his eye out with water, it still stings. (Drain cleaner is strongly alkaline – containing **60%** sodium hydroxide). He phones his doctor. "Wash out your eye until the ambulance arrives and while travelling to the hospital," is the advice, "then report to the accident and emergency department."

a) What safer ways are there to clear blocked drains?

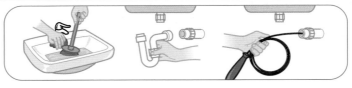

Ways to clear a blocked drain

A **titration** is an accurate method to find out the concentration of something. We check the amount of aspirin in aspirin tablets using a titration reaction. We determine the concentration of a metal in solutions using titration, e.g. the level of iron in blood.

Imagine that 'Trading Standards' has given you the task of measuring the concentration of sodium hydroxide in a bottle of drain cleaner.

Your teacher will show you how to carry out the titration. Your school or college technician will first dilute the corrosive drain cleaner solution by 20 with distilled water to reduce the risk. Take care – the drain cleaner solution you use is still an irritant.

A **risk assessment** for the titration is needed before you start.

STANDARD PROCEDURE

1 Using a **pipette** (and safety filler) transfer 25 cm³ of dilute drain cleaner (sodium hydroxide solution) into a conical flask.
2 Add a few drops of indicator (e.g. screened methyl orange) and put a white tile under the flask.
3 Using a funnel, fill a **burette** with your standard solution of 0.2 mol/dm³ sulfuric acid (meaning 0.2 moles of H_2SO_4 was diluted in 1 dm³ of water).

Drain some acid into a beaker to remove the air below the tap.

Record the starting volume to the nearest 0.05 cm³.

4 Slowly add the acid (1 cm³ at a time) to the flask of drain cleaner. Swirl the flask and stop at the **end point**, when the indicator just changes colour.

Record the final volume. Work out the volume of acid used.

This is your trial or **rough experiment**.

5 Repeat the titration more carefully, swirling and adding acid drop by drop near the end point.

Continue repeats until you get two accurate volumes within 0.1 cm³. Average the two accurate titrations.

Assume the average volume of sulfuric acid used is 23.8cm³.

Calculating concentration

The balanced chemical equation shows:

2 moles of NaOH reacts with 1 mole of H_2SO_4

Measure at the bottom of the meniscus

	sodium hydroxide	+	sulfuric acid	→	sodium sulfate	+	water
	2 NaOH	+	H_2SO_4	→	Na_2SO_4	+	2 H_2O

volumes: 25 cm³   23.8 cm³

concentrations: ?**M**?   0.2 mol/dm³

(?unknown concentration?)

Now use the **formula** to work out the unknown concentration:

(For NaOH) $\dfrac{\textbf{concentration} \times \textbf{volume}}{\textbf{number of moles}} = \dfrac{\textbf{concentration} \times \textbf{volume}}{\textbf{number of moles}}$ (For H_2SO_4)

$$\frac{M \times 25}{2} = \frac{0.2 \times 23.8}{1}$$

Therefore

$$M = \frac{0.2 \times 23.8 \times 2}{25}$$

$$M = 0.38 \text{ mol/dm}^3$$

Since the technician diluted the drain cleaner by 20,
the **concentration** of the drain cleaner = 20 × 0.38 = **7.6 mol/dm³**

The relative formula mass of sodium hydroxide (NaOH) = 23 + 16 + 1
$$= 40$$

Therefore   One mole of NaOH has a mass = 40 g
And   **7.6** mol of NaOH has a mass = 7.6 × 40
$$= 304 \text{ g}$$
or   the **concentration** of the drain cleaner = **304 g/dm³**

1 dm³ (or 1 litre or 1000 cm³) of water has a mass of 1000 g,
so the drain cleaner has 304 g of NaOH in every 1000 g of solution.
(304/1000) × 100% = 30.4% (or approximately **30%**).

This is about *half* the **60%** advertised on the bottle.

In this case *Trading Standards* would take the company that makes
'*Blockbuster*' to court!

TEST YOURSELF!

1   What measurements are made in a titration experiment?

2   Draw a results table for a titration experiment.

3   20.0 cm³ of hydrochloric acid reacted with 25 cm³ of 0.1 mol/dm³ sodium hydroxide. Calculate the concentration (in mol/dm³) of the acid, using the formula above.

	HCl	+	NaOH	→	NaCl	+	H_2O	(This equation is balanced)
	hydrochloric acid		sodium hydroxide		sodium chloride		water	

DID YOU KNOW?

We use sodium hydroxide (NaOH or caustic soda) to make paper, textiles and detergents. It is highly caustic, with a high risk of causing chemical burns, scarring and blindness.

1.10   Electrical properties – resistance

Both large and small, we use electric circuits every day.

The National Grid

A microprocessor

Long thin wires resist the flow of current and can get hot.

a) Why do we use thick wires to carry electricity across country?

Look at Naomi's model of an electric circuit below. People are carrying sacks of energy from the battery to the bulb. They must return to the battery to get more energy.

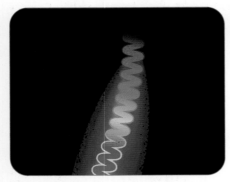

Infra-red image of hot wire carrying a current

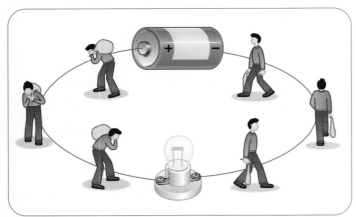

Model of electric current

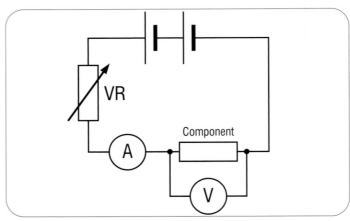

As you **vary** the variable resistor (VR), it alters the current flowing round the circuit

  Discuss what you think the people and their sacks represent.

You know that more voltage provides more energy to a circuit. More voltage also increases the flow rate or current. In metal wires the current is a flow of electrons. Current is measured in amperes (amps, A).

The greater the resistance of the component the less the current. **Resistance** is measured in ohms or Ω.

b) What is needed for electrons to flow?

We can measure resistance in two ways:

1 Using the formula:

$$\text{Resistance} = \frac{\text{voltage}}{\text{current}} \qquad (\text{or } \Omega = \frac{V}{A})$$

2 Using a multimeter.

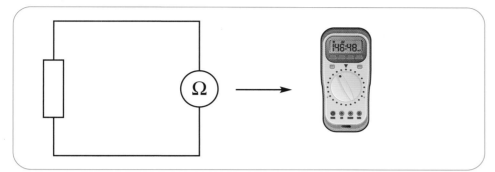

Using a multimeter

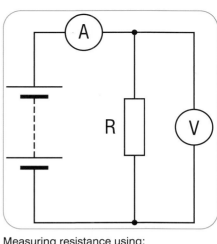

Measuring resistance using:
$\Omega = V \div A$

c) A current of 0.75 A flows through a wire when it is joined to a 1.5 V battery. What is the resistance of the wire?

Metals have small resistances.

You have probably seen carbon resistors. Carbon resistors have high resistances. We use them to limit the current in devices like computers. This prevents overheating and reduces running costs. Carbon resistors have different colour codes.

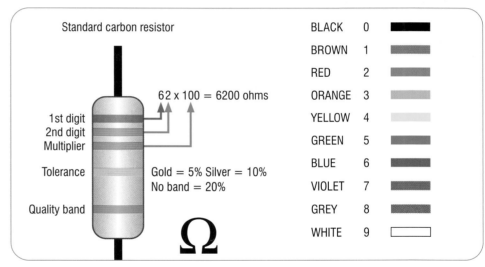

Standard carbon resistor

1st digit
2nd digit
Multiplier

62 x 100 = 6200 ohms

Tolerance

Gold = 5% Silver = 10%
No band = 20%

Quality band

Ω

BLACK	0
BROWN	1
RED	2
ORANGE	3
YELLOW	4
GREEN	5
BLUE	6
VIOLET	7
GREY	8
WHITE	9

A standard carbon resistor and resistor colour codes. You will use carbon resistors again in Unit 4 Electronic devices.

TEST YOURSELF!

1 Copy and complete the table:

Quantity	Units	Measuring instrument
	volts (V)	
Current		
Resistance		Multimeter

2 What is the resistance of a hair drier filament which draws a current of 5 A from a 230 V mains supply?

1.11

Electrical properties – investigation ideas

A live gig

Before a concert can go ahead, electricians must check the electric wiring.

It is not just a matter of tripping over loose cable. Some cables carry electricity better than others and offer less resistance to the current. The length and thickness of the wire affects the resistance.

Faulty installation can cause **electrocution** or fire.

Extension leads are useful in the garden

Imagine using a hedge trimmer with a 30 m extension lead. Every metre of the extension lead resists the flow of electrons through the copper wire. The resistance of a lightweight cable can make it overheat. Polyvinyl chloride (pvc) insulates the cable, but it softens above 70°C. Then the copper wire inside the cable can cut through the insulation. If pvc burns, it emits dense smoke and corrosive hydrogen chloride gas.

a) Why does cable for use in gardens often have orange insulation?
b) Why should extension leads be completely unwound before use?
c) Why is it dangerous to use powerful appliances with thin cable?

You can buy three core-cable of different widths.

In your investigation you could try the following **for each size of cable**:

1 Count the number of strands that make up the live (brown) wire. Measure the diameter of a single strand using a micrometer. (The micrometer dial is accurate to 1/100 mm.)

Calculate the area of a strand using:

$$Area = \pi \, (radius)^2$$

Then multiply by the number of strands to calculate the total area of each live wire.

2 Measure the resistance (in ohms: Ω) of a 10 m length of live wire using a multimeter.
Check to see whether the resistance of your connecting leads affects your measurements. If it does, adjust your readings. Compare the total area of each live wire to its resistance.

3 Select one strand of live wire. See how the resistance of this strand increases with length, every 20 cm up to 2 m.

4 The voltage applied affects the current flowing. The resistance can be measured another way using the formula:
resistance = voltage / current (or $\Omega = V / A$)

For a 2 m strand, plot voltage against current. (There is a risk of the wire getting hot if the voltage is not limited to 2 V maximum.)

Check the resistance at each voltage.

What conclusions can you make?

Extension leads have cables of different widths and lengths

GET IT RIGHT!

Remember – repeat readings.

Do not use mains voltage.

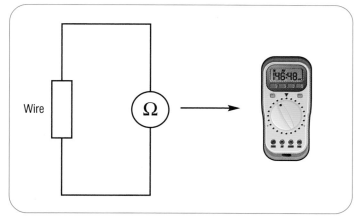

Multimeter

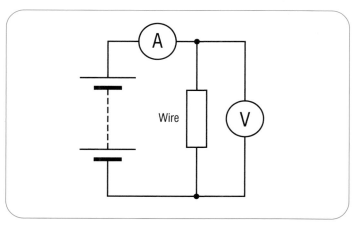

Measuring resistance using: $\Omega = V / A$

TEST YOURSELF!

1 Where are long extension leads useful?

2 If the diameter of a wire is 0.2 mm,
a) What is its radius?
b) What is its area? (Use $A = \pi \, r^2$)

3 The voltmeter reads 1.8 V.
The ammeter reads 0.9 A.
What is the resistance of the wire?

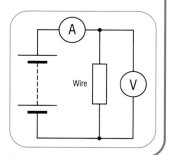

1.12

Mechanical properties – density investigation

1 How is density measured?
2 How can we carry out a coursework investigation about **density**?

The Californian gold rush

'Strike it rich' – the density of gold ($19.3\,\text{g/cm}^3$) was important to miners of the Californian gold rush of 1848. Very dense gold dust from mountain streams sank to the bottom of their 'pans'. Less dense **sediments** were shaken out of the pan with the water.

The table shows the density of various metals.

Metal	Density (g/cm^3)
Magnesium	1.74
Aluminium	2.70
Zinc	7.14
Tin	7.31
Iron	7.87
Copper	8.92
Lead	11.3
Gold	19.3
Aluminium alloy	2.6–2.8
Brass (Cu / Zn)	8.4–8.7
Bronze (Cu / Sn)	7.4–8.9
Steel (Fe / C / etc.)	7.7–8.1

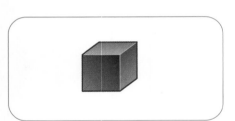

A cube – $1\,\text{cm}^3$

The density of a substance is its mass in grams, for $1\,\text{cm}^3$.

$$\text{Density} = \frac{\text{mass}}{\text{volume}} \quad \text{units: g/cm}^3$$

a) What is the mass of $2\,\text{cm}^3$ piece of aluminium?
b) $4\,\text{cm}^3$ of silver has a mass of $42\,\text{g}$. What is the density of silver?

A 14 karat gold ring

Pure gold is called 24 karat. 14 karat gold is more common for use in jewellery, as it is harder wearing. 14 karat gold is an **alloy** made by mixing other metals like copper and silver into the gold. 14 karat gold contains only 58% gold ($14 \div 24 = 0.58$). It is less dense than pure gold.

Pure aluminium is relatively soft. Alloys of aluminium are harder and stronger – more like steel – but far less dense. We make the alloy by adding small amounts of other elements to it, like copper, manganese, silicon, magnesium and zinc. Alloying changes the density of the aluminium.

c) When magnesium is added to aluminium, why does the alloy have a lower density than pure aluminium?

d) Aluminium alloy has a lower density than stainless steel. Why does aluminium alloy's low density make it useful for making:
  i) Aircraft?
  ii) Ladders?
  iii) Train carriages?

You could investigate some regularly shaped metals (cuboids, cylinders and spheres). By measuring their density you could find out whether they are pure metals or alloys.

Aluminium alloy wheels

REMEMBER

the volume of a cuboid = length × width × height   units: cm^3
radius = 0.5 × diameter   units: cm
the volume of a cylinder = $\pi r^2 h$ units: cm^3
the volume of a sphere = $(4/3) \pi r^3$ units: cm^3
$$density = \frac{mass}{volume}$$ units: g/cm^3

Use a digital balance (accurate to 0.01 g) to weigh your masses. You can measure lengths with a ruler, but more accurately with **digital callipers** or a **micrometer**. Digital callipers and micrometers measure to the nearest 1/100 mm. Your teacher will show you how to use them.

Digital callipers   A micrometer

GET IT RIGHT!

Designing a suitable results table for this investigation is tricky. You have many readings and calculations to do. Have a separate results table for each shape. Start with the simplest shape – the cuboid.

REMEMBER

1 To change mm readings to cm before you calculate the volumes of your solids.

2 To get reliable results, repeat your measurements.

Finally, calculate the density of each solid. Compare the densities against the values shown in the table on the previous page for pure metals and some alloys.

Other investigations are possible, based on the thermal conductivity or the strength of materials. (See page 284.)

TEST YOURSELF!

1 A certain metal cuboid has sides 3 cm × 4 cm × 5 cm. Its mass is 162 g.
  a) What is its volume?
  b) What is its density?
  c) What metal is it?

DEVELOPING SCIENTIFIC SKILLS

1.13

Heat conduction and the strength of materials

1 How would you compare conductivities?
2 How would you compare the strength of materials?

Look at the metal cooling fins on the motorbike. The fins have a large surface area, and **conduct** the heat away from the engine.

In the same way, we fit a 'heat sink' to the processor in a computer. The fan on top of the heat sink helps the metal cooling fins conduct the heat away from the processor.

Cooling fins on a motorbike engine

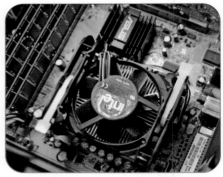

The heat sink sits over the processor

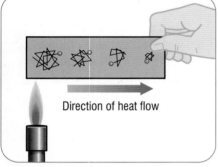

Peter's explanation of how metals conduct heat

Direction of heat flow

Peter explains how metals conduct heat in his diagram opposite.

a) Discuss whether or not it correctly explains conduction of heat.
b) Draw your own diagram to improve Peter's understanding. Pages 158 and 194 will help.

Investigation idea based on thermal conductivity

Find out which metal would be best as a heat sink for a computer processor.

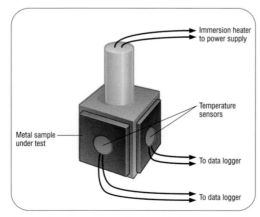

Apparatus to compare how metals conduct

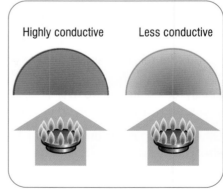

Different conductivities

One idea is to place temperature sensors on samples of different metals, like copper, iron and aluminium. You can compare the conductivities by noting the temperature rise of each sensor.

Investigations ideas based on the strength of materials

Steel is strong and stiff. Nylon, used in car seat-belts, is strong and flexible. Glass is strong but brittle.

 Discuss the uses of steel, nylon and glass based on their properties.

Testing for stiffness and flexibility in metals

You could see the effect of different cross-sectional areas.

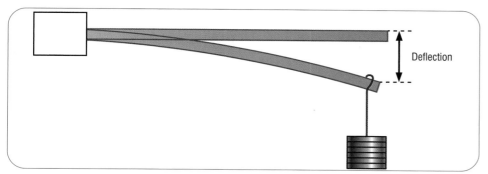

Flexibility test

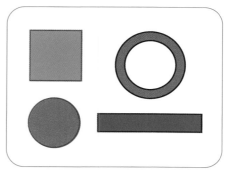

Possible cross-sections

Testing for hardness in metals

Place a ball bearing on your sample of metal. Drop the 1 kg weight onto the ball bearing. Measure the diameter of the dent in the metal with callipers.

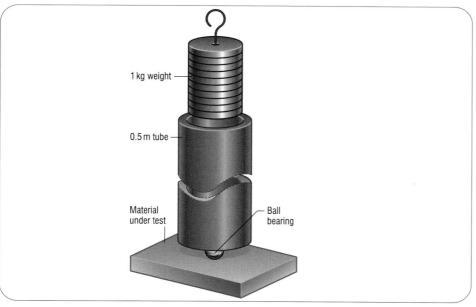

Hardness test

DID YOU KNOW?

Harder materials are more difficult to scratch. Ask your cat!

GET IT RIGHT!

Beware of falling weights – protect fingers, feet and floor.

TEST YOURSELF!

1 Think about these words: stiff, flexible, tough, brittle, hard. Why can concrete be broken?

2 Why do we reinforce concrete structures with steel rods?

3 What useful property has steel that is lacking in concrete?

1.14 The space elevator!

"Hello, ladies and gentlemen, welcome aboard the *Space Elevator*.

Your journey to the Space Station will take 5 hours, so sit back and enjoy the trip. As we go up, see the curvature of the Earth and the sky change from blue to black – truly one of the most breathtaking views you will ever see!"

Does this sound like a chapter out of Arthur C. Clarke's, '*Fountains of Paradise*'? Well, it's not.

Scientists believe a space elevator is a real possibility.

Artist's impression of the *Space Elevator* travelling on its taught cable

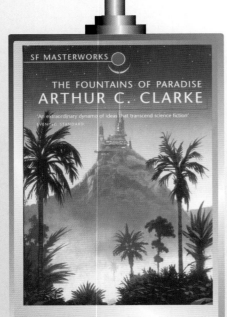

In '*The Fountains of Paradise*' by Arthur C. Clarke, Vannevar Morgan is the most famous architect of the 22nd century. He has built magnificent structures across the planet. Now he has decided to build what will be the greatest of them all. He's going to build the *skyhook*, the space elevator, from Earth to space.

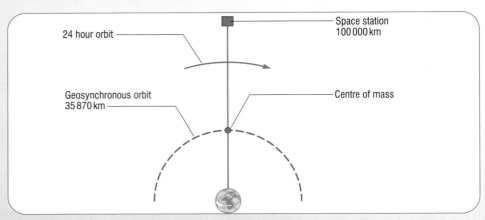

Scale diagram of the 24-hour orbit of the space elevator cable – 100 000 km long

Unlike Jack's 'beanstalk', an orbital *space elevator* uses a cable that 'hangs down' to the surface of the Earth. The centre of mass of the cable is 35 870 km high, in a geostationary (24-hour) orbit above the equator. Electric 'climber cars' travel up and down the cable, reaching speeds of up to 10 km/s. The material for the cable is able to endure tremendous stress, as well as being light-weight.

Activities

a) Why must the orbit be over the equator?
b) How long would it take you to travel 100 000 km at 10 km/s?

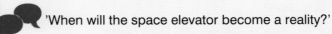 'When will the space elevator become a reality?'

'Probably about 50 years after everybody stops laughing!'

Discuss what you think.

Scientists are already working on its development.

Compared with current methods of getting off this planet – rockets, the Space Shuttle, etc., which can cost £10 000/kg – you could send people to geostationary orbit via a space elevator for 1/100 of the cost. However, the development costs of a space elevator are estimated at over $10 billion.

 Can this be justified? Discuss.

Physicist Brad Edwards overheard a colleague say that such an elevator couldn't be built for 300 years. Brad Edwards, though, was familiar with carbon nanotubes – fibres that are more than 100 times stronger than steel. He did some calculations and found no reason why a space elevator couldn't be built. NASA agreed and gave him $500 000 to develop his plan.

Activity

It needs a force of 1500 N to break a 1 mm wide steel cable. How many 1 kg bags of sugar could you hang on a carbon nanotube that is 1 mm wide? Remember 1 kg weighs 10 N.

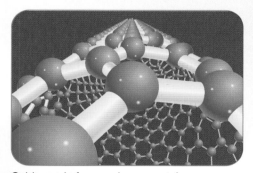

Cable made from carbon nanotubes. See the hexagon shape

In Brad Edwards's design, rockets blast off to 36 000 km and launch an 'anchor' satellite. Cables made from carbon-nanotube composite fibre unwind, one rising to 100 000 km. The other would be balancing this and falling to the ground. The biggest challenge is that the longest nanotube ever created is just 1/1000 mm in length. By combining nanotubes with an epoxy resin, though, "you can already make 'fishing line' strands as long as you want".

Problems remain, such as stability during hurricanes, collisions by meteorites and corrosion by oxygen, as well as building the transport system itself. "It's a big engineering challenge", Brad Edwards says. "There will be difficulties. But there's no reason why it can't be done." You can find out more information on the internet.

Activities

 "Once you're in Earth orbit... you're half-way to anywhere!" (Robert Heinlein, science fiction writer). Discuss this statement.
Discuss the problems of building a bridge from Liverpool in England to Dublin in Ireland.

1.1 Monitoring living organisms

LEARNING OBJECTIVE

1 Why do we look after organisms we study?
2 What are some of the moral and ethical issues involved in testing living organisms?

Introduction

Your coursework for Unit 4 shows you how scientists investigate problems for the benefit of society. You will need to apply the skills learnt in Unit 3 to carry out your own investigations into:

● Monitoring living organisms.
● Making a useful product.
● Assembling an electronic/electrical device.
● Using machines.

Monitoring living organisms

It is essential for scientists to work with living creatures at times, to find out how they grow and develop. Scientists look at plants and animals to find out all sorts of information.

It is important to care for the organisms that you work with, for many reasons. If something is not cared for properly it will not grow well.

Imagine you are trying to test which fertiliser helps plants grow best. You may carefully set up your experiment, making it a fair test by using the same sort of plant and the same amount of different fertilisers. You could use a large number of seeds to make your results more reliable. However, if you don't water the plants and keep them warm and allow them lots of sunlight, the experiment will not work.

a) Explain why we need to care for the organisms we study so that we get good results.

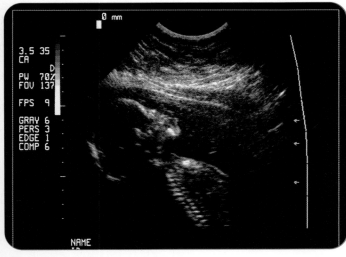

Ultrasound scan of a foetus

You have learned that X-rays can be used to take photographs of bones in the body. Soon after X-rays were invented, people started to use them to monitor the growth of foetuses in the womb. Parents could see the bones grow and develop. This made them both happy and more attached to the baby growing inside the womb.

Unfortunately, scientists didn't know that X-rays are dangerous and can cause cancer. Some of the babies born were very ill.

Today, scientists use **ultrasound scans**. These are completely safe and can give the parents good pictures of the developing foetus. They also allow doctors to monitor the growth and look for problems.

b) Here is an ultrasound scan of a foetus. Can you identify the head? Which way is it facing?
c) How can monitoring the foetus in the womb help mothers and doctors?

Animal testing?

Many people disagree with monitoring animals in tests. They say it is cruel. Other people say that it is impossible to learn if we don't do any testing. It is a very emotive subject.

Some people have been very violent, hurt people and broken the law to argue their point of view. There are very strict laws on how animals should be treated.

What are your opinions? Have a debate about testing living organisms. Be careful to consider all organisms – plants as well as animals. Make sure that all types of testing are considered.

Consider how religious views can be taken into account when discussing this matter.

TEST YOURSELF!

1 You need to produce a piece of coursework about monitoring living organisms. Select an organism that you can care for that you are going to monitor. Explain your choice.

2 Write a detailed essay discussing the morality of monitoring living organisms. Explain why we have to take the organisms' well-being into account when we monitor them. Try to see all points of view in your discussion.

1.2

Monitoring living organisms – the investigation

Wheat field

An athlete

GET IT RIGHT!

In your report, you should explain in detail how your research could be used to help a scientific industry.

Don't forget to do a risk assessment before you start!

You can choose to do a very wide range of things to complete this coursework. It is worth spending time on, as it makes up another 27.5% of your total GCSE marks.

As you saw on the previous page, monitoring living organisms must be completed with thought and care for the organism you study. You also need to consider how you are going to evaluate the investigation. What would make your investigation a success and how would you measure it?

You need to investigate the growth and/or development and/or responses of an organism under controlled conditions. (It is important that you show appropriate care and consideration to living organisms during this activity and follow procedures that are ethical.) Possible investigations may be to:

● Improve the yield of a plant / microorganism. Perhaps you could grow some seedlings and measure their growth in different conditions.
● Monitor the performance of a person in a physical or mental activity. Perhaps you could measure to see if the performance of some athletes improves.
● Monitor the effects of changing the environment on the behaviour and/or growth and/or development of an organism.

Make sure your report explains the purpose of the monitoring activity. Include a full plan which you discuss and explain before you begin to monitor the organism. Make sure your teacher has agreed to your plan before starting.

You should consider:

● The type of organism and a risk assessment.
● Why you are studying the organism.
● How the welfare of the organism is going to be taken into account.
● What conditions you are providing for the organism.
● What you are going to measure, for how long and how regularly.
● How you are going to evaluate the results of your investigation.
● How your investigation could be used in a scientific workplace.

a) Why do you think you should show your teacher your plan before you start?
b) Why do you think scientists make sure their plans are agreed before they start to monitor living organisms?

Monitoring living organisms

Stage 1	Stage 2	Stage 3
You need to: • Produce a simple safe plan for the investigation with guidance • Monitor the growth, development and response as appropriate of an organism with guidance • Record data obtained • Offer simple explanations for your findings • Give a simple evaluation of your activity • Suggest an application of your investigation	• Produce a safe plan, with little guidance which would enable the investigation to be carried out by another person • Monitor the growth, development and response as appropriate of an organism with little guidance • Record data obtained, identify and explain patterns within the data and, carry out calculations • Make and explain conclusions from the evidence • Give evaluations of your activities and suggest an improvement to their method • Describe an application of monitoring organisms in this scientific workplace	• Independently produce a safe plan described in a series of well ordered steps, which would clearly enable the investigation to be carried out by another person • Independently monitor the growth, development and response as appropriate of an organism • Record data obtained, analyse the data, explaining what they show, identifying any shortcomings in the evidence • Suggest improvement to the methods used that would enable more reliable evidence to be collected • Use scientific knowledge and understanding to explain why it is important to monitor organisms in the scientific workplace
1–6 marks	7–12 marks	13–17 marks

Measuring conditions in fieldwork

GET IT RIGHT!

It is often best to draw up a table of results that you are going to fill in when you are writing your plan. That way you can check if it is going to be easy or not to fill it in. If it is too complicated, think of another way of monitoring your living organism to make it easier.

Show how your investigation could provide useful information for a scientific workplace

Carefully phrase the question you are investigating

START HERE

Say why you have chosen to investigate that organism

State how you will look after the organism

Choose which conditions you will vary in your investigation

Say how you will measure any changes in the living organism, including how often you will take readings

Record your results systematically and look for any patterns in graphs you draw

Evaluate your investigation to improve your plans

GET IT RIGHT!

You have to work out a monitoring schedule that will get you your results. You should monitor your organism regularly enough to see small changes. Your schedule should also be over a long enough period of time to see significant growth or development of your chosen organism.

1.3   Completing the coursework

1 How should you present your results?
2 How do you express your conclusion?
3 What makes a good evaluation?

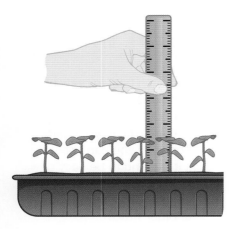

Measuring height

There is no point collecting precise, accurate, and reliable data under very carefully controlled conditions if you don't explain what you found out. Unfortunately, some students do not present their ideas well at this stage. Look at this piece of work:

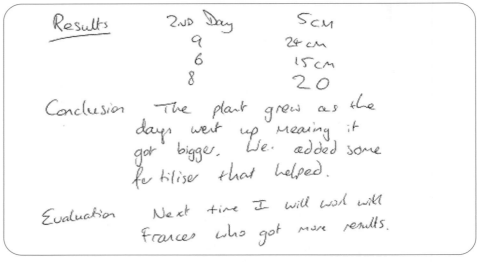

Some student data

a) Point out as many things as you can about this piece of work. Why is it not going to get many GCSE marks?
b) What advice would you give to students when working on a piece of coursework?

The work shown above is not good enough even to complete stage 1.
Look at the student's work below.

Results of plant growth experiment

Height (mm) of bean plant measured every day at 5 p.m. Every plant got same amount of water.			
Day	No fertiliser	Green's fertiliser	Bob's fertiliser
1	0, 0	0	1
2	0 1	0	1
3	2, 2	2	4
4	4, 3	4	8
5	6, 5	6	11

c) Describe how this table is better.
d) How could the second table of results be improved?
e) Could this student have taken more results, and how could they have been shown?

Conclusion

From my results table you can see that Bob's fertiliser helped the plants grow better. It is proof that Bob's fertiliser helps the plants grow. Bob's fertiliser had more nitrates in it that helps the plant grow more. Plants use nitrates to make proteins for growth.

We could use the results of this investigation in a farm. Farmers can spread Bob's fertiliser on the fields and their plants will grow better which will make more food for people.

GET IT RIGHT!

When making a conclusion, always refer to the graphs you have drawn.

Explain any patterns you find in your data.

f)   What improvements has this student made in their conclusion?
g)   How could graphs have helped?
h)   If the student had taken more results, how would that have helped to draw a firmer conclusion?
i)   How could the workplace applications section of the work been improved?
j)   What other information could have been put into the conclusion?

Evaluation

I could have taken more results in my experiment. I should have tested more fertilisers and seen which one was best because only using two isn't enough to get a really good conclusion. I also should have done at least 10 for each experiment because some people's bean didn't grow and that spoiled their experiment. If I had done more of each experiment I could have averaged the results. Farmers plant thousands of seeds not just a few.

I forgot to water the plants on the sixth day and they all died. I should have made sure that the plants had enough water so I could monitor them for longer. The fertiliser may have taken a long time to work.

I did the measurements by putting a ruler next to the bean every day. This wasn't always accurate because the stalks were not dead straight. If I did this experiment again I would make the plants grow up a stick so it was easier to measure.

GET IT RIGHT!

Get a friend to read your work before you hand it in. If they understand what you mean, then the examiner will as well. Sometimes you will need to redraft your work several times to get it right.

k)   How is this evaluation better than the conclusion above it?
l)   What more information would you have liked to see in the evaluation?
m) Does the evaluation above talk in enough detail about the quality of results?
n)   Did the student have any anomalous results? How can you tell? What could have been done better?

 Discuss how many marks the second student would have got by looking at the marking grid on page 291.

1.4   Making a useful product

LEARNING OBJECTIVES

1 What useful materials can you make from metals extracted from rocks?

2 What is involved in this coursework investigation task?

We make useful products from naturally occurring materials such as metals, rocks and minerals.

a) Match the raw material (1–4) to the useful product (A–D).

1 Malachite
$CuCO_3.Cu(OH)_2$

2 Galena
PbS

3 Bauxite
Al_2O_3

4 Haematite
Fe_2O_3

A Steel girder

B Water pipe

C Roof flashing

D Ladder

Increasing the rate of a chemical reaction

In industry, the faster the reaction happens, the more quickly the product is made (and the cheaper the process, the greater the profits).

We can make chemical reactions faster by:

- Increasing the **temperature**.
- Increasing the **concentration** of solutions.
- Increasing the **pressure** of gases.
- Increasing the **surface area** of solids (using smaller pieces of solid).
- Adding a suitable **catalyst**.

Collision theory

Increase the frequency of collisions and the rate of reaction increases.

Particles normally bounce off each other. To react together, the particles have to collide into each other with enough energy.

- Increasing the **temperature** gives the particles more energy, so they collide harder and collide more often.
- Increasing the **concentration** or **pressure** puts the particles closer together, so they collide more often.
- A large lump of solid has most of its particles below its surface. These particles never get hit. Increasing the **surface area**, by breaking the lump into smaller pieces, increases the number of particles open to attack. So collisions take place more often between the particles.
- Particles can react at the surface of a **catalyst** without needing as much energy when they collide.

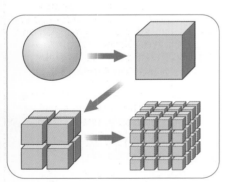

Decreasing particle size; increasing surface area

GET IT RIGHT!

A **catalyst** is a substance that speeds up a reaction without being used up in the reaction itself.

In this project you make a chemical product that benefits society. You put your final product into a suitable sample tube, with its name, hazard warning label and date of preparation.

You also calculate the cost of making your chemical product.

Coursework investigation checklist

1 Explain how people use your product and how it benefits society.
2 Write a word equation for your chemical reaction.
3 Write a balanced chemical equation for your reaction.
4 Explain the type of chemical reaction you are using.
5 Explain (using 'collision theory') factors that speed up your reaction.
6 Write a risk assessment before you start the experiment.
7 Knowing the **mass of reactant**, you can work out the maximum mass of the product that you could obtain (the *theoretical yield*).
8 Compare the starting mass of your raw material (the **mass of reactant**) with the actual mass of chemical product you obtain (the **actual yield**).
9 Calculate the **percentage yield** of the reaction using the **actual yield** and the *theoretical yield*:

$$\textbf{percentage yield} = \frac{actual\ yield}{theoretical\ yield} \times 100\%$$

10 Calculate the cost of making your chemical product.

The 'assessment evidence grid' or mark scheme for Making New Products is as follows:

Stage 1	Stage 2	Stage 3
You need to: • Given a procedure, obtain a pure chemical product safely, using a named chemical reaction and present it in a labelled sample tube, with guidance • Write a word equation for the reaction, with guidance • Measure the actual yield of the product • Give a use for the product • State one way that the rate of the reaction could be increased	• Given a procedure, obtain a pure chemical product safely, using a named chemical reaction and present it in a labelled sample tube, with little guidance • Write a word equation for the reaction • Calculate the percentage yield of the product, given the theoretical yield, and using the actual mass of the product obtained • Calculate the costs of making a given amount of the product • Describe the use of the product • Describe two factors that affect the rate of the reaction	• Independently, given a procedure, obtain a pure chemical product safely, using a named chemical reaction and present it in a labelled sample tube • Write a balanced chemical equation for the reaction and explain the type of reaction taking place • Calculate the percentage yield of the product, given the theoretical yield and using the actual mass of the product obtained to the appropriate number of significant figures, stating the correct units • Calculate the percentage yield of product obtained from a specified amount of reactant • Explain the industrial importance of the product and its impact on society • Use scientific knowledge and understanding to explain the factors that affect the rate of the reaction
1–5 marks	6–11 marks	12–17 marks

TEST YOURSELF!

1 How can we increase the surface area of a solid?

2 Explain what you mean by the 'concentration' of a solution.

1.5

Making a useful product – the investigation

LEARNING OBJECTIVES

1 How do you calculate yields?
2 What is involved in this coursework investigation task?

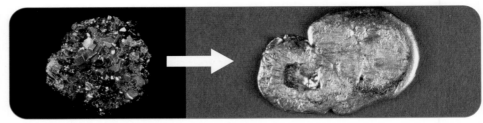
Galena ore to lead metal

The ore galena is *mainly* lead sulfide (PbS). To extract the metal, lead, from galena we crush the rock, then heat it in air and charcoal.
(It reacts with oxygen (O_2) in the air and the carbon (C) in the charcoal.)
The following reactions take place:

lead sulfide + oxygen → lead oxide + sulfur dioxide

$$2\,PbS + 3\,O_2 \rightarrow 2\,PbO + 2\,SO_2$$

then: lead oxide + carbon → lead + carbon dioxide

$$2\,PbO + C \rightarrow 2\,Pb + CO_2$$

KEY FACTS

The relative atomic mass of:

lead   Pb = 207
sulfur   S = 32

So, the relative formula mass of lead sulfide

PbS = 207 + 32
      = 239

The balanced equations tell us that:

	2 moles of lead sulfide (PbS)	produce	2 moles of lead (Pb)
So	1 mole of PbS	produces	1 mole of Pb
So in theory	239 g of PbS	could produce	207 g of Pb

Your teacher will explain this experiment. (See the student's results below.)

a) Why will the actual yield be less than the theoretical yield?

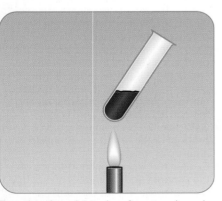
Roasting the mixture in a fume cupboard

Extracting lead from galena

We weighed out a spatula full of crushed galena and recorded the mass.
Then we added a spatula full of powdered charcoal and mixed well.
We put the mixture into a test tube and roasted it well over a bunsen flame in a fume cupboard.
We tipped the mixture out onto a heat-proof mat and let it cool.
We picked out the beads of lead we had produced and weighed them.

Results: the mass of reactant (= mass of galena)   = 5.34g
            the actual yield (= mass of lead produced)   = 1.42g

Calculations:

1. Theoretical yield:

If 239g of galena could produce 207g of lead.
       1g of galena could produce 207/239 = 0.87g
   So 5.34g of galena could produce 5.34 x 0.87 = 4.63g
               The theoretical yield = 4.63g

2. Percentage yield:

Percentage yield = $\dfrac{\text{actual yield} \times 100\%}{\text{theoretical yield}}$

         = $\dfrac{1.42 \times 100\%}{4.63}$ = 31%

Comments: Maybe the galena rock was not pure and contained only a little PbS.
                 Maybe we didn't extract all the lead out of the galena that was in it.

b) What else might be in the galena rock besides lead sulfide?

c) Why might it be difficult to extract all the lead from the ore?

You probably understand how to calculate theoretical yield and percentage yield. If so, try this investigation:

Producing copper sulfate crystals from malachite ore

Use a periodic table to calculate the relative formula mass of:

- Your reactant – malachite – $CuCO_3.Cu(OH)_2$
- Your product – copper sulfate crystals – $CuSO_4.5H_2O$

Method

Write a risk assessment before you start (e.g. remember copper(II) sulfate is harmful!).

1 Weigh out about 10 g of crushed malachite. Record this mass (m_1).

2 Put 50 cm³ of **dilute sulfuric acid** into a 250 cm³ beaker.

3 Very slowly add the malachite to the acid. Stir with a glass rod.

4 Stop adding malachite when fizzing stops.

5 (The solution is now neutral and not acidic. Check with pH paper.)

6 Weigh the malachite you haven't used. Record this mass (m_2).

7 Calculate the *mass of reactant* (mass of malachite used) = $m_1 - m_2$.

8 Filter the solution. Leave it in an evaporating dish until crystals form.

9 Weigh the crystals to get the *actual yield* (mass of crystals produced).

d) Remember: carbonate + acid → salt + water + carbon dioxide
and: alkali + acid → salt + water

Write a balanced chemical equation for the reaction.

e) How does your equation show that:
1 mole of $CuCO_3.Cu(OH)_2$ produces 2 moles of $CuSO_4.5H_2O$?

f) In theory: **how many grams** of $CuCO_3.Cu(OH)_2$ could produce **how many grams** of $CuSO_4.5H_2O$?

g) So 1 g of malachite could produce how many grams of $CuSO_4.5H_2O$?

h) Now calculate your theoretical yield.

i) Now calculate your percentage yield.

TEST YOURSELF!

1 Research question: why do we use copper sulfate in agriculture?

2 Explain the type of chemical reaction we use to make copper sulfate crystals from malachite.

3 Explain, using collision theory, ways to speed up the reaction between malachite and sulfuric acid.

GET IT RIGHT!

1 Put your final product into a suitable size tube, with its name, hazard warning label and date of preparation.

2 Your teacher or technician can provide you with the prices of malachite and sulfuric acid. Use this information to calculate the cost of making your copper sulfate crystals.

3 Use the Coursework Investigation Checklist on page 295 to help you *get it right!*

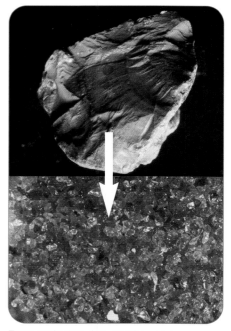

From malachite (reactant) to copper sulfate (product)

1.6 Electronic devices

LEARNING OBJECTIVES

1 What are the uses of electronic and electrical devices?
2 What are the functions of the components used?
3 How do you assemble and assess the effectiveness of a device?

We use a vast number of electrical and electronic devices in our homes, at work or during our leisure time. All are designed and built to do their job.

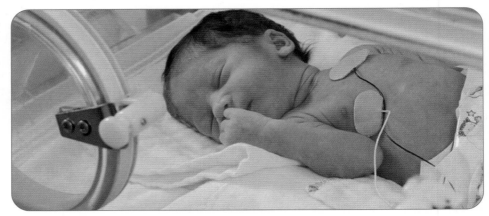

Premature baby in her incubator

💬 Discuss the benefits of how we use electronic machines for sensing, monitoring and controlling machines or the environment.

In this coursework task you will assemble, test and evaluate the effectiveness of an electrical/electronic device, explaining the function of the components used. The 'assessment evidence grid' or mark scheme for Assembling an Electronic/Electrical Device follows:

GET IT RIGHT!

You need to assemble and assess the effectiveness of one electrical or electronic device.

Stage 1	Stage 2	Stage 3
You need to: ● Safely assemble a useful electrical or electronic device, with guidance ● Test the electrical or electronic device, with guidance	● Safely assemble a useful electrical or electronic device, with little guidance ● Test the electrical or electronic device ● Explain the function of the components used in the device ● Evaluate the effectiveness of the device when used	● Independently, safely assemble a useful electrical or electronic device ● Independently, test the electrical or electronic device and suggest alternative tests that could be carried out ● Give a detailed evaluation of the effectiveness of the device and suggest improvements that could be made to make it more useful
1–2 marks	3–6 marks	7–9 marks

Electronic systems have four main parts: a **power supply**, **input** components, a **processor** and **output** components.

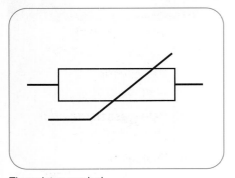

Thermistor symbol

a) Thermistors and light-dependent resistors (LDRs) are examples of **input sensors**. What does a thermistor respond to?
b) What **input sensors** do we use with a mobile phone?

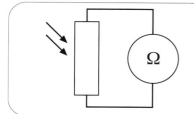

Experiment 1

Input sensor: *Experiment 1*
Connect your LDR to a multimeter on the resistance (ohm or Ω) scale. Cover the LDR and see what happens to its resistance.

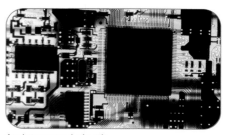

LDR symbol

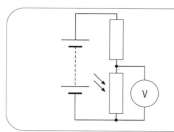

Experiment 2

Input sensor: *Experiment 2*
Now connect your LDR in series with a 10 kΩ resistor and a power supply. Cover the LDR and see what happens to the voltmeter reading.

When we put a sensor into an **input circuit**, we place the sensor in series with a resistor. Now the voltage in the circuit can change. We call an **input circuit** like this a '**potential divider**'.

c) Choose the correct words; In the dark, the resistance of the LDR **increases** /**decreases**, so the voltage across the LDR **increases** /**decreases**.

Processors take the voltage from the input, work out what needs to be done, and tell the output what to do. In modern electronic devices, the processors are usually integrated circuits built on a silicon chip. These contain large numbers of electronic switches or 'transistors'.

An integrated circuit

Transistors switch to give a **low** or a **high** voltage output.

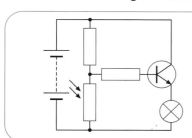

Experiment 3

A nightlight: *Experiment 3*
Connect this circuit. It will switch on a lamp when it gets dark.
*The LDR is the **input** sensor.*
*The transistor is the **processor**.*
*The lamp is the **output** device.*

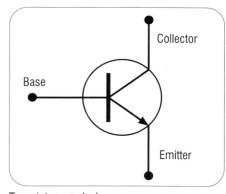

Transistor symbol

d) Buzzers, motors, heaters and relays are examples of other **output** devices. What does a relay do?

TEST YOURSELF!

1 How is the nightlight useful to the baby in her incubator?

2 To open a window when the kitchen gets too hot:
   a) What input sensor would you use?
   b) What output device would you use?

3 **Digital** pulses of light in optical fibres have replaced **analogue** currents in copper wires for telecommunication.
   a) What do the words **digital** and **analogue** mean?
   b) In what other ways has there been a 'digital revolution'?

GET IT RIGHT!

In your coursework project you will need to:

● Select your components.

● Safely assemble and test your device.

● Evaluate it, commenting on how well it does its job.

1.7 Electronic devices – the investigation

1 What is involved in this coursework investigation task – selecting and carrying out your investigation?

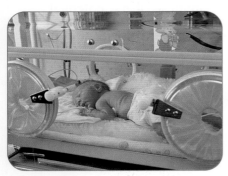

Baby incubator

For this coursework task I'm going to make a device for a premature baby incubator.

Great, but what sensors are you going to use?"

What sensor?

 Discuss what we must monitor and control in baby incubators. Think about what sensors we need to have in the incubator.

Before planning your coursework investigation, try to understand:

● The difference between **block diagrams** and **circuit diagrams**.
● How can **variable resistors** and **relays** help us with control.

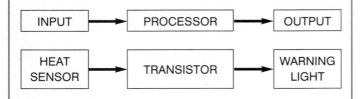

Block diagrams show the input – processor – output arrangement of a system

a) What could a system like this be used for?

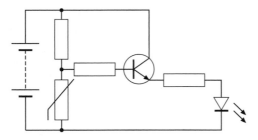

Circuit diagrams show the way components are wired together

b) What is the **input sensor** in this circuit?
c) What is the **output device**?
d) What happens if the temperature decreases?
e) What could this circuit be used for?

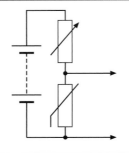

We can adjust the variable resistor in this input circuit. It will control the temperature when the device is activated

f) In what systems could this be useful?
g) Electronic circuits use low-voltage power supplies. Why could this be an advantage?

However, some powerful output devices, like heaters and motors, operate on high voltages.

A **relay** is an electromagnetic switch.

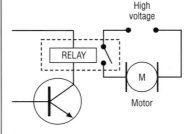

We can use a relay to switch on/off a high-voltage circuit from a low-voltage electronic circuit

For your coursework task, decide which input sensor you will need. To start with, have an indicator as your output device. Modifications to the output can be added later. Draw a block diagram and circuit diagram of your system before trying to assemble it. Explain the function of the components used. After testing, plan modifications. For example, up to now, you may only have a warning that it is too hot or too cold. Ask yourself, "What am I going to add to the circuit to control the temperature, so that it stays just right?"

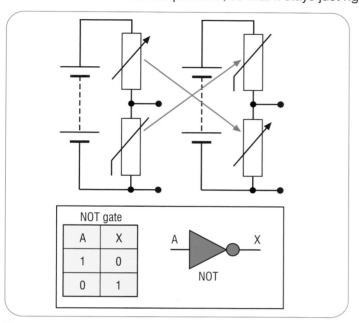

Two ways to reverse control

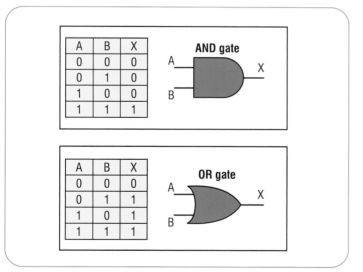

Two ways to combine inputs

TEST YOURSELF!

Farmers try to control the environment in which mushrooms grow. The systems are similar to those in the premature baby unit.

1 To get the best growing conditions, temperature, moisture level and light intensity have to be controlled in a greenhouse.

What sensors could we use to monitor these variables?

GET IT RIGHT!

Remember these words in your evaluation:

Effectiveness – Does it do the job it is designed for – e.g. does the heater come on if the temperature is too low?

Accuracy – Does it do the job well – e.g. can it control the temperature to +/– 1°C?

Improvements – What would make your device even more useful as a real-life product?

GET IT RIGHT!

Do not experiment with mains electricity.

Mushroom farmer:
"Climate control is the key to our business success and controlling temperature is the critical factor"

1.8   Using machines

LEARNING OBJECTIVES

1 What mechanical machines are used in the workplace?
2 What forces are involved in these machines?
3 How are energy transfers and efficiency measured?

From one corkscrew to another one, mechanisms are all around us!

A corkscrew

The Colossus corkscrew at Thorpe Park

A brake lever

Although times have changed, we still use mechanisms that we used over 100 years ago:

levers, wheels and axles, pulleys, gears, ramps, screws, and pneumatic and hydraulic machines.

Visit your school, college or local gym and note how many of these mechanisms you can spot in the fitness studio.

Discuss what you find out.

In this coursework task, you will research how we use mechanical machines in the workplace. The 'assessment evidence grid' or mark scheme for Using Machines follows:

Stage 1	Stage 2	Stage 3

You need to:
 	
• Give and describe an example of how mechanical machines may be used in the workplace
	• Describe how mechanical machines used in the workplace act as force multipliers
	• Describe why the effects of friction are important in mechanical machines
		• Measure the applied force and the force produced by a machine
		• Calculate:
		  – The amount the machine multiplies force
		  – The work done by the machine
		  – The efficiency of the machine

1 mark	2–3 marks	4–7 marks

Usually, we design mechanical machines to be **force multipliers**. With force multipliers, we can raise heavy loads with small efforts. This is a great advantage when raising people in wheel chairs into a minibus. Pulleys also give **mechanical advantage**.

$$\text{mechanical advantage} = \frac{\text{load}}{\text{effort}}$$

Hoist in a minibus

a) Why is the mechanical advantage of a force multiplier greater than one?

Friction is not always a disadvantage in mechanical machines. It provides grip and can stop loads slipping. However, friction does cause wear and produces heat.

The **efficiency** of machines is less when more energy is wasted as heat. In this case, not as much input energy to the machine ends up as useful output energy.

 Discuss other advantages and disadvantages of friction in machines.

$$\text{efficiency} = \frac{\text{useful energy output}}{\text{total energy input}} \times 100\%$$

b) Why is the efficiency of all machines less than 100%?

We calculate the work done (or energy transferred) by a mechanical machine using the formula:

work done = **force** × **distance moved**
(energy transferred) (in the direction of the force)

The units are: work done in joules (J)
force in newtons (N)
distance moved in metres (m).

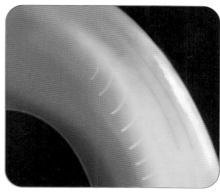
An infra-red image of car tyre after braking

GET IT RIGHT!

You could visit a Theme Park. Then, back in the lab, you could base your 'Using Machines' project on an aspect of the ride.

TEST YOURSELF!

1 'Magic Mouse' is a small roller coaster. Look at its photo opposite.

 What would happen if there was no friction between the 'mouse' and the track?

2 The two main hazards for customers are:
 ● 'slipping on the wet metal entrance to the ride' and
 ● 'being hit by an object while on the ride'.

 How do you think these risks are controlled?

3 It needs an effort of 8 kN for the chain to haul the 'mouse' up the 30 m long incline.

 What is the work done on the mouse? (This answer is the total energy input.)

4 The weight of the mouse and its riders (i.e. the load) is 10 kN. They rise to a height of 15 m.

 What is the useful energy transferred to them? (This answer is the useful energy output.)

5 Calculate the efficiency of the machine that pulls the mouse up the incline.

6 What is the mechanical advantage of this machine?

Magic Mouse

1.9   Using machines – the investigation

Coursework task

LEARNING OBJECTIVE

1 What is involved in this Unit 4 coursework investigation task to investigate a mechanical machine?

You have probably seen lots of mechanisms:

levers, wheels and axles, pulleys, gears, ramps, screws, and pneumatic and hydraulic machines.

Examples of machines

 Discuss examples of mechanisms and workplaces that use them.

Look at the diagram of the crowbar – a simple lever.

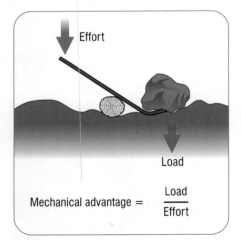

Effort

Load

Mechanical advantage = $\dfrac{\text{Load}}{\text{Effort}}$

A crowbar

a) Why is the crowbar able to multiply force?

b) The load weighs 240 N. If the effort needed to move it is 80 N, what is the **mechanical advantage** of the lever?
Look at the photo of the rowing machine.

c) The rower pulls with an effort of 1000 N and the cord moves 2 m. What is the energy transferred by the rower?
(Remember:
work done = force × distance)

A rowing machine

Your coursework task can *either* involve taking measurements from a machine in real life *or* modelling that machine in the laboratory.

d) Why would taking measurements from a model helicopter be both difficult and dangerous?

A model helicopter

In your investigation you will need to...

1 Identify a mechanical machine used in the workplace, and its usefulness.

2 Explain how it works, with the aid of diagrams.

3 Explain how effective the machine is at performing its task.

4 Describe advantages and disadvantages of friction in the machine.

5 Write a risk assessment for your experiment and describe the experiment.

6 Measure the applied force (the effort).

7 Measure the force produced by the machine (the load).

8 Calculate the amount the machine multiplies the force (i.e. the mechanical advantage: load ÷ effort).

9 Calculate the work done (or energy transferred) by the machine (i.e. the effort: force × the distance moved by the effort).

10 Calculate the energy transferred to the load (i.e. the load × the distance moved by the load).

11 Calculate the efficiency of the machine (i.e. (useful energy output ÷ total energy input) × 100% = (energy transferred to the load ÷ work done by the machine) × 100%).

A stair lift

You could model the incline of the 'Magic Mouse' roller coaster.

e) Why is the 'Mouse' ramp like a stair lift? How is it different?

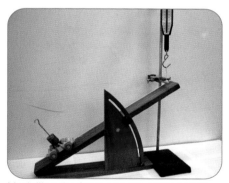

Modelling the forces on the roller coaster incline

Close-up of the incline for the 'Magic Mouse'

How does the load affect the power needed?

 Discuss the experiments you could carry out in the laboratory.

TEST YOURSELF!

1 In the investigation, what mechanical machines could we use?

2 a) Choose one machine and say why it is useful.
   b) Explain how it works, with the aid of diagrams.
   c) Explain how effective the machine is at performing its task.
   d) Describe advantages and disadvantages of friction in the machine.

DID YOU KNOW?

The first 'scream machines' were not roller coasters but blocks of ice. Sledges ran down ice-covered man-made hills.

Glossary

A

acceleration speeding up, going faster (also a change in velocity)

addiction severe craving for a drug, which makes you believe you can't survive without it

aerobic respiration a chemical reaction in cells in which oxygen is used to release energy from glucose

aerosol a mixture of a solid or liquid in a gas

alkane a family of hydrocarbons including methane and ethane

alleles different forms of the same gene

alloy a mixture formed when another substance has beeen added to a metal to change its properties

ammeter a device to measure electrical current

anaerobic respiration process in which cells break down glucose without oxygen

antibiotic chemical which kills bacteria

antibody chemical produced by white blood cells which destroys a specific microorganism

antiseptic chemical which kills microorganisms without damaging your skin

anti-toxin chemical produced by white blood cells which destroys a specific toxin produced by a microorganism

atom the building-block of matter. Contains protons, neutrons and electrons

atomic number the number of protons in an atom

B

Big Bang the explosion that is thought to have started the universe

biological control when living organisms are used to control a pest population

black hole the remains of a huge old star – so dense that even light gets pulled into it

braking distance how far a car travels between the brakes being applied and the car coming to a stop

C

cancer a disease in which some cells in the body become abnormal, and start multiplying without stopping

carbohydrate compound containing carbon, hydrogen and oxygen. They are a major source of energy in animal diets and include sugars and starches

catalyst a chemical that affects the speed of a chemical reaction, without being used up itself

catalytic converter device to remove pollutants from vehicle exhaust gases

cement made by roasting limestone with clay. Used for making mortar and concrete

ceramic a material like china, brick or clay. Ceramics are very hard and have high melting points

chemical energy stored in the bonds between atoms in compounds (see exothermic and endothermic)

chemical formula a way of describing a chemical using symbols

chlorophyll green pigment in leaves that traps light for photosynthesis

chromatography a way of separating mixtures of many solutes, usually pigments

chromosomes strands of DNA which contain genes

circuit breaker device that switches off a circuit when too much electricity flows

clone identical copy of a parent

coal solid fossil fuel consisting of the fossilised remains of ancient plants

combustion when a chemical reacts with oxygen and releases energy

comet an icy, rocky object orbiting the Sun on an eccentric orbit

composite a material made by combining the best properties of two other materials

compound a substance made from two or more elements which are chemically bonded to each other

concrete a mixture of cement, water, sand and small stones. Concrete is used by the building industry

D

conduction flow of energy (either electricity or heat) through a material

conductor a material that allows energy to flow through it

covalent bond a type of chemical bond in which atoms share outer electrons

convection how warm fluids rise when warmed

crude oil a liquid fossil fuel, formed over millions of years from the remains of sea creatures

current the rate of flow of electricity in a circuit, measured in Amperes (Amps, A)

D

decelerating slowing down; a decrease in velocity

deoxygenated blood blood which is lacking in oxygen

diaphragm sheet of muscle which flattens to draw air into the lungs

diesel a fuel commonly used by larger vehicles; one of the products of crude oil

diffusion movement of molecules from an area of high concentration to an area of low concentration.

disinfectant chemical which kills microorganisms, but damages skin

distillation a way of separating mixtures of liquids with different boiling points (or liquid from solutions)

DNA (Deoxyribonucleic acid) – the chemical that carries our genetic information

dominant gene a gene which is always expressed if present in an organism

Doppler shift change in frequency of a wave due to its source moving towards or away from you

droplet infection method by which diseases are spread through coughing and sneezing

drug chemical which alters the way the body works

ductile a word to describe a material which can be pulled out to form wires

E

effectors muscles or glands which cause a response

efficiency how good a device is at turning its input energy into useful output energy

electric motor a device that turns electrical energy into kinetic energy

electrolysis using electricity to split up compounds

electromagnet a device that uses electricity to make magnetism

electromagnetic spectrum a family of waves which all have similar properties; includes radio, micro, infra-red, visible, ultraviolet, X-rays and gamma-rays

electron an atomic particle. Electrons have a negative charge and almost no mass. Electrons are involved in making chemical bonds

element a substance containing only one type of atom

emulsifying agent a substance added to immiscible liquids that keeps them mixed together

emulsion a mixture of immiscible liquids

endothermic a chemical reaction which needs heat energy to take place

energy is transferred (changed from one type to another) whenever anything happens

energy efficient making good use of an energy supply, without wasting much

energy resource a source of energy, such as crude oil or wind power

ethanol one type of alcohol, produced from fermentation of sugars

eutrophication process by which water sources become enriched with nutrients, eventually causing the death of water inhabitants

evaporation when a liquid turns to a gas

exothermic a chemical reaction which releases heat energy

F

fat oily compound that provides a store of energy. It also protects organs and insulates against heat loss

fermentation another name for anaerobic respiration

fibre food group which is not digested but is important to help remove waste products from the body

fibreglass a composite material made from fibres of glass set in polymer

fibre-optic cable thin glass threads that carry light along them by internal reflection

filtration a way of separating insoluble solids from liquids

fission the nuclear reaction when unstable elements break apart, releasing energy

flaccid floppy without structure

fluorescent a material that absorbs energy and gives it back out as visible light

foam a mixture in which bubbles of gas are trapped inside a liquid or solid

fossil fuel fuels formed over millions of years from the remains of plants and animals (coal, oil, gas)

fraction part of crude oil separated out for a specific use

fractional distillation the process that is used to separate out the different fractions in crude oil

frequency the number of waves in each second, measured in Hertz (Hz)

fuel a chemical burnt to release energy

fuel rods the source of energy in a nuclear power station, usually uranium

fuse a small device that contains a small central wire which melts when too much current flows through it, breaking a circuit

G

galaxy a group of billions of stars in space; our galaxy is called the milky way

gamma ray high energy electromagnetic wave. Highly ionising

gasohol alcohol used as a fuel

gel a mixture in which a liquid is trapped inside a solid framework

gene a small section of DNA which codes for a characteristic

gene pool the variety of genes which exist within a species

generator (also called a dynamo) – an electromagnetic device that creates electricity from movement

genetic engineering artificially changing an organism's genetic material

giant structure huge molecules with thousands of atoms

gland organ in the body which produces a hormone

glucose sugar with the chemical formula $C_6H_{12}O_6$

glycogen carbohydrate that stores excess glucose in the liver

graphite a type of carbon used as pencil lead

greenhouse effect the Earth's atmosphere traps more of the Sun's heat than it should, causing the Earth to warm up

H

homeostasis the maintenance of a constant internal environment

hormones substance produced by a gland, which travels in the blood and has an effect on another part of the body

hydrocarbon a type of chemical compound which only contains hydrogen and carbon atoms

hypothermia abnormally low body temperature

I

immiscible liquids which will not normally mix together

immunisation causes immunity to an infectious disease through the use of a vaccine

immunity resistance of the body to infection by a specific microorganism

incomplete combustion when fuels burn but there isn't enough oxygen for complete combustion, meaning that more pollution is produced

incubation period the period between the time of infection and the time the first symptoms appear

infra-red electromagnetic wave, heat energy

inherited passed on from parents to their offspring

insulator a material that does not allow energy to flow through it

intensive farming method of farming to minimise costs yet maximise production

ion a charged particle. Atoms become ions when they lose or gain electrons

ionic bond a type of chemical bond in which atoms have exchanged electrons

ionising radiation radiation which removes / adds electrons to atoms, making them into ions

J

joule unit of energy

K

kilowatt hour a unit of electrical energy – the amount used by a 1 kW electrical device in one hour

L

lime kiln large oven in which limestone is heated to become quicklime

limestone rock containing calcium carbonate ($CaCO_3$). Used by many industries, especially construction

M

malleable a word to describe a material which can be hammered into different shapes

mass number the number of protons plus neutrons in an atom

medical imaging doctors use X-rays, gamma rays and ultrasound to produce pictures of patients to diagnose problems

metallurgist a scientist specialising in the properties and chemistry of metals

microwave a type of electromagnetic wave – used in communications as well as cooking

minerals essential nutrients required for healthy animal or plant growth

mitochondria the cell structures in which respiration occurs

mixture a substance made from two or more elements which are not bonded together

molecule more than one atom joined together with chemical bonds

monomer a single unit repeated many times in a polymer such as plastic

mortar a mixture of cement, water and sand. Mortar is used to hold bricks together

N

natural gas a fossil fuel, formed over millions of years from the remains of sea creatures

nebula a huge cloud of dust and gas in space

neurone nerve cell

neutron an atomic particle. Neutrons have no charge and a mass of 1

neutron star the super dense remains of a dead star that is not quite big enough to form a black hole

nicotine addictive chemical found in cigarettes

non-renewable a resource that will run out because it cannot be replaced

nuclear energy energy stored in the nucleus of an atom; used to produce energy in nuclear power stations

nucleus 1. structure in the cell which contains the cell's DNA
2. the name given to the centre of an atom

O

ore a rock containing enough metal for it to be worthwhile extracting

organic farming production of food and other materials without the use of chemicals. Animals have an agreed standard of living

organic solvent a solvent containing the element carbon

osmosis movement of water molecules from a high concentration to a low concentration through a selectively permeable membrane

oxygen debt the amount of oxygen needed to break down lactic acid produced as a result of anaerobic respiration

oxygenated blood blood that is rich in oxygen

P

pathogen an organism which causes disease

Periodic Table a list of all the elements in order of atomic numbers

petrol a fuel commonly burnt in cars; one of the products of crude oil

pH a way of measuring how acidic or alkaline a solution is; pH above 7 = acidic

photosynthesis process by which green plants convert water and carbon dioxide into glucose and oxygen using light energy

pitch how high a note is; linked to its frequency

plasma liquid component of blood – mainly water

plasticiser a substance added to a plastic to make it more flexible

platelets fragments of cells which are involved in blood clotting

pollutant a harmful chemical that is added by humans to the environment

polymer a huge molecule made from many small units linked together

power how fast energy is used or work is done, measured in Watts (W)

power rating description of the power of a device, measured in watts – how much energy it uses each second

primary energy resource an energy source that can be used straight from the ground, without needing to be processed first

producer organism which makes its own food by the process of photosynthesis

protein food group which provides the body with material for the repair of tissue, growth and energy

proton an atomic particle. Protons have a positive charge and a mass of 1

Q

quicklime calcium oxide (CaO). Produced by heating limestone in a lime kiln. Used for making cement

R

radar a system that uses reflected radio waves to detect how far away objects are (used by planes, as well as weather scientists)

radiation energy emitted from an object. See also ionising radiation

radioactive decay/radioactivity the nucleus of an unstable atom breaks down and gives out radioactive particles

radioisotope an unstable form of an element that will decay radioactively

radiotherapy treatment of a disease using ionising radiation

radio wave an electromagnetic wave, used mainly in communication

reactivity series a list of elements in order of their reactivity

receptors groups of cells that detect a stimulus

recessive gene a gene which is only expressed if there are two copies of it present in a nucleus

recyclable an object that can be broken down and turned into something else after use

red blood cells carry oxygen around the body

red-shift the change to longer wavelengths that is seen in the light of galaxies and stars that are moving away from us

reduced the removal of oxygen from a compound

reducing agent a chemical that removes oxygen from another compound

renewable a resource that will not run out because more can be created

respiration process by which glucose is converted to energy in cells

S

satellite an object in orbit

sclerosis a liver disease, commonly suffered by alcoholics

selective breeding process by which a farmer chooses his best organisms and breeds them together to produce offspring with desired characteristics

sensory neurones carry messages from receptor cells to the central nervous system

sieving a way of separating solids of different sizes

slag a waste material produced by a blast furnace

slaked lime calcium hydroxide $(Ca(OH)_2)$. Produced by adding water to quicklime. Used for neutralising areas affected by acid rain

solar power the Sun's light and heat, used as an energy resource

Solar System our Sun and the bodies that orbit it (e.g. planets, moons, asteroids and comets)

soluble a substance which can dissolve in a solvent

solute a substance which is dissolved in a solvent

solution a mixture in which a substance has been dissolved in a liquid

solvent a liquid which can dissolve a substance

sound wave sound is carried through the air by the vibrations of air particles

spectrum a group of waves of a similar type

speed how fast something moves (= distance ÷ time), measured in m/s

sterile an environment without microorganisms

sterilise technique used to kill microorganisms to produce a sterile environment

stimulus a change in the environment

stomata tiny openings in leaves which allow gas exchange to occur

supernova the explosion of a large star as it ends the stable, main part of its life

suspension a mixture of an insoluble solid and a liquid

sustainability the ability of a resource to last for a longer time because it can be renewed

T

tar produced by smoking tobacco. Contains many chemicals, some of which cause cancer

telescope a device used to study distant objects by focusing waves (usually light or radiowaves)

thermal decomposition when a chemical is broken down by heat

thinking distance how far a vehicle travels from when the driver sees something to when the brakes are activated

thorax upper part of the trunk of the body in animals, containing the heart and lungs

total internal reflection how light travels along the inside of a fibre-optic cable

total stopping distance the sum of thinking distance and braking distance – the total distance a car travels while stopping

toxin a chemical that is poisonous to the body

tracers chemicals inserted into the body to track movement e.g. blood flow

transpiration movement of water through a plant

turbine large, propeller-like blades that are made to spin e.g. in power stations to generate electricity

turgid rigid (not flaccid)

U

ultra-violet electromagnetic waves with frequency slightly higher than visible light; causes tanning of skin

uranium a radioactive element used as an energy source in power stations

V

vaccine normally contain dead or weakened microorganisms which trigger white blood cells to produce immunity

variation differences within a species

vasoconstriction narrowing of capillaries

vasodilation widening of capillaries

velocity the speed of an object in a particular direction, measured in metres per second, m/s

vibration a regular, repeated backwards and forwards motion

visible spectrum the range of colours of light that we can see

vitamin nutrient needed in small quantities to keep you healthy

voltage the push that makes electrical current flow – measured in volts

voltmeter a device that measures voltage

W

watt unit for power; equals one Joule used each second

wavelength how long a wave is (the distance from one peak to the next)

weather satellite a device that orbits the earth, monitoring weather conditions from above

white blood cells responsible for protecting the body from disease

withdrawal symptoms unwanted side effects people suffer when they stop taking a drug

X

X-ray high energy electromagnetic waves used, for example, in medical imaging

xylem vessels in a plant which transport water

Index